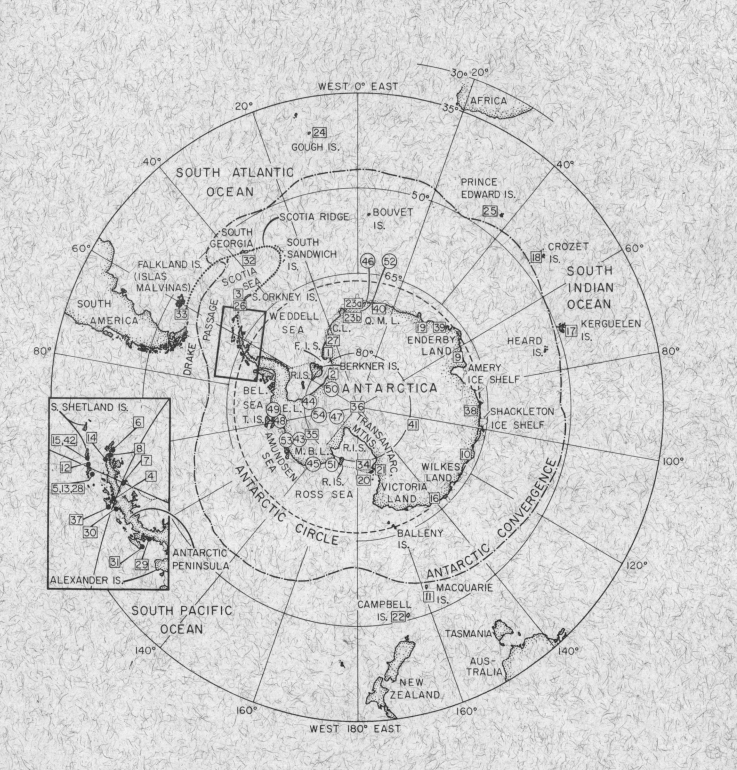

POLAR RESEARCH
A Survey

POLAR RESEARCH

A Survey

COMMITTEE ON POLAR RESEARCH
NATIONAL RESEARCH COUNCIL

86152

National Academy of Sciences

Washington, D.C.

1970

STANDARD BOOK NUMBER: 309-01753-X

AVAILABLE FROM

PRINTING AND PUBLISHING OFFICE

NATIONAL ACADEMY OF SCIENCES

2101 CONSTITUTION AVENUE

WASHINGTON, D.C. 20418

FIRST PRINTING, March 1970
SECOND PRINTING, May 1971

LIBRARY OF CONGRESS CATALOG CARD NUMBER: 78-603320

Preface

This report is concerned with scientific research in the north and south polar regions. Its primary purpose is to identify and assess important scientific problems that should be studied in the next few years. The report considers similarities and differences in the scientific problems relating to each polar region and to the over-all earth environment and touches on operational features and international collaboration. The Arctic and Antarctic encompass substantial portions of the earth's surface, and the unraveling of their many secrets will contribute to a better understanding of the earth—its life, climate, oceans, interior, and the solar and interplanetary forces that dominate it. At the same time, from a practical standpoint, a better understanding of the polar regions can assist mankind in meeting various problems, for food is present in polar waters and mineral and petroleum resources are present in the Arctic.

The Committee on Polar Research is concerned with research activities in the Arctic and Antarctic. Periodically the Committee reviews the status of knowledge and needs and opportunities for future investigations, making recommendations to operating agencies of the government. The present report builds on the foundations of three earlier studies: *Science in Antarctica, Part 1: The Life Sciences in Antarctica* (1961); *Science in Antarctica, Part 2: The Physical Sciences in Antarctica* (1961); and *Science in the Arctic Ocean Basin* (1963).

This report draws on extensive information, both scientific and operational, supplied by federal agencies, on the scientific literature, and on the experience and special knowledge of polar scientists in many research institutions. Each of the eight discipline chapters has been the responsibility of a specialized panel. In developing their respective sections, the panels (see page 201) met both individually and jointly; that several members served on more than one panel helped to coordinate the individual sections.

As Chairman of the Committee on Polar Research, I wish to express gratitude to many individuals who have given so generously of their time and knowledge in the preparation of this report, both the members of the scientific panels and those identified in the Acknowledgments. Particularly warm appreciation is due the Committee's Steering Group—M. A. Pomerantz (convenor), W. S. Benninghoff, and A. L. Washburn, who guided the project from its inception. We acknowledge with appreciation the support of the National Science Foundation, which helped to make this study possible.

L. M. GOULD, *Chairman*
Committee on Polar Research

Acknowledgments

The Committee on Polar Research and its scientific panels, in preparing this volume, have drawn on the talents of many individuals and groups. We wish to acknowledge their assistance with appreciation and gratitude, and to single out a few especially valuable contributions.

The first draft of Chapter 4 was compiled by Henri Bader, University of Miami, who also participated in Glaciology Panel deliberations. A special working group, under the chairmanship of E. R. LaChapelle, consisting of C. M. Keeler, U.S. Army Cold Regions Research and Engineering Laboratory; J. H. Smith, U.S. Forest Service; W. V. Tangborn, U.S. Geological Survey; Paul Bock, University of Connecticut; and J. M. Wallace, University of Washington, put together the section on "Snow Research and Control" of Chapter 4.

Specialists contributing to Chapter 5 included L. M. Sebert, Canada Department of Energy, Mines and Resources; R. P. Peat, U.S. Army Topographic Command; and, from the U.S. Geological Survey, D. G. Anderson, W. H. Chapman, D. Landen, and personnel of the Space Technology Applications Office.

Arne A. Wyller, Bartol Research Foundation, is the principal author of Chapter 8. He wishes to acknowledge valuable suggestions from B. J. Bok, Steward Observatory, University of Arizona; J. W. Evans, Sacramento Peak Observatory; W. J. Luyten, University of Minnesota; N. U. Mayall, Kitt Peak National Observatory; M. Schwarzschild, Princeton University; O. C. Wilson, Mt. Wilson and Palomar Observatories; F. B. Wood, University of Florida; and H. Zirin, California Institute of Technology.

Several specialists contributed generously to Chapter 9. They were C. R. Goldman, University of California, Davis; E. K. Eric Gunderson, U.S. Navy Operational Psychiatry Division; J. Kalff, McGill University; G. L. Kooyman, Scripps Institution of Oceanography; G. A. Llano, National Science Foundation; K. Norris, Hawaii Oceanic Institution; D. L. Pawson, Smithsonian Institution; E. D. Rudolph, The Ohio State University; and W. M. Smith, Walter Reed Army Institute for Research.

Throughout the preparation of the report, the secretariats of several committees of the National Academy of Sciences provided valuable advice and suggestions: the Committee on Atmospheric Sciences, the Committee on Oceanography, and the U.S. National Committee for the International Hydrological Decade. C. L. Dunham and R. B. Stevens of the Divisions of Medical Sciences and of Biology and Agriculture, respectively, reviewed Chapter 9.

The Committee wishes especially to thank members of the staff of the Physical Sciences Division for their contributions: Louis DeGoes, Executive Secretary of the CPR; Pembroke J. Hart, Dean P. Kastel, and Herbert G. Shepler, who shared in the scientific preparation of the report; Mrs. Jacqueline Boraks, for her editorial contributions; and Miss Ann Wagoner, for her work on Chapter 1.

Contents

1. **Summary and Recommendations**   1

Introduction   1
Geology and Solid-Earth Geophysics of the Polar Regions   2
The Polar Oceans   3
Polar Glaciology   4
Polar Geodesy and Cartography   5
Polar Meteorology and Climatology   6
Upper-Atmosphere Physics in the Polar Regions   7
Polar Astronomy   8
Polar Biology and Medicine   9
International Cooperation   10
Logistics   11

2   **Geology and Solid-Earth Geophysics of the Polar Regions**   12

Arctic Alaska   12
   History of Geological Exploration   ·   Summary of Present Knowledge   ·   Scientific Problems   ·
   Recommendations
Arctic Canada, Greenland, and the Northernmost Atlantic Ocean Basin   17
   Present State of Investigations and Study   ·   Summary of Present Knowledge   ·   Scientific Problems   ·
   Recommendations
Antarctica   28
   Physiography of the Antarctic Continent   ·   East Antarctica   ·   Transantarctic Mountains   ·
   West Antarctica and the Scotia Arc   ·   Antarctic Geophysics and Crustal Structure   ·
   Scientific Problems   ·   Recommendations
General Recommendations   42
References   42

3.   **The Polar Oceans**   49

The Floor and Underlying Crust of the Arctic Ocean and Its Bordering Seas   49
   Topography and Sediments   ·   Crustal Structures   ·   Theories on the Origin of the Arctic Ocean Floor   ·
   Recommendations
Topography and Crustal Structure of the Seas Surrounding Antarctica   56
   Ocean Floor Surrounding Antarctica   ·   Recommendations
Waters of the Arctic Ocean and Subarctic Seas   57
   Circulation of the Arctic Ocean   ·   Circulation of Subarctic Seas   ·   Opportunities for Research   ·
   Recommendations

Antarctic Water Masses and Currents   64
    Antarctic Circumpolar Current · *Antarctic Convergence* · *Formation of Antarctic Bottom Water* ·
    Recommendations
Air–Sea Interaction in Polar Oceans   67
    Basic Scientific Problems · *Recommendations*
Chemical Oceanography in Polar Regions   68
    Scientific Problems · *Recommendations*
Logistics   69
International Cooperation   70
References   71
Bibliography   71

4.   Polar Glaciology   73

Introduction   73
    Problems of Glaciology · *Research Areas and Priorities*
Sea Ice: Energy Balance and Dynamics   75
    Arctic Sea-Ice Cover: Stable or Unstable? · *Numerical Models of Atmosphere and Ocean* ·
    Sea Ice: Volume, Condition, and Dynamics · *Recommendations* · *Antarctic Pack Ice*
Snow Research and Control   77
    Large-Scale Phenomena · *Small-Scale Phenomena* · *Areal Studies* · *Recommendations*
Glacier Surges and Sliding of a Glacier on Its Bed   79
    Recommendations
Energy-Balance Studies of Glaciers   80
    Recommendations
Flow and Diffusion through Snow and Frozen Ground   81
    Recommendations
Ice Formation in Running Water   82
    Recommendations
Physical Properties of Ice   82
    Recommendations
Quaternary Glaciology   83
    Recommendations
International Cooperation   85
    Cooperation in the Antarctic · *Cooperation in the Arctic* · *International Hydrological Decade* ·
    Recommendations

Appendix A. Glaciology in the Arctic   87

Glaciers   87
    Recommendations
Seasonal Snow Cover   88
    Recommendations
Frozen Ground   88
    Recommendations
Quaternary Chronology   89
    Recommendations
Logistics and Support   89
Summary   90
Acknowledgments   91
References   91

Appendix B: Antarctic Glaciology   91

Geographic Description   92
    Recommendation
Mass Balance of the Ice Sheet   92
    Recommendations

Dynamics of the Ice Sheet   93
    Recommendations
Physical and Chemical Properties of the Ice   94
    Recommendations
History of the Antarctic Ice Sheet   95
    Recommendations
Techniques   95
    Recommendations
Operations and Facilities   96
    Recommendations

Appendix C: Snow Research and Control   97

Introduction   97
The Large-Scale Relations of Snow to Its Environment   98
    A New Approach to Snow Hydrology · Artificial Regulation of Snow Storage · Recommendations
The Small-Scale Relation of Snow to Its Environment   99
    Recommendations
Areal Studies   100
    Remote Sensing of the Snow Cover · Environmental Effects on Snow · Mesoscale Phenomena ·
    Recommendations
General Recommendations   102

5.   Polar Geodesy and Cartography   103

Arctic Alaska   104
    Past Cartographic Accomplishments · Current Cartographic Programs · Recommendations
Arctic Canada   105
    History of Cartographic and Geodetic Programs · Current Programs in Geodesy and Cartography ·
    Recommendations
Greenland and Surrounding Waters   112
    Status of Cartographic Coverage · Current Mapping and Charting Programs · Recommendations
Arctic Ocean Basin   113
    Recent and Current Cartographic Programs · Geodetic Control Networks · Recommendations
General Recommendations for the Arctic   115
Antarctica   118
    East Antarctica · West Antarctica · Antarctic Oceans · Recommendations
Systems Applicable to Polar Geodesy and Cartography   128
    Geodesy · Photogrammetry · Other Remote-Sensing Systems
Polar Gravity Programs   134
    Argentina · Australia · Belgium · Chile · France · Japan · New Zealand · South Africa ·
    Soviet Union · United Kingdom · United States · Summary
References   137
Bibliography   137

Appendix A: Index Maps Showing Coverage of Greenland at Various Scales   138

6.   Polar Meteorology and Climatology   139

Synoptic Meteorology and Tropospheric Processes   139
    Scientific Problems · Recommendations
Stratospheric and Mesospheric Circulations   140
    Scientific Problems · Recommendations
Climatology   143
    Scientific Problems · Recommendations
Heat Balance   144
    Scientific Problems · Recommendations

Atmospheric Chemistry   145
    Scientific Problems   ·   *Recommendations*
The Global Atmospheric Research Program in the Polar Regions   146
    Recommendations
Automation, Logistics, and Data   147
    Recommendation
References   148
Bibliography   148

7.   **Upper-Atmosphere Physics in the Polar Regions**   149

Galactic and Solar Cosmic Rays   150
    Progress in the Field   ·   *Outstanding Problems*   ·   *Recommendations*
Auroral Phenomena   153
    Progress in the Field   ·   *Outstanding Problems*   ·   *Recommendations*
Photochemical Effects   159
    Recent Progress   ·   *Outstanding Problems*   ·   *Recommendations*
Upper-Atmosphere Dynamics   162
    Recent Progress   ·   *Outstanding Problems*   ·   *Recommendations*
Logistics   166
    Unmanned Automatic Observatories   ·   *Rocket and Aircraft Support*   ·   *Facilities and Logistic Support
    in the Arctic Basin*   ·   *Recommendations*
References   167

8.   **Polar Astronomy**   170

Introduction   170
Solar Research   171
Planetary Research (Moon, Planets, and Comets)   172
Stellar Research   173
Stations and Instruments   174
Recommendations   176
References   176

9.   **Polar Biology and Medicine**   178

Systematics and Biogeography   178
Terrestrial Ecosystems   180
Freshwater Ecosystems   181
    Recommendations
Marine Ecosystems   184
    Recommendations
Comparative Physiology   189
Animal Behavior   191
    Recommendations
Human Biology   192
    Health and Morbidity   ·   *Physiological and Biochemical Studies*   ·   *Psychological Studies*
Conservation   195
Logistics   197
International Cooperation   198
References   198

Committee and Panel Members   201

POLAR RESEARCH
A Survey

1

Summary and Recommendations

INTRODUCTION

The north and south polar regions are dominated by rigorous cold and characterized by months of continuous daylight alternating with equal periods of darkness. In almost every other respect, the Arctic and Antarctic are strikingly different.

The North Pole lies near the center of a deep oceanic basin surrounded by land areas that, except for a breach at the Bering Strait and the expanse of sea between Greenland and Norway, isolate the arctic waters from the other northern oceans. By contrast, the south polar region is dominated by a mile-high land mass surrounded by frigid waters of the earth's three great oceans, the Atlantic, Pacific, and Indian. Antarctica is the fifth largest continent, with an area of 5.5 million square miles—larger than the United States and Mexico combined. This area doubles in the winter as the sea freezes around the periphery of the continent. Antarctica has been referred to as a "hump" and the Arctic as a "hollow," reflecting the continental character of the one region and the oceanic nature of the other.

Antarctica is a vast desert, burdened by glacier ice that is pierced by isolated nunataks and fringed by narrow belts of glacial deposits and rock outcrops. Only penguins, a few other bird species, and rare insects inhabit the bleak continent. Terrestrial life in Antarctica, both plant and animal, is as poor as the oceanic life is rich. The oceans surrounding Antarctica are potentially richer food-producing areas than any other on earth; they are the home of the great blue whale, which can eat a ton of krill a day—and which weighs fully five times as much as any dinosaur that ever lived.

The arctic lands, on the other hand, are carpeted with green tundra and boreal forest and are inhabited by men and a great variety of animal life. Early man used the Siberian-Alaskan land bridge more than 10 thousand years ago as a stepping-stone in his first migration to the New World. The extreme isolation of the Antarctic and the lack of indigenous food and fuel prevented a comparable invasion by peoples from the South Seas.

For centuries, the poles have driven hardy men to exploration, motivated by curiosity, adventure, promise of rewarding harvests of seals and whales, or by the search for shorter trade routes across the Arctic to the Orient. The annals of early polar exploration tell of daring exploits and killing hardships. Ironically, some of the more tragic early expeditions contributed most to our knowledge of the polar regions, as, for example, the ill-fated Franklin expedition into the Arctic and Shackleton's remarkable journey after his ship, *Endurance*, had been crushed by pack ice in the Weddell Sea. The ships *Jeannette*, *Fram*, and *Sedov*, drifting ice-bound in the Arctic, gathered much information on the little-known Arctic Ocean Basin. Because survival in the harsh environment demanded so much of the early explorers, their contributions to our knowledge of the polar regions were largely limited to the discovery and mapping of land features.

Polar investigation has entered a new era. The unprecedented magnitude and comprehensiveness of the cooperative polar research carried out during the International Geophysical Year (IGY) 1957–1958 mark the end of the age of random exploration and reconnaissance and the beginning of scientific research in the true sense. Broad features of the polar environment are now known; future polar work must be focused on the search for solutions to specific significant problems, largely interdisciplinary in nature, that will lead to a better understanding of the total global environment.

The polar regions are integral parts of the total global environment, and understanding of polar processes and phenomena is essential to the solution of earth-wide problems. For example, polar atmospheric circulations strongly influence weather and climate at the lower latitudes, and the polar oceans can be considered the high-latitude portions of the world oceans. Much of the energy generated in the magnetosphere tens of thousands of kilometers above the earth's surface is guided toward, and dissipated in, the polar upper atmosphere. Removal of the sea-ice cover of polar seas, either accidentally or deliberately, would almost certainly have a profound effect on the global heat balance and hence on the world's weather and climate.

To illustrate the pressures and urgency that bear on polar research, the technological implications of an ice-free Arctic Ocean are of great import to the exploitation of rich natural resources and to northern development as a whole. In 1968, an oil field was discovered on the arctic coast of Alaska—the province likely extending into arctic Canada—which shows promise of being part of one of the largest petroleum accumulations known in the world today. Already millions of dollars are being invested in seeking means to deliver the crude oil to markets by reinforcing the hulls of large tankers, building pipelines and airfields, and launching massive over-land-and-ice tractor trains. Ships passing through an ice-free Arctic Ocean and nearby waters would reduce shipping distances between the Far East and Europe by about 6000 miles; tankers could deliver crude oil directly to world markets. But would adverse effects outweigh commercial benefits? Will the ecological effects of industrialization or massive oil spillage be grave and irreversible? While accelerated development in the Far North is upon us and is desirable in many ways, we have yet to uncover and explain many of the basic secrets of the arctic environment, to relate them to their global counterparts, and to weigh the interlocking consequences of any environmental modification we propose to undertake.

To formulate recommendations and plans for future action in the polar regions, we have believed it necessary to review past research and present knowledge and to identify critical areas for scientific investigation. The remainder of this chapter summarizes the principal recommendations of our study, numbered consecutively for the reader's convenience.

GEOLOGY AND SOLID-EARTH GEOPHYSICS OF THE POLAR REGIONS

Geology and solid-earth geophysics are concerned with the structure, composition, and physical history of the earth and with the nature of its surface under changing environmental conditions. In the geologic past, the north and south geomagnetic poles were in very different locations than they are today, the polar climate was warm, and fossils give evidence of a rich, semitropical plant and animal life. Compelling evidence is accumulating that the world's great land masses were once a single protocontinent which slowly separated, perhaps by sea-floor spreading, and drifted apart. The polar

regions have a key role in testing these concepts. The evolution of the polar regions to their present structure, geography, and climate is one of the exciting problems in science.

The interest of geology and geophysics is twofold. Scientifically, knowledge of the structure, composition, history, and dynamics of surface and deep-lying features will permit us to obtain a unified concept of the evolution of the solid earth, the life that inhabits it, and the processes that govern it today. Thus we are interested in the bedrock and the mountain range, the deep crust of the earth and the floor of the sea, the typical and the anomalous. On the practical side, such knowledge is our best indicator of hidden natural resources and our best protection against the consequences of natural disasters like earthquakes.

As we review our present information, we see that the land areas of arctic Canada, Greenland, and the northernmost Atlantic Ocean Basin have been reasonably well mapped at reconnaissance scale and the general structure and stratigraphy of the bedrock are known. Knowledge of surficial deposits and of the effects of glacial and periglacial processes is less satisfactory. Base-map and air-photo coverage is extensive, but many areas appear only on small-scale maps and some have not been photographed at all. Detailed bathymetric maps, essential to topographic and structural information on the sea floor, are almost lacking. Geophysical data are sparse, confined mainly to low-density gravity surveys, widely spaced aeromagnetic profiles, and a few heat-flow and seismic crustal observations. In arctic Alaska, very little information was available until 1944, when limited geologic studies and drilling were undertaken in search of oil. Further investigations have been made subsequently, particularly during the IGY, but the great impetus to geologic exploration throughout the entire western Arctic has been the discovery of oil at Cook Inlet in 1957 and at Prudhoe Bay in 1968.

Of the many scientific problems we wish to resolve on the geology and geophysics of the Arctic, we give particular importance to the following: the relationships between the Alpha Cordillera, Lomonosov Ridge, Innuitian orogen, and Cordilleran orogen; the great depth of the edge of the continental shelf off the Canadian archipelago; the age and nature of the Mackenzie River delta; the origin and history of Baffin Bay and the Nares Lineament; the relationships between the geosynclines and basins of arctic Canada and their contemporaneous equivalents in Greenland; the tectonic history of northeast Greenland; the late Tertiary and Quaternary history of Greenland; the history of the Brito-Arctic volcanic province and its relation to the Mid-Atlantic Ridge; and the nature of the crust below Iceland. Important problems to be studied in arctic Alaska include the succession and age of the stratified rocks; the relation of the Brooks Range to the Cordilleran and Innuitian orogens; the origin of the Brooks Range overthrusts; the age and structure of the basement rocks; and the nature of crustal and mantle structure.

1. Recent oil discoveries in the Arctic have emphasized both the economic potential of that region and the inadequacy of our present knowledge of its geologic structure and history. The completion of reconnaissance geologic mapping in all mountainous regions is needed, together with detailed geologic mapping of selected critical areas. Systematic aeromagnetic, gravity, and heat-flow surveys of the entire region should be made, along with bathymetric surveys of the continental shelf and slope and inland waters. Further geological and geophysical study, including deep drilling, of the northern Mid-Atlantic Ridge would have great scientific value. Additional seismograph stations should be established in the Arctic to provide an adequate network for the study of earthquakes and global structure.

Our knowledge of the geologic history of Antarctica has been gathered during the past 70 years, most of it since the beginning of the IGY, and is now reasonably good in broad outline. The broad outlines of antarctic stratigraphy and structure are also fairly clear, and geophysical data have revealed the general morphology of the subglacial bedrock surface. Rock outcrops constitute less than five percent of the continental area and most have been photographed and mapped at some scale. Considerable geophysical work has been accomplished on oversnow traverses and from ships in the surrounding oceans. These studies include seismic soundings and refraction shooting, gravity observations, magnetic measurements, and paleomagnetic determinations.

We single out for particular attention the following scientific questions: the ages and boundaries of crustal geologic provinces; the past geographic relationships of these provinces to each other and to other continents; the history of the Scotia Submarine Ridge; the possible continuation of the circum-Pacific mobile belt across West Antarctica; the aseismic character of Antarctica; the age and structural relations of the basement rocks in West Antarctica; and the relationships between the circum-Pacific mobile belt, the Ellsworth Mountains fold belt, and the Transantarctic Mountains. Other significant problems include the age and correlation of the strata in the Transantarctic Mountains; the nature of the boundaries of the Transantarctic Mountains with East and West Antarctica; the early Precambrian history of East Antarctica; the morphology of the subglacial bedrock surface; the response of the crust and mantle to the ice load; the cause of the uplift of the Transantarctic Mountains and the coastal rim of East Antarctica; and the great depth of the edge of the continental shelf.

2. Great advances have been made in antarctic geology and geophysics during the past 15 years, but many basic questions remain unanswered. The reconnaissance geologic mapping of the continent is nearing completion, and increased support for the study of specific geologic problems, commonly requiring large-scale geologic mapping, is needed. Systematic aeromagnetic surveys and topographic mapping of the subglacial bedrock surface by airborne radiosounder should be undertaken. Studies of deposits below the grounded and floating parts of the Antarctic Ice Sheet will help to clarify both the history of the continent and the mechanics of subglacial erosion. Additional paleomagnetic determinations will help to test the reality of continental drift, and geological and geophysical studies of the antarctic continental shelf and slope and the adjacent midocean ridges should be undertaken.

We make the following recommendations that apply to both polar regions:

3. Knowledge of the Arctic and the Antarctic has matured to the point that individual scientists or small groups, as well as larger organizations, can make important contributions. Field studies by small parties are logistically possible and should be encouraged. Additional radiometric age determinations should be made on systematically collected rocks from the polar regions. Support for systematic laboratory study of existing polar rock collections, and for reduction and analysis of scientific data now on hand, should be encouraged. Increased support for the preparation and publication of maps and manuscripts on work already accomplished would assure wide dissemination of this new knowledge.

THE POLAR OCEANS

The deep circulations of the world ocean are strongly influenced by the temperature differences between the polar and equatorial regions. The cold, dense polar waters sink to the ocean floor and spread outward to form the deep and bottom waters of the Pacific, Indian, and Atlantic Oceans. The Weddell Sea of Antarctica is the primary region of these sinking cold waters, while a secondary source is in the Greenland and Norwegian Seas. Polar fronts or convergences mark the interfaces with the major oceans. The polar regions similarly force global atmospheric circulations, exerting major influence on world climate. The interactions between atmosphere, ocean, and ice are significant and complex—and imperfectly understood.

The Arctic and Antarctic Oceans present some of the most fundamental and still unsolved problems in geophysics. The structure of the earth's crust underlying the polar oceans is one of the basic unanswered questions relating to the origin and evolution of land forms. Although we now know the topography of the sea floor in these regions fairly well, the geophysical parameters, such as gravity, magnetics, and heat flow, are still only poorly charted. These parameters give important clues to crustal composition and structure and permit integration of the regional pattern into the global tectonic pattern. Recent hypotheses on continental drift and the origin of ocean basins by means of sea-floor spreading, which are providing a great stimulus to the earth sciences, need to be tested in the polar regions. The history of movements of the antarctic continent and the spreading of the Arctic Ocean Basin can now be investigated by magnetic surveys and studies of paleomagnetic cores.

To understand the dynamics of global oceanic circulation and the processes of climatic changes, we must study the polar heat sinks—the conditions of bottom-water formation and processes occurring along the polar fronts. These heat sinks differ greatly in intensity and fluctuate widely in time. With its perennial cover of sea ice, the Arctic Ocean is considered to be a key factor in climatic changes by some scientists who believe that removal of sea ice could produce major changes in world weather. This hypothesis, bearing on a subject so important to man's welfare, deserves to be tested fully by field, laboratory, and theoretical studies. Stability of the ice cover depends on air–sea interaction processes such as energy transfer and the solar-radiation budget and the general circulation of ice and water in the ocean. These processes must be better understood to predict the future of the ice cover and its climatic effect.

In studying the circulation and heat budget of the Arctic Ocean, we believe it necessary to carry out the following programs: to monitor the larger year-to-year variations in the heat budget, which result from variations in albedo and from exchanges of ice and water through the entrances to the Arctic Ocean, particularly through the Greenland-Svalbard strait; to monitor ice and water movements by means of an array of automatic telemetering stations on the ice that continuously record meteorological and oceanographic data; to conduct theoretical studies of Arctic Ocean circulation which draw on analytical, simulator, and numerical models as well as on field work; to monitor water transport across the Greenland–Iceland–Faeroes–Scotland Ridge so that the ways in which arctic bottom water and north Atlantic deep water are exchanged can be determined; and to identify and utilize radioactive isotopes, organic compounds, and trace metals as tracers of water masses.

To determine the interaction between the world ocean and antarctic circulation, direct measurements of the Antarctic Circumpolar Current passing through the Drake Passage should be made using floats or other techniques; a multiship survey should be carried out along a section of the Antarctic Convergence, possibly in cooperation with other nations; and the surface heat exchange associated with the formation of bottom water should be monitored in detail through at least one winter, possibly from a barge or similar platform frozen into the pack ice of the Weddell Sea.

With regard to climatic changes, year-to-year variations in sea-ice area and albedo should be monitored; field and laboratory experiments should be conducted on the freezing processes of seawater with special attention to the structure and depth of convection (a ship or buoy platform could be placed in an area of seasonal ice cover to monitor conditions during sea-ice formation); the internal stresses of sea-ice sheets should be measured under both natural and laboratory conditions; and carbon dioxide exchange between ocean and atmosphere should be monitored.

A historical approach to the study of climate should also be pursued. Glacial fluctuations on land can be traced by studying sediments on the ocean floor. Ice-rafted rocks, shells of organisms, and sedimentation rates all give clues to past climates. Long piston cores should be obtained in quantity from the arctic and antarctic sea floor: cores taken to date have given a very incomplete climatic history of the polar oceans, and more complete areal coverage by longer cores is needed to provide adequate geographic distribution and to push the record back further in time.

4. We give priority to the following oceanographic research problems and recommend that they be the object of comprehensive study: the structure of the earth's crust underlying the polar oceans; relationships of polar to global ocean-water circulations; influences of sea-ice cover on climatic changes; and the correlation of bottom sediments with past climates.

POLAR GLACIOLOGY

Glaciology—the study of snow, ice, and frozen ground—is a young, interdisciplinary science. The scientific, engineering, and economic aspects of glaciology are highly significant to today's society because of our ability, within limits, to control or manage these resources. Snow control could directly influence water supply in many densely populated areas of the world, and ice control could determine the navigability of many water bodies. The presence or absence of snow, ice, and frozen ground may depend on a delicate climatic balance. If this balance is unstable, attempts to control snow or ice might trigger a reaction that could have wide environmental implications. Thus our understanding of glaciological processes has high relevance for both short-range and long-range planning concerned with weather, water, and ground conditions in many parts of the world.

Most of the problems of glaciology concern the relation of snow and ice to the environment in which they form and evolve. The "easy" problems of glaciology are concerned with such things as the inventory (size, shape, and location of ice masses) and physical properties (for example, density, temperature, deformation, and metamorphism). The "difficult" problems deal with the effects of weather and annual climatic cycles; they have to do with the exchange of energy and water substance across a number of interfaces. The "very difficult" problems bear on the effects of secular climatic changes on the nature and spatial distribution of ice masses. The effects of these changes can be almost instantaneous or, as in responses of large ice caps and continental ice sheets, for example, can have a time delay of millennia or hundreds of millennia. Glacial geology, biology, synoptic meteorology, and two powerful new tools—geodetic satellites and remote-sensing techniques—have central contributions to make in resolving these problems. It should be understood that we have no intent to de-emphasize those basic, on-going research trends in glaciology whose significance and importance are well established.

5. **We single out three problems of glaciology as the most timely and urgent to man's understanding of his environment and to his ability to use this knowledge for efficient utilization and management of resources. In order of priority they are: sea-ice energy balance and dynamics; snow-cover research and control; and glacier surges and the sliding of a glacier on its bed.**

6. **We direct attention to five additional research problems for which new or increased emphasis is warranted and which should lead to the most rapid advances toward solutions of problems of practical and theoretical importance. They are (with no priority order): comprehensive energy-balance studies of glaciers; flow and diffusion through snow and frozen ground; ice formation in running water; physical properties of ice; and certain aspects of Quaternary glaciology, especially the analysis of long cores from glaciers and ocean-bottom sediments.**

We note that some of the above problems involve very large-scale studies and international exchange of data, which require formal procedures for international collaboration. Glaciology has benefited enormously from international cooperation, and its future progress will be affected by the measure of cooperation that obtains. We attach particular importance to effective U.S. participation in the International Hydrological Decade.

POLAR GEODESY AND CARTOGRAPHY

Geodesy and cartography are often thought of as service disciplines, in the sense that they do not study or inquire into naturally occurring phenomena but rather provide a means whereby the scientific investigation of any area may be conducted. Without maps, accurately and precisely portraying an area of interest, the geologist, glaciologist, or oceanographer would have no way of locating or delineating a region of investigation nor any graphic means for illustrating research results. Cartographers, in turn, would be unable to produce quality maps without having access to the precisely located points in a geodetic control network from which they can extrapolate distances and elevations. To the simple questions "Where is it? What does it look like? How

big is it?" geodesy and cartography supply indispensable answers.

During the course of investigations of large areas, the needs of the user disciplines for maps change gradually and consistently. As program planning shifts from early reconnaissance stages to systematic investigation of selected areas, geodesists and cartographers must support and anticipate these changes in emphasis by providing larger-scale, more detailed, more precise maps, thereby slowly filling in the gaps left by earlier, cursory stages.

The supportive services of geodesy and cartography are not, however, limited to scientific investigations. As is often the case, their services are called upon to aid in matters of economic interest. For example, the Prudhoe Bay oil discovery has already prompted a great increase in demand for larger-scale maps of adjacent areas to support further exploration. And the decision to transport the crude oil to lower-latitude markets, whether by land or sea, must be weighed in the light of precise information gathered and depicted on land-surface maps and bathymetric charts.

Reviewing the status of antarctic geodesy and cartography, we note that most of the nations active on the continent have produced maps from both ground-based surveys and aerial photographs, with varying amounts of ground control. Reconnaissance mapping is nearing completion. Mapping continues to improve and expand, and maps of selected coastal and mountainous regions of West Antarctica at a 1:250,000 scale will probably be completed by 1982. Looking to the future, we give importance to larger-scale maps of specific regions selected for scientific study and to U.S. participation in the preparation of maps at a 1:250,000 scale of the unmapped mountainous regions and at a 1:1,000,000 and smaller scale of the continent as a whole. We see a particular need for aircraft specially instrumented for mapping and the acquisition of geophysical data with remote and thermal sensors, sounders, side-looking radar, precise cartographic cameras, and other camera systems for solar, infrared, and multispectral photography.

With respect to the north polar regions, coverage of arctic Alaska is fairly good; the region has been photographed and mapped at scales of 1:250,000 and 1:1,000,000, the coastal areas at a 1:50,000 scale, and most of the interior at a 1:63,360 scale. Nevertheless, in view of rapidly evolving scientific investigations and economic developments, the status of mapping programs in Alaska should be reviewed to assure that current user requirements are met.

Arctic Canada has all been mapped at scales of 1:250,000 and 1:1,000,000, and limited coverage at a 1:50,000 scale is available. Here we believe it important to extend geodetic control westward to the Alaskan border and to the Mackenzie River valley and delta to permit an expanded program of larger-scale mapping.

Greenland is mapped at various scales, but the quality of the maps is not uniform nor is the entire region mapped at a single scale. A major effort should be made to improve the maps and charts, using both existing cartographic data and new techniques such as side-looking radar, so that a synoptic view of the Greeland Ice Sheet may be derived. We also give importance to the initiation of a program of high-altitude photography and orthophotomaps of Greenland for use in glaciological studies. Synoptic mosaic coverage of Iceland by radar imagery is recommended to record the present configuration of glaciers and to give topographic coverage of the interesting neovolcanic zone. Radio echo-sounding should be carried out as well to determine the Icelandic subglacial topography.

Referring to both polar regions, we single out the following tasks: (1) Nautical charts should be updated and corrected. To do so requires continued acquisition of large quantities of data, in the face of the special problems in positioning and data interpretation which the polar regions present. (2) Tidal stations should be established in polar areas for the extension of precise leveling operations. These geodetic data, combined with meteorological and glaciological data, would provide improved knowledge of the state of the ice masses. (3) Terrestrial gravimetric data should be obtained at the poles by means of continuous recording systems combined with astronomic determinations. Gravity measurements at sea should be expanded.

In this discussion, we have called for the application of recently developed techniques and instruments to geodetic and cartographic work. These, in complement with traditional methods, are working a revolution in mapping. Particularly significant is the role of artificial satellites either through on-board instrumentation for earth observations or by precise tracking of their orbits, which, by giving a known point of reference, establishes distances with remarkable accuracy between specified points on the earth. High priority should be given to the use of satellites and electronic techniques in establishing geodetic control. Specifically, a need exists to establish geodetic connections across the Bering Strait and between Greenland, Iceland, Svalbard, and Norway to tie together existing work and to permit adjustment to the National Geodetic Satellite Program. Geodetic control in other areas should be worked out using the most economical method commensurate with desired accuracy, that is, classical triangulation or trilateration using Shoran, Loran, Aerodist (with aircraft), or Doppler satellites. Present technology for establishing geodetic control to measure ice movement is not entirely suitable, and new procedures such as hovering helicopters and portable Doppler satellite receivers are recommended.

We believe that high priority should be given to the utilization for polar work of satellite return-beam Vidicon imagery under the proposed Earth Resources Technology Satellite (ERTS). In particular, we urge that Vidicon imagery be considered in the compilation of a planimetric supplement to the 1:1,000,000-scale map series of the Antarctic,

and that the technique be used to monitor and map short-term changes in the surfaces of polar ice caps, in coastal ice features, and to provide synoptic up-to-date coverage for compilation of the recommended 1:5,000,000-scale map of the Arctic.

7. Advances in technology and new, imaginative techniques should be applied to polar geodesy and cartography. Among these we include: satellites and electronic equipment to establish necessary geodetic control; utilization of satellite imagery under the Earth Resources Technology Satellite program to map short- and long-term changes in polar ice caps and for small-scale mapping; tidal stations in conjunction with precise leveling; continuous gravity readings at the poles combined with precise astronomical observations; gravity measurements at sea; and aircraft specially instrumented for mapping and acquisition of data by remote sensors. New techniques and equipment must also be applied to mapping of snow-covered areas of low relief where measurements of ice movement are required.

8. The preparation of up-to-date maps and charts of the polar regions is a continuing, essential facet of polar research and development. Of the many needed tasks highest priority should be given to the following: large-scale and bathymetric charts of the polar oceans; large-scale antarctic maps of areas selected for detailed study; exploration of existing cartographic data and recently developed cartographic techniques to prepare uniform-scale maps of Greenland; and review of the status of current mapping programs in Alaska to include requirements generated by the recent large oil strike on the arctic coast.

POLAR METEOROLOGY AND CLIMATOLOGY

Meteorology and climatology constitute a broad field of study which has been investigated on virtually every polar expedition and which will continue to be one of the main fields of scientific and practical interest in polar research. We have noted above how closely intertwined are meteorological and climatological processes in the polar regions with other geophysical phenomena. Understanding of the interaction of the air, sea, and ice, for example, is critical to an understanding of the dynamic systems that govern both the Arctic and Antarctic and the entire globe. To approach this kind of problem, synoptic or coordinated observations at many different points on the surface and at altitude are necessary. In the past, limitations of observational techniques and areal coverage of data have handicapped such studies. Although the possibilities for improving conventional observation systems in the polar regions may be limited, we believe that remote and automated sensing techniques and the use of mathematical models offer inviting prospects. Thus we can single out five specific subjects which are now more than ever susceptible of study and which are likely to be of particular importance in the next decade: synoptic meteorology and tropospheric processes; stratospheric and mesospheric circulations; climatology*; heat balance; and atmospheric chemistry.

Polar meteorology and climatology will probably be advanced most in the next decade by the application of new technologies. Utilization of satellites, sounding rockets, and balloons is already planned under the Global Atmospheric Research Program (GARP). We attach great importance to the development of a low-cost automatic weather station for polar use. Aircraft should continue to collect important data unattainable by other means. The high-altitude vehicles combined with automated ground stations and instrumented aircraft would give vital synoptic coverage of the two polar regions and, simultaneously, would relieve logistic problems and costs by reducing the need for manned surface stations.

To exploit these new techniques for polar meteorological and climatological studies, we emphasize the importance of the following specific measures: the meteorological rocket network should be expanded to give adequate coverage in the northern hemisphere; special chaff, or other economical rocket payloads, should be used to measure tidal motions in the 60- to 80-km region; radiometeor equipment should be installed in both polar regions to measure winds at 80- to 110-km altitudes; measurement of stratospheric and mesospheric temperatures should be made by remote sensing from meteorological satellites in nearly polar orbits; aircraft should be provided by the appropriate agencies for use in logistic support and as data-acquisition platforms in the Arctic Ocean Basin; and a ground station, equipped with cloud-sensing radar, should be established in the Arctic to permit visual cloud studies in conjunction with instrumented aircraft flights. While the development of unmanned stations is under way, the three U.S. meteorological operations at McMurdo, Byrd, and South Pole Stations should continue to record basic meteorological parameters until superseded by other observational means.

Recent advances in numerical modeling, together with the high cost of logistic support of polar research, suggest that a change of emphasis is necessary in the traditional relationship between theory and observation in polar meteorology and climatology. More effort is needed in theoretical modeling of atmospheric processes and related phenomena at ocean and ice interfaces to ensure that expensive observational programs are properly directed toward specific scien-

tific objectives. To improve models, aircraft measurements are essential, especially to study small-scale processes. Routine synoptic weather reconnaissance flights, such as those flown daily by the U.S. Air Force between Alaska, 90° N, and England, should include monitoring of large-scale year-to-year variations in ice extent and albedo.

The kinds of scientific problems we wish to resolve and the types of tools required to do so make logistic support especially important. This is true for most polar research. With respect to the Arctic, much of the necessary logistic support for our recommended programs may already exist, particularly for aircraft. But steps must be taken to ensure optimal use of these expensive facilities and vehicles through program coordination and determination of appropriate priorities for scientific observations on arctic missions undertaken for other than scientific purposes. Moreover, the scientific community and other interested groups should be informed of facilities and new opportunities for arctic research.

There is evidence that many of the data required by researchers have already been obtained but are not fully used, either because they are not processed in a suitable manner or because their sources are not widely known. Other data from both polar regions are readily available but are not being utilized to the maximum. Such material is invaluable for home-based programs, particularly at universities which have an educational role and serve to bring new workers into polar research. We emphasize that support for such programs is an essential complement to field programs and must continue to be given high priority.

Finally, it is important not to jeopardize research by logistic compromises. Facilities, transportation, and other logistic and administrative support should be available for small, independent, short-term research efforts which aim to solve specific problems requiring limited observations.

9. To advance polar meteorology and climatology, the application of new techniques—satellites, balloons, rockets, automated ground stations, and specially instrumented aircraft—is of primary importance. Greater effort should be given to mathematical modeling of atmospheric processes and related studies, especially those pertaining to the air-ocean-ice interfaces. Aircraft should collect needed data unavailable from other sources, particularly on small-scale atmospheric processes and on large-scale year-to-year variations in heat budget. A review of coordination of arctic logistics and of the management of arctic data is necessary.

*The RAND Lake Arrowhead Study (J. O. Fletcher, ed., *Proceedings of the Symposium on the Arctic Heat Budget and Atmospheric Circulation*, RAND Corp. Memo No. RM-5233-NSF, Dec. 1966) correctly identified the probable directions of rewarding projects in climatological research in the Arctic during the next decade. A similar analysis of the influences of antarctic regions on global climate is also now available (J. O. Fletcher, "Ice Extent on the Southern Ocean and its Relation to World Climate," RM-5793-NSF, The RAND Corp., March 1969).

UPPER-ATMOSPHERE PHYSICS IN THE POLAR REGIONS

The field of upper-atmosphere physics embraces all phenomena in the regions beyond the domains of classical meteorology: it is the study of the earth's spatial environment and its interaction with and control by the sun. The advent of space-vehicle techniques for scientific research has revolutionized our methods of studying the upper atmosphere and our understanding of its processes. It has caused us also to change our way of looking at upper-atmosphere problems: all aspects of each phenomenon must be considered as a totality, irrespective of the region of space in which they occur. Thus we stress carefully coordinated measurements from both space vehicles and ground stations and, in view of the over-all limitation on resources, we move toward specially mounted experimental programs rather than toward extensions of the ground-based monitoring networks that characterized earlier synoptic studies. However, the importance should not be discounted of maintaining a sufficient network of ground monitors to display the key features of the long-term variations of the upper atmosphere.

This unified approach to atmospheric investigations can be illustrated by the study of auroral phenomena. The polar upper atmosphere has very different characteristics from that at lower latitudes, primarily because the geomagnetic field lines re-enter the earth in the polar regions. The geomagnetic field exerts a dominant influence on the movement of charged particles in the polar upper atmosphere, which must be considered a part of the magnetosphere that extends tens of thousands of kilometers in front of the earth as it orbits the sun and hundreds of thousands of kilometers behind. To understand how auroras arise, we must trace the energetic particles from their initial capture by the magnetosphere from the solar wind, through their acceleration and transport in the magnetosphere, until their precipitation into the upper atmosphere at the poles. Studies of these processes require not only ground-based measurements but also coordinated rocket and satellite measurements of auroral fluxes, plasma, emitted radiations, and electric and magnetic fields. Similarly, studies of solar cosmic rays require ground-based and balloon observations coordinated with a variety of satellite measurements during specific events. Another example of this unified approach is the investigation of airflow morphology by means of particle detectors and photometers on satellites, together with rocket or ground-based measurements of wind and turbulence in the E region of the ionosphere.

We see a need for more sophisticated instrumentation, both in space vehicles and on the ground. Satellite instruments capable of measuring protons and alpha particles in many energy intervals with high sensitivity and directional capabilities would greatly aid in understanding the propagation of solar cosmic rays. Very-low-frequency transmitters, located both on satellites and on the ground, will permit probing of the magnetosphere and emission stimulation; artificial injection of identifiable particles into the ionosphere can provide needed information on electric and magnetic field variations. The development of unmanned automatic observatories, possibly using satellites for data relay, offers a promising opportunity for much improved geographic coverage in ground-based sensing of the upper atmosphere.

Small-rocket techniques should be employed much more extensively in the polar ionosphere for studies of ion chemistry and neutral-atmosphere dynamics, and these measurements should be carefully integrated with ground-based and satellite observations. The global patterns of composition, temperature, and eddy diffusion should be explored with combinations of rocket and satellite techniques.

10. Space-vehicle techniques, together with balloons, automatic unmanned ground observatories, and other sophisticated instrumentation aloft and on the ground, should be fully exploited in the study of the polar upper atmosphere and its relation to the total terrestrial environment. Global observations from ground stations, rockets, and satellites should be fully coordinated in order to achieve maximum benefits. A capability for quick reaction to specific solar-particle events should be established; and there is urgent need to develop a dependable real-time communications link between home stations and polar field stations to achieve rapid access to data, especially during specific events, and to acquire more meaningful data.

POLAR ASTRONOMY

Two characteristics of the polar regions are particularly advantageous for observational astronomy. Continuous darkness during the winter months and daylight during the summer offer the possibility of long periods of uninterrupted observations, while the exceptionally dry polar atmosphere should allow excellent "seeing" and observations in the infrared not feasible elsewhere from the earth's surface. Compared with lower latitudes, polar stations may enjoy an order-of-magnitude improvement in both factors—more than 100 hours of continuous observing time and less than 0.04 mm of precipitable water vapor in the atmosphere. These factors are of special significance to stellar, planetary, and solar research, as in the study of the evolution of long-lasting events and in determining temperatures and emissions of astronomical objects.

A third factor bears on the value of polar astronomical observations. When we look at the longitude and latitude distribution of present-day observational facilities, we are struck by the fact that there are no truly high-latitude stations, that there are 13 stations in the southern hemisphere compared with 103 in the northern hemisphere, and that the worldwide longitude coverage is far from satisfactory. The consequences are that it is not now possible to observe astronomical objects when they are below the horizon of the midlatitude stations nor, in many cases, to overcome the brevity of coverage by a single station as the object passes beyond the field of view as the earth rotates. Polar astronomical facilities would aid materially in solving these problems.

To date, very little attention has been given to the establishment of polar observatories, in part because of the remoteness and earlier logistic inaccessibility of the regions. Logistic systems are now adequate to the task, and polar research stations at Thule, McMurdo, and South Pole, for example, are well-equipped bases of a permanent nature. Cold-weather technology has made great strides in the past decade, so that diverse equipment and instruments are now operated under polar conditions.

Thus we believe it timely to evaluate the feasibility of a program of polar astronomical observation. We would begin by conducting preliminary seeing tests at South Pole Station, which weather records indicate is the most promising site, and by determining whether the state of the art of mechanical technology is adequate for the operation and maintenance of medium-sized (24- to 30-inch) telescopes in polar environments.

11. The long periods of time available in polar regions for continuous observations and the extremely low water-vapor content of the atmosphere should be exploited for stellar, planetary, and solar astronomy. We recommend, as a first step, that seeing tests be conducted at the South Pole Station, together with feasibility studies for operating and maintaining a medium-sized telescope at that station.

POLAR BIOLOGY AND MEDICINE

Despite their seemingly inhospitable environment, the polar regions are the home of a remarkably large number and variety of life forms. Plants and animals, marine life, and, in the Arctic, human beings, have over the ages adjusted to, and thrive in, a milieu which to those in the temperate latitudes would be insupportable. Even today we know very little about many of these unique organisms and less about their physiological, ecological, and behavioral systems. Research on any systematic basis into polar biology and medicine could be said to date back only twenty years or so, having been initiated under the impetus of World War II and by the realization of the significance of polar life forms for any biological theory, for the inventory of world biological resources, and for wise management of our ecology. More recently, striking similarities in the problems of adaptation and survival between the polar regions and spaceflight and habitation undersea have motivated further close inquiry.

One of the most important objects of biological research—and among the most difficult to analyze—is the ecological system (or ecosystem), the manner in which living things and their environment exist as an interdependent totality. Ecological systems of the polar land masses have the advantage of being relatively uncomplicated and, in part for that reason, are increasingly coming under study; but progress is slow because our knowledge of the life history and population ecology of most of the species involved is so incomplete. We

must give particular attention to increasing that knowledge. Not to be neglected are the input of nutrients from marine sources to near-shore areas and the role of microorganisms in soils. We note that terrestrial ecosystem research and, to a degree, limnological research are deficient with respect to criteria for comparing the relationships of organisms to their environments, units of measurement, and levels of accuracy.

Freshwater ecological systems of polar regions differ from those in temperate latitudes largely as a consequence of the polar light regime and the long duration of heavy ice cover. Primary producers and consumers of microplankton are not well identified nor are the organisms that live on the upper and under surfaces of lake ice. Lakes in Antarctica are special cases, extremely interesting scientifically: limited to the fringe of the continent and almost always heavily covered with ice, they contain microorganisms with unusual metabolic characteristics. Very little biological research has been carried out in arctic streams; in Antarctica, streams are rare. We would emphasize that research programs on polar terrestrial and freshwater ecosystems have been too isolated from each other: correlated investigations should be made or, at the least, results collated.

As we review our understanding of polar marine organisms and their ecosystems, we must conclude that our knowledge is meager despite 150 years of biological observations in the polar seas. We single out the following areas for particular attention: studies of the marine biology of pack ice and shelf ice using specially designed platforms or submersibles; further investigations using conventional vessels with increased international collaboration; studies of life histories ranging from common marine organisms to microscopic plankton to fish; relationships between trophic levels and the flow of energy through the antarctic marine ecosystem; and the acquisition of further data on arctic marine ecosystems needed by planners of fish resources.

With regard to ecological systems in general, we see a continuing need for systematics, morphology, descriptive ecology, and biogeography—the biological disciplines longest established in polar regions—because they are fundamental to an understanding of the precise identities, relationships, and distribution patterns of plants and animals.

Psychrobiology and cryobiology—studies of responses to cold environment and of reactions of organisms, tissues, and cells to cold far below the freezing point of water—are outstandingly important in polar biology. These fields are relatively new in terms of concentrated study and are ripe for imaginative investigation in plants as well as animals. Improved facilities and logistics will, however, be required to secure and maintain specimens for study. We would stress the remarkable opportunities available in the polar regions for other, related physiological and behavioral investigations: circadian rhythms, periodicity, and endocrine function because of the unusual day–night cycles; diving physiology, metabolism, and thermoregulation in polar marine mammals; unusual adaptations of circulatory and respiratory function in polar fish; and animal behavior, especially among marine mammals and birds. Although significant contributions have been made in recent years to the science of animal behavior (or ethology) through studies of polar species, we still know little of the undersea behavior of penguins and seals, the species which have been studied most. Here again improved facilities and techniques are required for proper research, and better equipment is needed to observe animals in the sea and to track their movements.

Until recently, studies of human biology in the polar regions were oriented primarily toward medical and public-health programs related to endemic and chronic disease. As in medical research generally today, the focus has shifted from the goal of curing disease toward prevention of disease and toward optimizing performance of healthy individuals. We have also become aware of the need to study human biology in a more complete, integrated manner that includes, especially, both physical and psychological responses to the environment. Sociopsychological factors account for the major gaps in the knowledge required to gain these new goals. We stress the importance of an academic-based program of fundamental research on biomedical and biobehavioral aspects of man in the polar regions. A wide range of problems should be included—circadian rhythms, sleep, high-altitude hypoxia, responses to cold and dryness, and initiation and evolution of group behavioral patterns. The progressive impact of European and Asiatic technological cultures upon indigenous Eskimo populations in the Arctic requires continuing study, and increasingly refined multidisciplinary studies should be made of the behavior of temperate-latitude peoples who form transient populations in the Arctic and Antarctic.

The polar regions are the last extensive areas to be exploited by man, and their ecological systems are among the most easily damaged of any in the world. Planning to protect endangered species and habitats therefore becomes the first step in resources utilization and management in these regions. The Antarctic is protected in some measure by natural isolation and by conservation provisions in the Antarctic Treaty. The Arctic is less fortunate: comparable protection is urgently required. We see a critical need for international accords governing the exploitation of biological resources in the polar seas and coastal regions, and we urge that every effort be made toward this goal.

12. **The polar regions provide unparalleled opportunities for studies of specialized life forms, life processes, environmental adaptations, and relatively uncomplicated ecological systems. Polar biological and medical research should be pursued vigorously to better understand the unique polar organisms and their physiological, ecological, and behavioral systems. Special emphasis should be given to research in comparative and environmental physiology, including psy-chrobiology and cryobiology; key organisms in major ecosystems; animal behavior, especially among marine mammals and birds; and human biology and sociopsychology. The established disciplines of systematics, morphology, descriptive ecology, and biogeography should continue to be supported in order to achieve meaningful results from research. Additional facilities, new or improved equipment, and better coordination and logistics are required in some facets of the research program.**

13. **We underline in the strongest terms the critical importance, both practically and scientifically, of the protection, conservation, and intelligent harvesting of polar biological resources. We urge that the most diligent efforts be made on the national and international levels to achieve this goal.**

INTERNATIONAL COOPERATION

Polar research is almost synonymous with international scientific cooperation. Formal, multinational collaboration has roots dating back to the first and second International Polar Years in 1882–1883 and 1932–1933, which focused on exploratory research in the Arctic. The International Geophysical Year 1957–1958 was originally conceived as the third International Polar Year and represents the greatest international scientific undertaking the world has known. The IGY antarctic program involved the combined and cooperative efforts of twelve nations, with 48 stations on the margins and in the interior of the continent, and in the IGY arctic program fourteen nations established some 302 stations north of the 60° parallel. Scientific investigations were made in 14 disciplines.

Scientific cooperation in Antarctica during the IGY led to the creation of an unprecedented political document, the Antarctic Treaty, which took effect on June 23, 1961, following ratification by the 12 signatory nations: Argentina, Australia, Belgium, Chile, France, Japan, New Zealand, Norway, the Republic of South Africa, the Soviet Union, the United Kingdom, and the United States. By this treaty, the antarctic continent is a scientific and biological preserve, protected for peaceful purposes and for scientific study; military-oriented activities are prohibited, and freedom of scientific investigation is guaranteed. The antarctic cooperative program that began during the IGY has continued without interruption under the auspices of the International Council of Scientific Unions' Scientific Committee on Antarctic Research (SCAR).

Arctic research would benefit greatly from the existence of a formal international scientific body such as SCAR; and attractive opportunities and returns for multinational scientific collaboration in the Arctic are evident, especially in the Arctic Ocean Basin. Although we do not make a formal recommendation on this subject, we wish to emphasize strongly that the promotion of expanded international scientific cooperation in the Arctic is a critical need.

LOGISTICS

The problem of logistic support for implementing polar research is a unifying element shared by all field investigators. This is largely due to the remoteness, inaccessibility, and extreme cold of the polar regions, the extended periods of daylight and darkness, and, because all these conditions must be overcome, the cost is exceptionally high. While the problem is more severe in the Antarctic, it nevertheless poses uncommon limitations on arctic work. Scientific programs are critically dependent on logistics. The transition from broad exploratory investigations to problem-oriented research programs increases the complexity of logistic support, because the latter involve more numerous, detailed, and sophisticated measurements, all of which must be coordinated with each other. The great cost of polar logistics, especially for the support of personnel, underlines the importance of developing automatic unmanned stations for remote locations.

We must continually re-examine research programs in terms of logistic capabilities for transportation, communications, and subsistence and attempt to devise imaginative new approaches to support future programs and to exploit new tools and techniques afforded by modern technology. Satellites, remote-sensing techniques, automatic unmanned surface stations, rockets, balloons, aircraft serving as both data collection platforms and logistical support vehicles, air-transportable vans for use as temporary mobile stations, turbine-powered helicopters, airborne radio-echo sounding equipment for rapid and accurate mapping of subice topography, deep-drilling equipment for extraction of ice-cores, buoys, submersibles—all these and more should be fully investigated with a view toward drastically reducing logistic costs. These new techniques may also permit comprehensive data acquisition on a real-time basis and provide better control for analysis and exchange of data.

Operational, logistic, and technological matters are beyond the scope of this report. However, for such a study, there is an overriding need to delineate the scientific problems and goals that dictate the direction for future support efforts. This we have attempted to do.

14. In this study, we have of necessity returned time and again to the constraints and limitations imposed on polar research by the problems of logistic support in the harsh polar environment. In many instances we have suggested alternative methods of obtaining data as, for example, by remote sensing or automatic stations. That is only a partial answer, for much work must be done on site. We believe that the problems, opportunities, and potentialities of logistics in the polar regions should be examined thoroughly and systematically, both from the point of view of support for scientific investigations and of providing a better operational capability in the polar environment. We consider such a study to be of immediate scientific and practical importance and recommend that it be initiated without delay.

2

Geology and Solid-Earth Geophysics of the Polar Regions

This chapter reviews the current geological and geophysical knowledge of the polar regions, focuses attention on a number of significant and unsolved problems, and recommends a research program for solving these problems.

Some working definitions of the polar regions are necessary to delineate the areas under review. In the north, the Arctic Circle is used as the general southern boundary of our study area, even though a number of structural provinces lie transverse to it. We do not discuss the entire arctic region but rather limit our coverage to arctic North America, Greenland, and the northernmost Atlantic Ocean Basin from the Mid-Atlantic Ridge westward. The marine geology and geophysics of the Arctic Ocean Basin are treated in Chapter 3. In the south, attention is centered mainly on the emergent antarctic continent, including the Scotia Arc, and on certain problems from the submarine realm surrounding Antarctica.

The hostile polar environment is common to both the arctic and the antarctic regions, but important geologic contrasts exist between the two. The geographic North Pole lies in the Arctic Ocean, the site of a deep marine basin transected by three major seafloor ridges and bordered by the North American and Eurasian continents, as well as by some interesting groups of islands. On the other hand, the geographic South Pole lies high in the interior of Antarctica, which is a remote continent surrounded and isolated by the southern oceans. In the Arctic, much of the land is now ice-free and contains some of the best rock exposures in the world. In the Antarctic, however, bedrock appears above the surface of the ice sheet in only a small fraction of the continent.

Except for some processes unique to this environment, the geologic problems of the polar regions are similar to those elsewhere in the world. Geologists and geophysicists seek to understand the structure, composition, and history of the earth, as well as the processes that have brought it to its present state. Spatial distribution of rock bodies must be established by geological and geophysical field studies. Ages of rock units can be determined in many cases, either by isotopic measurements or by fossils. From field observations and laboratory analyses, conclusions are drawn on such matters as the environments of rock deposition, geography, and climate in the geologic past. One of the most interesting and important ideas in earth science today is the hypothesis of continental drift, and it is clear that the polar regions are destined to play a critical role in the testing of this fundamental concept. Geological and geophysical studies in the Arctic and the Antarctic will contribute significantly to our understanding of the earth's history and processes and will also provide the knowledge essential for the evaluation of the economic potential and future usefulness to man of polar lands.

ARCTIC ALASKA

HISTORY OF GEOLOGICAL EXPLORATION

Up to 1945, the geology of arctic Alaska was known only from a few widely scattered reconnaissance traverses made by a few intrepid geologists (Schrader, 1904; Leffingwell, 1919; and Smith and Mertie, 1930). This early work resulted in six published reports along with some maps at scales ranging from 1:1,250,000 to 1:250,000. These documents outline the regional geologic pattern, point out the petroleum potential of the Arctic Slope, and focus attention on detailed problems of petrology, paleontology and stratigraphy, structure, and processes and conditions unique to the arctic environment, such as permafrost.

In 1923, an area of about 78,000 km², thought to have

the greatest petroleum potential, was set aside by executive order as Naval Petroleum Reserve No. 4 (NPR-4). Geologic exploration continued until about 1927 when systematic studies and surveys were interrupted until 1944, at which time the U.S. Navy began its program of petroleum exploration in the area. As before, the United States Geological Survey (USGS) was asked to undertake the geologic part of this program.

Between 1944 and 1953, virtually all the exposed bedrock within NPR-4 and adjacent foothills south, east, and west was studied and mapped. The results were published between 1957 and 1963 in USGS Professional Papers 303A–303E. Seismograph surveys were made in many areas within NPR-4 and in a few adjoining areas. In addition, gravity stations were established throughout much of the northern part of NPR-4, and reconnaissance aeromagnetic traverses were flown across most of NPR-4 and part of the adjacent area to the south and east. The results of these geophysical surveys were published (Woolson *et al.*, 1962). The drilling program carried out between 1945 and 1955 included 36 test wells and 44 core tests with a total penetration of about 53,000 m. A major oil field at Umiat, a major gas field at Gubik, a minor gas field at Barrow, and several prospective fields were discovered. The geologic and engineering data collected during this drilling program were also published (Robinson and Rucker, 1958–1964), along with a complete chronological history of the U.S. Navy's oil exploration program, with charts and maps showing the work accomplished (Reed, 1958). Additional detailed technical data, as well as subsurface samples, have been preserved in the care of the USGS and are available for study.

During the U.S. Navy's exploration program, facilities at Point Barrow and Umiat were made available to a variety of scientists interested in working on arctic problems. The Arctic Research Laboratory established at Point Barrow continues to operate as the main base for scientific study in the Alaskan Arctic. Financial support for this facility is provided largely by the Office of Naval Research (ONR).

Intensive geological and geophysical field studies in support of the U.S. Navy's program ceased in 1953, but a few geological field projects continued, partly or wholly supported through the Naval Arctic Research Laboratory. The USGS shifted emphasis to the southern Brooks Range and began a regional mapping program designed to map the entire range at a scale of 1:250,000. To date about 47,000 km² have been mapped, including the Coleen, Christian, Chandalar, and Wiseman quadrangles.

From 1958 to 1960, areal geologic mapping and other geologic studies were made by the USGS in the vicinity of Cape Thompson, situated in the northwest corner of arctic Alaska. These studies were done in connection with the proposed nuclear excavation test, Project Chariot, and papers on several scientific investigations were published (Wilimovsky and Wolfe, 1966; Campbell, 1967).

In 1957, the discovery of oil at Cook Inlet in southern Alaska and the opening of lands adjoining NPR-4 for public leasing the following year brought a new surge of field activity and interest in the geology of Alaska's possible petroleum provinces, including the North Slope. In the past ten years nearly all major, and many independent, oil companies have reviewed the geology of arctic Alaska and fielded geological and geophysical parties throughout the region. Since completion of the U.S. Navy's drilling program in 1953, twelve additional exploratory test wells and two development wells at the Barrow and Gubik gas fields have been drilled, but no new oil or gas fields have been discovered in this area.

In March 1968, the Atlantic-Richfield Company and Humble Oil and Refining Company announced the discovery of a new well at Prudhoe Bay, on the arctic coast of Alaska about 200 miles east of Point Barrow. Oil and gas were found in several horizons in the upper Paleozoic in both detrital and carbonate rocks. Geologic exploration activities in the period 1953 to the present have produced important new data, but most of these data are commercially significant and not generally available. With the cooperation of oil companies, Lathram attempted to compile and synthesize this recent work along with that from the U.S. Navy's program; his geologic map (scale, 1:1,000,000) of all northern Alaska was made available in the open files of the USGS in 1965.

Other than continuing commercial oil exploration, current geologic research in arctic Alaska includes limited projects in Pleistocene geology, paleontology, and geomorphology, supported mainly through the Arctic Research Laboratory at Point Barrow. The USGS, at the request of the Office of Naval Petroleum Reserves, is studying the distribution and geology of oil shales along the north front of the Brooks Range. In addition, a palynologic study of subsurface samples collected during the drilling programs has been started. Reconnaissance geologic mapping is continuing by the USGS in the southern Brooks Range and in the Ipewik-Kukpuk area of the western Brooks Range.

SUMMARY OF PRESENT KNOWLEDGE

In Alaska, the Arctic Circle intersects a series of lowlands and plateaus that border the irregular south flank of the Brooks Range. These and other geomorphic provinces of Alaska have been described (Wahrhaftig, 1966). The geology along the Arctic Circle is more closely related to that of central Alaska and the intermontane plateaus of western Canada and the United States than to that of northern Alaska.

In general terms, the major geologic and geomorphic features of northern Alaska are the Brooks Range, a continuous east–west geanticlinal belt of predominantly sedi-

mentary and metasedimentary rocks of Paleozoic age, and
the North Slope, a foothills and plains region underlain by
an elongate trough of mainly Mesozoic age sedimentary
rocks. The most recent general descriptions of the geology
of northern Alaska are by Payne *et al.* (1951) and Miller
et al. (1959) and the 1:1,000,000-scale geologic map by
Lathram (1965).

Stratigraphy

The Brooks Range consists of subparallel belts of predominantly Paleozoic sedimentary rocks. Rocks of the southern
half are chiefly middle and upper Devonian strata that have
been metamorphosed to slates, phyllites, and greenschist
and locally intruded by granite. The northern half of the
Brooks Range, excluding the DeLong Mountains, consists
chiefly of unmetamorphosed upper Devonian, Mississippian,
Permian, and Triassic strata. Descriptions of these rocks have
been published by Bowsher and Dutro (1957), Sable and
Dutro (1961), Tailleur and Sable (1963), Brosgé *et al.*
(1962), Sable (1965), Porter (1966), Reed (in press), Gryc
et al. (in press), Tailleur *et al.* (in press), and Campbell
(1967).

North of the Brooks Range in the arctic foothills and
coastal plain subprovinces sedimentary rocks continue dominant and, in general, become progressively younger to the
north. In the southern part of these foothills, the exposed
bedrock consists chiefly of Jurassic and lower Cretaceous
graywacke and mudstone, with lesser amounts of Triassic
and Permian shales and cherts; a few fault-bounded blocks
and slivers contain Paleozoic limestone. In the northern foothills and the coastal plain, conglomerate, sandstone, shale,
coal, and pyroclastic rocks of mid-Cretaceous, late Cretaceous, and Tertiary age are the principal lithologic types.
This trough of Cretaceous sedimentary rocks apparently
steepens sharply near the front of the mountains, and at
Umiat, basement rocks may be present at about 6000 m
and at lesser depths to the north. At Point Barrow, basement rocks of Paleozoic age are within 730 m of the surface,
and elsewhere along the coast they rise to within 900 to
1500 m.

Tertiary beds have been mapped in the coastal plain area,
and thicknesses up to 2100 m have been measured on
Carter Creek (Morris, 1957).

The stratigraphy and structure of various parts of the
arctic foothills and coastal plain have been described in some
detail in USGS Professional Papers 302, 303, and 305, by
Collins and Robinson (1967), and in several shorter stratigraphic paleontology papers.

Paleontology

During the NPR-4 program of 1945–1953, extensive studies
were made of the surface and subsurface Mesozoic and

Quaternary microfauna by Tappan (1951, 1955, 1962).
Later, Berquist (1966) published a definitive report on his
studies and interpreted the surface and subsurface stratigraphy in the light of the microfaunal zones. His studies
concern mainly foraminifera, but radiolaria and other elements of the microfauna are noted. Detailed studies of other
microforms such as pollens and dinoflagellates could add
significantly to stratigraphic knowledge and could be very
helpful in petroleum exploration.

Microfloras of the subsurface samples were not studied
during the NPR-4 program. Recently, the techniques and
knowledge of stratigraphic palynology have progressed to
the point where they can be very useful in petroleum exploration and in regional geologic studies. Accordingly, with
the support and cooperation of the Office of Naval Petroleum and Oil Shale Reserves, the USGS is processing the
subsurface cores for microfloras and preparing slides of the
material for study by all who are interested.

Extensive collections of plant fossils from throughout
northern Alaska have been used to establish megafloral zones
for the region (Hollick, 1930; Smiley, 1966, 1967). This
work has been supported by the Arctic Research Laboratory
through contracts with the Arctic Institute of North America
(AINA) and the Office of Naval Research (ONR). Studies of
this type should be continued and completed through the
stage of detailed taxonomy and published in full.

Studies of several groups of invertebrate megafaunas have
been reported (Tappan, 1951; Imlay, 1955, 1959, 1961;
Gordon, 1957; Todd, 1957; Jones and Gryc, 1960; Yochelson and Dutro, 1960; Cobban and Gryc, 1961; Swain, 1963).

Igneous Rocks

Although rocks of sedimentary origin predominate in
northern Alaska, both intrusive and extrusive igneous rocks
are widespread and include granitic plutons, mafic and ultramafic plugs, dikes, sills, flows, and pyroclastic strata. Regional mapping and a few radiometric age determinations
suggest periods of igneous activity in mid-Devonian, early
and middle Jurassic, early and late Cretaceous, and early
Tertiary.

Radiometric age determinations are presently available
for only a few localities. A 370 million year (m.y.) (mid-
Devonian) radiometric age (K–Ar) for mafic dikes in the
central Brooks Range has been reported (Reiser *et al.*, 1965).
Radiometric age data for a granitic pluton on the Hulahula
River in the eastern Brooks Range are also available (Sable,
1965). The lead-alpha age on a zircon fraction is reported to
be 360 ± 45 m.y., but K–Ar determinations on a mica fraction indicate 125 and 128 m.y. ages (early Cretaceous). A
Permian age (237 and 253 ± 45 m.y.) is reported from a
whole-rock K–Ar determination on some mafic igneous rocks
near the Canadian border in the eastern Brooks Range (Wanless *et al.*, 1967).

Structure

The major Mesozoic and Cenozoic structural features of Alaska have been named, described, and correlated, including the Brooks Range geanticline and the Colville geosyncline in northern Alaska (Payne, 1955). Positive and negative elements within these major units were also described, and these were more thoroughly treated and modified by later work (Miller *et al.*, 1959). The suggested framework is that of a Brooks Range geanticline, which originated in Jurassic time, superimposed on a Paleozoic miogeosyncline, and a Colville geosyncline, which also originated at about the same time and was gradually filled and moved northward on a subsiding shelf region. This pattern has been largely substantiated by subsequent studies. However, recent work suggests a series of major thrusts in the Brooks Range and arctic foothills with northward displacement of as much as 240 km (Jones and Grantz, 1964; Tailleur *et al.*, in press; Tailleur and Snelson, 1966; Snelson and Tailleur, 1968; Lathram and Gryc, 1966). During at least two major episodes, mid-early Cretaceous and early Tertiary, thrusting may have affected virtually all the region at least as far north as the Colville River (Lathram and Gryc, 1966). This thrusting may be related to rifting in the Arctic Basin and to continental drift to the south and west (Tailleur and Snelson, 1968).

Exploration Geophysics

Between 1945 and 1953, the Navy's investigation of NPR-4 led to the only comprehensive and well-coordinated geophysical exploration program that has been sponsored by the U.S. Government in arctic Alaska. Aeromagnetic measurements covered almost the entire reserve, excluding its mountainous southwest corner, and extended across the coastal plain south and east of the reserve. A gravity survey covered the northern half of the reserve with a station spacing varying from 0.4 to 8 km. Approximately 13,000 reflection and 400 shallow refraction profiles were completed in more than 100 crew-months of seismic work. Electric, seismic-velocity, and temperature logs were made of most of the test wells, and interpretation of the geothermal data provided basic information on frozen ground.

The 1945-1953 geophysical surveys were helpful in defining the general configuration of the sedimentary basin, particularly in the coastal plain area. Seismic reflection surveys discovered and defined several anticlines and buried structures in sufficient detail to establish drill sites. A few profiles were run outside of NPR-4, and some extended into the southern foothills. However, the results from these areas were inconclusive, and not enough work was done to identify with confidence specific structures or the tectonic style. Additional profiles in the foothills near the mountain front could be useful to check thrust interpretations and to evaluate the petroleum possibilities of that structural province.

Aeromagnetic surveys were carried out in the developmental stage of airborne technique, and the accuracy of the horizontal control has been questioned. The surveys revealed large anomalies which could not be related to the known geology at that time (1945-1946).

This work has been summarized (Woolson *et al.*, 1962), and detailed data such as field reports, profiles, and notes are available in USGS open files. Recently, reflection records have been digitized and reinterpreted.

Publication of the NPR-4 data and the upsurge of interest in Alaska's petroleum potential after 1957 have stimulated commercial companies to undertake detailed seismic and gravity measurements on the coastal plain east of NPR-4. Atomic Energy Commission (AEC) studies at Cape Thompson included geothermal measurements, reconnaissance aeromagnetic and radioactivity surveys, a few seismic measurements, and a local gravity survey (Wilimovsky and Wolfe, 1966). The USGS has flown a few other reconnaissance aeromagnetic traverses in the southern Brooks Range and in 1965 attempted a systematic aeromagnetic reconnaissance of northeast Alaska. Weather and equipment failures curtailed the planned north–south flight lines, spaced 10 miles apart, designed to cover the area north of 64° N and east of 148° W. Nevertheless, the data distinguished important tectonic elements and should stimulate more detailed geophysical and geological investigations in parts of the area. Better progress has been made on a systematic gravity reconnaissance of Alaska. More than 2000 stations north of the Arctic Circle were used in the preparation of a 10-mgal contour interval map of the whole state. However, a few important gaps remain in the coverage, and two to three weeks of helicopter support will be needed to complete this gravity reconnaissance of arctic Alaska.

SCIENTIFIC PROBLEMS

The review of the preceding section draws attention to important gaps in our knowledge. Although many significant geological questions remain unanswered, some of them are now the object of intensive research, while others have received scant attention. Most of these questions will yield only to detailed studies and measurements in critical localities, many requiring the contributions of several scientific disciplines. Some important scientific questions are:

1. What is the sequence and age of rocks in arctic Alaska?

Stratigraphic and paleontologic studies are critical to a general geologic understanding and regional synthesis of the entire polar region. Much has been done on the subject of paleontology and the stratigraphic succession, but much more remains to be done. The results are directly applicable to mineral-resource evaluation, particularly petroleum.

Upper Paleozoic strata, especially those of the Lisburne

Group, are locally highly fossiliferous, but definitive studies of the several invertebrate groups have yet to be completed and published. Extensive fossil collections were made during the NPR-4 program in the Brooks Range mapping project and during recent exploration activities by the oil industry. Some of the latter collections have been made available to the USGS and are under study. Additional fossil collections and detailed stratigraphic studies of the upper Paleozoic strata are needed, particularly in the Shublik and Franklin Mountains of the eastern Brooks Range. Lower Paleozoic strata are only generally known, and detailed stratigraphic and paleontologic data are missing in critical areas, particularly in the northeastern part of the Brooks Range.

Certain groups of Mesozoic invertebrates have been studied and the results published, but additional work is needed on Triassic stratigraphy and paleontology, Cretaceous mollusks, and Tertiary stratigraphy, microfossils, and megafloras. These projects all require additional field work in rather inaccessible areas. Tertiary rocks exposed in the Sagavanirktok region and eastward into Canada are very poorly known.

Radiometric age determinations discussed in the previous section are the only published pre-Pleistocene isotopic ages from this vast region. Other rock specimens are currently being studied, but much more work is needed. Careful petrologic and geochemical studies should accompany these geochronology programs.

2. What is the relationship between the Cordilleran, Brooks Range, and Innuitian orogenic systems?

Perhaps the most intriguing geologic problem in the North American Arctic is that of the historical and structural relationships of these three major tectonic elements. Does the Brooks Range bend sharply south to join the Innuitian system? Or are the Brooks Range and Innuitian systems two prongs of the Cordilleran system which have been rifted and have drifted apart? The solution of these problems requires at minimum a complete reconnaissance of the geology of the entire North American Arctic and a detailed knowledge of selected critical areas to determine age, succession, and structural style.

The NPR-4 program made possible extensive geologic mapping, especially in the northern foothills area. However, parts of the Brooks Range, particularly the Romanzof, Franklin, and Shublik Mountains, have been mapped only by widely separated reconnaissance traverses and by photogeology, with some notable exceptions (Sable, 1965; Reed, in press). Field reconnaissance mapping at a scale of 1:250,000 and detailed geologic mapping at a scale of 1:63,360, coupled with thorough stratigraphic studies in selected areas, would provide many of the data needed for regional tectonic synthesis and for correlation with the Canadian Arctic, the northern part of Greenland, and the arctic marine basin.

Large areas of outcrop south of the Brooks Range in the Yukon–Porcupine drainage area are still unknown geologically even at reconnaissance scales.

3. What is the origin of the overthrust belt in the Brooks Range?

The presence of large thrust features in the Brooks Range was apparent from the beginning of geologic studies in the region. However, the range has been generally described as a geanticline with complex thrust faults extending northward into the arctic foothills province for perhaps a distance of 15 to 30 km. Recent more detailed structural and facies studies and palinspastic reconstructions suggest that thrusting on an alpine scale may be the predominant structural style. Much of the Brooks Range may be allochthonous and displaced northward as much as 190 km. Mechanical explanations based on continental drift include underthrusting and oroclinal bending.

The juxtaposition of sharply contrasting facies and the evidence for large-scale thrusting seem to be exposed best in the western Brooks Range and the foothills of the upper Colville River region. Further detailed geologic mapping and detailed stratigraphic studies are required to prove or disprove these highly speculative generalizations.

4. What is the age and structure of the basement rocks in arctic Alaska?

Although rather extensive aeromagnetic, reflection seismograph, shallow velocity, and refraction studies, as well as gravity observations, have been made over large areas of arctic Alaska, the basement features that have been delineated remain largely unexplained. Many of these data are not of the quality now obtainable by modern technology, and others, such as the recent gravity observations, are incomplete. Current reflection and refraction studies by the oil industry are not generally available.

More complete knowledge of the basement rocks that underlie the Colville geosyncline and their relationship to the older rocks of the Brooks Range can provide a vital link in the geologic history of the region and is an important need in petroleum exploration and development.

5. What is the crustal and mantle structure below central and arctic Alaska?

Data bearing on this question are presently very scarce. No deep seismic refraction or telluric-current soundings of the crust have been attempted in the Alaskan interior, but the abundance of water bodies and auroral activity might make both such measurements nearly as easy in Alaska as in more southerly latitudes. Gravity data suggest significant areal variations in crustal properties. A new seismograph station at Northeast Cape on St. Lawrence Island might provide valuable data from travel paths across the distinctive crustal units of southwest Alaska and the Bering Sea.

The arctic environment does not necessarily present a severe handicap to geophysical programs. When seismic investigation of NPR-4 was first organized, its planners believed that productive work would be limited only to summer months. At the end of the investigation, however, these months were recognized as the least profitable working period. Similarly, the abundance of swamp and water in Alaska has inhibited many types of development, but profitable use has been made of such water bodies for both transportation and elevation control in the gravity reconnaissance of the state. The Canadians and Russians have also used lakes as seismic shot points to reduce drilling costs in seismic investigations of crustal thickness and upper-mantle properties.

A rapidly accelerated program of airborne geophysical studies is an obvious need in central and arctic Alaska, and it should provide a real stimulus to the development of mineral resources. Although magnetic measurements are the most obvious objective of such a survey, the possibilities of using the same aircraft for radioactivity measurements, electromagnetic soundings, and laser altimeter measurements to control more detailed gravity surveys should be seriously considered. The nearly completed reconnaissance gravity map can aid in establishing the proper local density of airborne coverage. Acquisition of these data from the air will almost inevitably stimulate further ground surveys and geologic mapping.

6. What are the causes of modern tectonic activity in arctic North America?

Arctic Alaska, unlike southern Alaska, appears to be a region of low seismicity. Southern Alaska includes the circum-Pacific belt of high volcanic and earthquake activity, and major strike-slip faults dominate the tectonic framework. These structural elements extend into central Alaska and may be present on the south slope of the Brooks Range.

RECOMMENDATIONS

Implementation of the following recommendations for polar research in arctic Alaska should be undertaken in the near future as a start toward solving the problems discussed above. It is evident that such a list cannot be considered comprehensive, but these approaches seem most promising at this time. The dissimilar nature of the various suggestions makes comparison of their importance difficult, but the items on the same general subject are ranked in rough order of priority.

1. Continued and increased support should be provided to complete reconnaissance geologic mapping at the scale of 1:250,000, especially in the Sadlerochit, Romanzof, Franklin, and Shublik Mountains and in the central Brooks Range.

2. Increased support should be provided to individual scientists for study of specific geologic problems in arctic Alaska.

3. The systematic gravity survey of the State of Alaska should be completed.

4. An Alaskan seismograph network, comparable with that of Canada and the contiguous United States, should be established. Approximately six new stations are urgently needed.

5. Bathymetric and gravity surveys should be conducted, with adequate positioning control, to produce maps of the continental shelf and slope at the scale of 1:500,000.

6. Detailed geologic mapping at a scale of 1:63,360 should be undertaken in selected critical localities.

7. Aeromagnetic surveys should be conducted, with adequate positioning control, to produce maps at the scale of 1:250,000 of arctic Alaska, including the continental shelf.

8. Aeromagnetic profiles at 20- to 25-km spacing should be obtained over the arctic continental slope.

9. A series of long seismic refraction profiles should be obtained in arctic Alaska, with the Chukchi Shelf proposed as a practical and significant initial site.

ARCTIC CANADA, GREENLAND, AND THE NORTHERNMOST ATLANTIC OCEAN BASIN

PRESENT STATE OF INVESTIGATIONS AND STUDY

Bedrock geology of the exposed land areas of arctic Canada, Greenland, and the islands of the northernmost Atlantic Ocean has been fairly well mapped on a reconnaissance scale, and there are few areas where the general stratigraphy and structural relations are unknown. Some parts of western Baffin Island and Greenland have been studied only in a sketchy fashion or are known only from expedition reports written decades ago by scientists covering the whole field of natural history; most of the available geological information from these areas is of an elementary, descriptive nature. Enough is known of the general region to require but little further reconnaissance mapping or exploratory investigation; future work should be directed at specific problems of stratigraphy and structure, crustal relationships, geological history, and geological processes.

Knowledge of surficial deposits and of the effects of glacial and periglacial processes in arctic Canada and Greenland is, on the whole, less satisfactory than that of bedrock. For example, extensive areas are covered with unconsolidated material that has been described only through interpretation of aerial photographs, and the few detailed ground studies that have been made have encountered evidence of such a complex recent geologic history that careful workers have been reluctant to extrapolate their results to unstudied areas. Satisfactory general reconstruction of the Pleistocene and Recent history of the Canadian arctic archipelago, Greenland, or Svalbard has not yet been possible; a great deal more careful observation, description, and dating, as well as interpretive and comparative studies, are required.

Topographic mapping on scales adequate for physiographic analysis is proceeding well in Canada, Greenland, and Svalbard. Arctic Canada is now entirely covered by modern maps at a scale of 1:250,000. Systematic mapping of Greenland and Svalbard is incomplete, but some detailed maps are available for representative parts of all major physiographic regions. Vertical, as well as tricamera or trimetrogon, aerial photographic coverage of good quality is available for all arctic Canada and for Svalbard. Much of the ice-free land of Greenland is covered by trimetrogon photography only, and some areas, particularly in the north, have not yet been photographed.

Any study of the Recent geologic history or of physiographic processes in the lands bordering the Arctic Ocean must consider the morphology and composition of floors of fiords, channels, straits, and continental shelves surrounding the land masses. For this purpose, detailed hydrographic or bathymetric charts, as well as information about the bottom materials, are necessary. Charts and information of sufficient accuracy and detail to be useful for geological purposes are almost nonexistent. Only for a few bays and channels in the Canadian Arctic, and for harbors in Greenland and Svalbard, which are not representative from a physiographic aspect, are there charts sufficiently detailed (1:100,000 or larger) to show, for example, bottom morainal deposits. The form of the continental shelf, the continental slope, and of the channels that impinge onto the shelf, is known accurately only for the area adjacent to the western Queen Elizabeth Islands and for the Lincoln Sea northwest of Greenland, where there has been systematic bathymetric mapping on a scale of 1:500,000 or larger. Elsewhere the topography of the sea floor is known only from random or widely spaced ship-track profiles or reconnaissance soundings.

Our knowledge of geophysical phenomena is sparse. Essentially all the Canadian arctic islands are covered with a regional gravity base loop network with base stations 150 km or less apart and tied to the continental gravity network. Systematic regional gravity mapping, on scales of 1:500,000 or larger, has been completed for about two thirds of the Canadian Archipelago and intervening waters, and for about one third of the continental shelf off the Queen Elizabeth Islands and north Greenland. Gravity observations in Greenland include looped networks on the southeast and southwest coasts, ties with the Canadian regional network on the northwest, about six traverses across the icecap, and scattered individual observations near some settlements and air bases. No gravity information is available across the Mid-Atlantic Ridge north of Iceland. A regional gravity survey has been made of Iceland, and some detailed traverses have been made across the median zone.

Considerable information about the magnetic character of the north polar regions is available from the observations of various continuing and temporary magnetic stations, as well as from studies over the past 120 years, of the nature and movement of the north magnetic pole. Most of these observations have contributed little to our knowledge of arctic geology or crustal structure, but recent studies of the regional geomagnetic gradient and of local areas of anomalous electrical conductivity in the Queen Elizabeth Islands have helped to define structural units and areas of distinctive geologic history. Widely spaced aeromagnetic flights have measured the total residual magnetic field over all the North American and Atlantic arctic regions; these measurements have been useful in delimiting major geologic and tectonic features and in demonstrating the typically symmetrically banded, magnetic character of the crust underlying the northernmost Atlantic and adjacent parts of the Arctic Ocean.

Data from systematic aeromagnetic mapping, on scales of 1:250,000 or larger, providing information on the shape and orientation of magnetic anomalies and the depth to crystalline bedrock are, however, available only for the Canadian Arctic. Maps published to date cover about 250,000 km^2, or about one third of the Queen Elizabeth Islands and the adjacent continental shelf and continental slope.

Seismograph stations in the northern hemisphere are well placed to record earthquake waves passing under the Arctic Ocean Basin, northern North America, and Greenland, in a variety of directions from the main seismic belts. Analyses of these records are contributing significantly to our knowledge of crustal and subcrustal structure and of the intrinsic seismicity of the Arctic. Although explosion seismic methods have been employed extensively to measure the thickness of glaciers and ice caps in northern Canada, Greenland, Iceland, and Svalbard, this work has contributed little to our understanding of the geology of these regions. Explosion seismology has been used to obtain structural information in the sedimentary basins of the Canadian arctic islands and continental shelf, on Iceland and its associated shelf, and on the Faeroe Islands.

Measurements of the flow of geothermal heat have been made in Iceland, southwest Greenland, western Queen Elizabeth Islands in or near areas of anomalous geomagnetic behavior, and at some isolated points in the central Canadian Archipelago and arctic mainland.

SUMMARY OF PRESENT KNOWLEDGE

From the above investigations it is apparent that the arctic portions of North America and the north Atlantic Ocean are a direct continuation of the geologic provinces to the south. Short of the Arctic Ocean basins themselves, there is no valid geologic boundary to the arctic regions.

In general, the stratigraphy and structure of arctic North America and the transition from the North American continental platform to the Arctic Ocean Basin typify the classic concept of an "ideal" continental margin. The central stable region or continental core is formed by the Canadian and Greenland shields, which together surround Baffin Bay and constitute the Canadian mainland west to about longitude 125° W. The shields have had a complex Precambrian history. The arctic part of the Canadian shield has been assigned to the Churchill Precambrian province with the last known major period of intrusion and deformation taking place about 1700 million years ago (Stockwell, 1964; Wanless *et al.*, 1967). Apparent ages of latest major deformations affecting the Greenland shield range from 2200 million to 1100 million years (Kulp *et al.*, 1962; Moorbath *et al.*, 1960). These central shields have been unaffected by orogenic movements since Cambrian time, although locally subjected to repeated block movements as shown by the Minto Arch, Boothia uplift, and East Greenland uplift. Two important geosynclines developed within or adjacent to the shield in Precambrian time. One lies across Victoria Island and contains more than 3500 m of upper Precambrian sandstones, limestones, evaporites, shales, and basalts, now exposed in the Minto Arch (Thorsteinsson and Tozer, 1962). The other in north and northeast Greenland, is shown by the presence of more than 3000 m of "Thule Group" pre-Lower Cambrian strata (L. Koch, 1961). Volcanic rocks are characteristic of both troughs, and both have been deformed in the Carolinidian disturbances of Precambrian times (Haller, 1961a). In some locations the deformed and metamorphosed rocks of the shields have been eroded to relatively smooth surfaces and are overlain by unmetamorphosed, undeformed upper Precambrian strata as shown on northwestern Baffin Island, eastern Ellesmere Island, and western central Greenland; elsewhere, the shield is overlapped from the north by a thin assemblage of lower and middle Paleozoic sedimentary rocks, now comprising the arctic lowlands and plateaus. These strata, which are mainly flat-lying or gently tilted with only local deformations, include a high proportion of carbonate material; clastic components were derived from a well-weathered terrain. These rocks were deposited in shallow, stable seas that once must have extended over the now exhumed area of the Precambrian shield. Aeromagnetic and gravity surveys indicate that the crystalline shield underlies these areas at relatively shallow depth, with a smooth upper surface that appears to be a continuation of the present exposed surface of the shield. A few north–south block structures interrupt the otherwise undisturbed pattern of both exposed and covered shield. Careful study of some block structures suggests that repeated movements have taken place in some cases from Precambrian to Recent times (Kerr and Christie, 1965).

North of a line that curves eastward and northeastward from about latitude 75° at the west edge of the Canadian Archipelago to latitude 80° at the east side, and continues across northern Greenland, Paleozoic formations thicken abruptly and change character; the central stable region is thus bounded by the Franklinian and east Greenland geosynclines. The Franklinian geosyncline includes a miogeosynclinal trough which extends completely across the Canadian Archipelago and northwest Greenland. From Cambrian to late Devonian time the Franklinian geosyncline received an aggregate of more than 12,000 m of carbonates, evaporites, and well-weathered clastic sediments apparently derived mainly from the northwest but with minor input from the southeast (Kerr, 1968). It is flanked at its northern end by a complementary eugeosyncline comprising great thicknesses of poorly weathered material, including much that is of volcanic origin. Recent studies have subdivided the Franklinian eugeosyncline into two subprovinces: a magmatic belt that formed the flank of a borderland rising intermittently during the Ordovician, Silurian, and probably the Devonian and shedding detritus toward the miogeosyncline and an axial trough separating the magmatic belt from the miogeosynclinal shelf, which received turbidity currents from the northwest during late Ordovician and early Silurian time (Trettin, 1968a, 1968b).

The folded Franklinian geosynclines form the basis of the Innuitian orogenic system. The eugeosyncline shows evidence of deformation in early Cambrian or earlier time, in middle Ordovician or earlier, in late Silurian–early Devonian, and in middle to late Devonian times (Blackadar, 1960; Trettin, 1964, 1966, 1967, 1968b). The associated miogeosyncline was deformed in late Silurian–early Devonian and again in late Devonian–early Pennsylvanian times (Thorsteinsson and Tozer, 1960; Kerr, 1968).

The formations comprising the lower half of the Franklinian miogeosyncline are known only from the margins of the geosyncline; in the central part they are covered with younger rocks and cannot be mapped by geophysical means because they are comprised mainly of heavy carbonate rocks whose physical properties do not allow them to be differentiated by seismic or gravity methods from the underlying crystalline rocks. Nevertheless, reconstructions from stratigraphic, structural, and magnetic evidence suggest that the base of the miogeosyncline along its axis lies 20,000 m or more below its rim. The northwest edge of the geosyncline is not exposed except possibly at the north end, but geophysical and facies evidence suggests that before deformation the basin was roughly symmetrical, with its northwestern boundary somewhere near the present seaward edge of the archipelago (Douglas *et al.*, 1963; Trettin, 1967, in press).

In east Greenland, geosynclinal development at the edge of the Greenland shield started earlier than in the Queen Elizabeth Islands, with the deposition of more than 11,000 m of varied clastic sedimentary rocks with minor carbonates, followed by a tillite below Eocambrian and lower Cambrian strata in the "central east Greenland geosyncline" (L. Koch, 1961; Haller, in press). The central east Greenland geosyncline developed separately from the Precambrian geosyncline that gave rise to the "Carolinides" of north Greenland; it is also distinct from the northeast Greenland geosyncline, which is an extension of the Innuitian system, although it appears that some formations can be traced with change of facies and of thickness from one area to the other. Although both the Franklinian and east Greenland geosynclinal belts underwent orogenic and diastrophic movements at about the same times, the style of deformation was different in the Innuitian and east Greenland systems. The first of the major deformations to affect the Franklinian geosynclines produced structures that cross the long axis of the basin in fairly regular open folds with curving axes and subparallel steeply dipping faults of moderate displacement. At least some of these structures appear directly related to block movements in the underlying basement. More severe and widespread late Devonian–early Pennsylvanian orogeny resulted in long regular folds parallel to the axis of the geosyncline. These folds are relatively open at the west end of the belt but become tighter toward the northeast where major thrust faults indicate movement from the north and west toward the central stable region (Ellitsgaard-Rasmussen, 1955; Fraenkl, 1956; Thorsteinsson and Tozer, 1960; Fortier *et al.*, 1963; Kerr and Temple, 1965). Significant regional metamorphism or igneous action connected with the Paleozoic deformations are rare in the Franklinian geosyncline at the present level of exposures. They are confined to late Precambrian or early Cambrian metamorphism in northern Ellesmere Island and northwest Greenland and small Devonian, or probably Devonian, intrusions with local metamorphism in northern Ellesmere Island and northern Axel Heiberg Island (Blackadar, 1960; Frisch, 1967; Trettin, 1967). In contrast, the Silurian (Caledonian) orogeny in east Greenland has resulted in extensive regional metamorphism, with locally important granitization and migmatization, with a wide variety of structural trends and forms which, at higher stratigraphic horizons and in marginal parts of the fold belt, resolve themselves into complex north-northeast-trending folds and thrust slices (sometimes themselves folded) which indicate an overriding toward the west (Haller, 1961b). The younger Paleozoic (Devonian) structures superimposed on the Caledonian structures of east Greenland are mainly those of extension or relaxation: steep dip-slip faults, monoclinal folds, and belts of horsts and down-dropped blocks, some of which trend parallel with, and some obliquely to, the older structures. These movements were accompanied by volcanism and granitic intrusion (Fraenkl, 1953; Haller, 1958; Butler, 1959).

In the Queen Elizabeth Islands of the Canadian Arctic Archipelago the deformed Franklinian geosyncline suffered further downwarping, with the development of a major structural basin—the Sverdrup Basin—that received essentially uninterrupted sedimentation from middle Pennsylvanian until early Tertiary time (Thorsteinsson and Tozer, 1960; Fortier *et al.*, 1963; Tozer and Thorsteinsson, 1964).

Sediments deposited in the basin include limestones and evaporites in the lower part, but above the Permian deposits, they are entirely clastic, dominantly shallow water, alternating marine and nonmarine in nature, and for the most part apparently derived from the south and east. Limited volcanism occurred in the Cretaceous period. Almost continuous sedimentation appears to have taken place along the axis of the basin, but the center of subsidence and deposition shifted repeatedly so that the aggregate thickness of the formations, as inferred from isopach studies, is much greater than the thickness at any point. Nevertheless, aeromagnetic and seismic data confirm the stratigraphic inference that the assemblage of conformable middle Pennsylvanian to lower Tertiary strata on Axel Heiberg Island is probably more than 13,000 m thick (Douglas *et al.*, 1963; Hobson and Overton, 1966). The area of deposition and the nature of the sedimentation varied greatly from formation to formation so that there is typically a pronounced lateral change in facies within formations across the basin. Along the margins of the basins there is much overlap and interruption of the stratigraphic sequence with local angular unconformities testifying to a fluctuating shoreline and local movements at the edge of the subsiding area. The rocks of the Sverdrup Basin were deformed by strong earth movements in Tertiary (probably early Tertiary) time, producing complex but generally fairly open folds and steeply dipping thrust faults, and at the same time Permo-Pennsylvanian evaporites intruded into younger strata to form piercement domes and diapirs. Numerous sills and ring dikes found widely throughout the Sverdrup Basin may have been emplaced at this time.

In east Greenland, marine and continental beds of late Carboniferous and Permian age including clastic sediments, limestones, and evaporites, pass conformably or transitionally to Mesozoic (Eotriassic) beds. These strata are similar to the lower portion of the Sverdrup Basin sequence, but the fossils have northern European, rather than North American, affinities (Trümpy, 1961; Maync, 1961; Dunbar, 1961). Similarly, deposition of largely clastic sediments of both marine and nonmarine origin continued, with minor interruptions, through the Triassic, Jurassic, and Cretaceous, in rough equivalence to that in the Sverdrup Basin. Except for a few wide-ranging species, the east Greenland Mesozoic fauna and flora are related to Europe and Asia and not to North America—not even to the nearby Innuitian Mesozoic rocks (Donovan, 1957, 1961; Callomon, 1961; Harris, 1961).

Sedimentary basins in which deposition took place during the Cretaceous and into early or middle Tertiary time are widespread in arctic Canada and Greenland. In the Queen Elizabeth Islands, the upper Cretaceous (?) and lower Tertiary Eureka Sound Formation, composed of typical coal measures, transgresses from the Sverdrup Basin and rests disconformably over older formations throughout an extensive area of the Franklinian geosyncline and the central stable region (Troelson, 1950; Tozer, in Fortier *et al.*, 1963, pp. 92–95). In places these rocks have been involved in Tertiary orogeny; in other places they appear essentially undisturbed by movements which affected underlying Mesozoic strata.

Around the shores of the Arctic Ocean, forming a belt apparently continuous from the coastal plain of Alaska to Meighen Island, is a remarkable sheet of unconsolidated cross-bedded sand and gravel, laden with logs and sticks of wood, and known as the Beaufort Formation (Tozer, 1956, 1961; Craig and Fyles, 1960; Thorsteinsson and Tozer, 1962; Tozer and Thorsteinsson, 1964; Fyles and Craig, 1965). The contained wood is mainly northern conifer, but some pollen from temperate hardwoods is also present. This formation has baffled attempts to interpret its origin or to date it; dates range from late-middle Tertiary to Pleistocene, although individual collections of fossils suggest restricted horizons within this range (Fyles and Craig, 1965; Hills, in preparation). Its pebbles are largely chert and quartzite, and the sands are highly quartzose; it appears to have been deposited by vigorous streams draining well-weathered shield terrain to the southeast. It appears undisturbed, although no mappable horizons have been identified; however, it shows long linear features which are almost certainly the traces of faults. Locally, it overlies deformed coal measures that are probably Eocene and, at least locally, is overlain by Pleistocene deposits. Continuity of the formation across channels separating the islands of the archipelago suggests that it was laid down before the dissection of the archipelago, and it appears to continue seaward as the floor of much of the presently submerged continental shelf. The pollen content indicates a relatively warm climate at the time of deposition of the lower beds.

In west Greenland, a well-defined basin contains several thousand meters of essentially conformable, mainly nonmarine strata, ranging from early Cretaceous to probably Eocene age, including the commercially important upper Cretaceous coal measures (E. B. Koch, 1964). In east Greenland there are small deposits of lowermost Eocene sedimentary rocks which, like those on the west coast, are covered by great floods of Tertiary plateau basalts with minor sedimentary intercalations (Backlund and Malmquist, 1932; Wager, 1934, 1947; Hassan, 1953; Wenk, 1961; Haller, in press). The basalts are extensively exposed in the Disko area of west Greenland and from latitudes 69° N to 76° N in east Greenland; they are part of the "Brito-Arctic" volcanic province which extends from the British Isles to Cape Dyer on Baffin Island. The flows are subhorizontal, extruded subaerially or locally subaqueously on a seaward-dipping erosion surface on both the east and west coasts of Greenland. Intercalated sediments have yielded fossils of Eocene to Miocene age, which bear closer relationships to the arctic faunas of Europe and Asia than to those of the Americas. Tertiary igneous activity in Greenland is also characterized by a great variety of local intrusions and dike swarms, many of which

are alkaline in character with unusual mineralogy and structure (Wager and Deer, 1939; Bearth, 1959; Kapp, 1960). Many of the older faults were reactivated in Tertiary time, accompanied by local folding. A major flexure, parallel to the east coast, has developed subsequent to the deposition of the basalts; it has caused more than 8 km of relative vertical displacement, submerging the easternmost flows beneath the waters of Denmark Strait while elevating the western ones to form the highest mountains in Greenland.

The Brito-Arctic volcanic province is traceable across the Atlantic Ocean by means of the Wyville-Thompson submarine ridge which intersects the Mid-Atlantic Ridge in Iceland. Iceland is by far the largest and best exposed outcrop of a midoceanic ridge (Björnsson, 1967). Composed primarily of Tertiary plateau basalts with the oldest at the east and west extremities, dipping inward and becoming progressively younger toward a median rift zone characterized by active fissures and aligned craters, it affords an impressive display of many features known on the ocean floor only from indirect evidence (Walker, 1964; Kjartansson, 1965; Gibson, 1966). Seismic, gravity, magnetic, and heat-flow data from Iceland are all consistent with a continuous intrusion of magma into the crust beneath the median zone, and the sequence and rate of formation of dike-filled fissures are sufficient to account for an east–west extension of the island of 0.6 to 2 cm per year since the beginning of the Tertiary (Palmasson, 1963; Bodvarsson and Walker, 1964; Einarsson, 1965; Thorarinsson, 1966; Björnsson, 1967). The eruption of the modern volcano Surtsey, which developed in the last decade in the median rift zone just south of Iceland, has provided an unparalleled opportunity to study crustal processes in action. The thorough and continuing work of the Surtsey Research Society, which has already led to more than forty papers on the geochemistry, geology, and geophysical aspects of the eruption, constitutes an outstanding and invaluable example of multidisciplinary investigation (Surtsey Research Society, 1965, 1966, 1967; Thorarinsson, 1967).

In contrast to the complex history of Iceland, the next "outcrop" to the north on the Mid-Atlantic Ridge, Jan Mayen Island, shows evidence of only two periods of eruptive construction; it apparently represents a much smaller time span (Nicholls, 1955; Carstens, 1961). In the absence of detailed studies, the position of Jan Mayen Island with regard to midocean ridge development remains uncertain (Demenitskaya and Dibner, 1966; Johnson and Heezen, 1967).

Much remains to be learned about the Pleistocene and Recent history of arctic Canada and Greenland. Nearly every careful study results in information that challenges previously held concepts. To date, two, and doubtfully three, periods of Pleistocene glaciation have been identified in arctic Canada. The rhythm and duration of ice advance and retreat have not been positively correlated with those of temperate North America with any degree of certainty, although it is obvious that the last general advance corresponds to the "classical" Wisconsin. Evidence of a "pre-Wisconsin" glaciation comes from the western Queen Elizabeth Islands and Mackenzie River delta area, outside the area reached by "Wisconsin" ice, where glacial till lying on the Beaufort Formation is overlain by freshwater silts with wood (some of it chewed by beavers) and peat yielding a radiocarbon age greater than 35,000 years and indicating a climate warmer than today (Craig and Fyles, 1960). The silts are overlain by stony material which might be another "pre-Wisconsin" glacial deposit, and this in turn is overlain by uncompressed peat, never overridden by glacial ice, which has yielded a radiocarbon age of more than 38,000 years. On western Victoria Island, plant-bearing silts and gravels between two layers of till have a radiocarbon age of 28,000 years (Fyles, 1963). "Pre-Wisconsin" deposits that appear to be inter-glacial have been described from Baffin Island, Bathurst Island, Ellesmere Island, and the mouth of the Mackenzie River (Terasme, 1959; Blake, 1964; Fyles and Craig, 1965; Terasme et al., 1966).

The "Wisconsin" glaciation in arctic Canada comprised two major ice sheet complexes which evidently coalesced at the period of greatest advance. The Laurentide ice sheet spread northward from the Canadian mainland and the Hudson Bay area, advancing almost to the sea in the Mackenzie River delta area. It covered Victoria Island and reached southeastern Banks Island, where it deposited impressive terminal moraines, and also spread across Viscount Melville Sound to southern Melville Island (Craig and Fyles, 1960; Fyles, 1963, 1965). In the central and eastern archipelago, the Laurentide ice sheet, at its maximum extent, coalesced with a Baffin–Ellesmere–Greenland glacier complex that surrounded and possibly largely covered Baffin Bay. The west central Queen Elizabeth Islands and most of Banks Island were not covered by an active regional ice sheet in Wisconsin time but instead had local icecaps and large areas of permanent and apparently stagnant snow cover. There is evidence that active ice tongues may have occupied many of the channels between the islands (Savile, 1961; Fyles, 1963; Horn, 1967). Small areas of Baffin Island and possibly northern Ellesmere Island appear to have escaped Wisconsin glaciation (Løken, 1966). The "Wisconsin" ice sheet began to diminish about 9500 to 9000 years ago. During its retreat, it rapidly developed into a number of centers of outflow, building extensive moraine complexes, some of which appear contemporaneous throughout large sections of the Canadian Arctic (Falconer et al., 1965; Blake, 1966). By 8000 years ago the Laurentide ice sheet had disintegrated sufficiently for the sea to penetrate through the center of its former mass and reach James Bay at the south end of Hudson Bay. Approximately 6000 years ago the last remnants of the Laurentide ice sheet appear to have disappeared from the mainland west of Hudson Bay. This ice sheet had also disappeared from southern Baffin Island by 4500 years

ago, from the north coast of Victoria Island 12,400 years ago, from the north coast of Devon Island 15,500 years ago, from central Ellesmere Island 6500 years ago, and from the coast of northeast Ellesmere Island by 7200 years ago (Fyles and Blake, 1965; Blake, 1966; Müller and Barr, 1966; Hattersley-Smith and Long, 1967; Christie, 1967).

There is no certain proof for the survival of glaciers in arctic Canada from Pleistocene to Recent times. Although the largest existing ice masses, the icecaps on Ellesmere Island, Baffin Island, and Devon Island, are remnants of once much larger bodies, all the small present glaciers in the Canadian Archipelago that have been carefully studied appear to be modern and to have grown to their present size within the past five centuries or less (Crary, 1960; Hattersley-Smith, 1961; Koerner, in press; Ives, 1962; Roots, in Fortier et al., 1963; Christie, 1967). In their present marginal retreat, these bodies sometimes reveal vegetation that is found today only in warmer regions to the south (Arnold, 1965; Falconer, 1966). Plant material from post-Pleistocene deposits in many places indicates that 5000 years ago much of arctic Canada must have been warmer than it is today (Lee, 1962; Blake, 1964; Christie, 1967).

The history of glaciation in Greenland is known only in a fragmentary fashion. During the period of maximum glaciation, which has not yet been dated, the icecap, though thicker than at present, apparently did not bury the higher peaks inland from the east coast (Lister and Wyllie, 1958; Pessel, 1962). Off the southwest coast, the icecap spread at least to the edge of the continental shelf. In the northwest, it carried boulders across Nares Strait and deposited them on the shore of Ellesmere Island, but parts of the north coast may have escaped glaciation (Christie, 1967). The outer islands off the southwest coast appear to have been deglaciated about 10,000 years ago, the central part of the east coast was free of ice at the then sea level by 9000 to 8500 years ago, and on the north coast, retreat has been recorded between 6000 and 3700 years ago (Davies, 1961; Kelly, 1966; Washburn and Stuiver, 1962; Lasca, 1966). Evidence exists that during the "Climatic Optimum" the ice cover was less than at present. Since then, the glaciers have advanced prior to their modern cycle of retreat (Boyd, 1948; Jacobsen, 1961; Soen, 1965).

The history of glaciation in Iceland is complicated by abundant local volcanism, with eruptions both beneath or through the ice and in ice-free areas or during ice-free periods. There is evidence of repeated coverage of the entire island by ice, but the pattern of deglaciation is in most places masked by a confusing mixture of eruptive, glacial, fluvial, and eolian material (the Palagonite Formation) of heterogeneous texture and lithology but with a limited range of composition and a lack of datable horizons (Einarsson, 1962). The most useful clues to the glacial and postglacial history are obtained from investigation of the land forms (Kjartansson, 1966; Thorarinsson, 1966).

An integral part of the study of the glaciation and Recent history of the entire area is the physiographic development, the changes in sea level, and the present geomorphic processes. From the very scanty information available to date, it appears that the topographic configuration and relief of the Canadian Arctic Archipelago and Greenland must have been, prior to the Pleistocene glaciations, generally similar to the present. The archipelago was apparently a more or less continuous land mass in mid-Tertiary times, and it has been dissected by stream erosion to roughly its present pattern by rivers flowing toward Baffin Bay and the Arctic Ocean, from a divide running roughly north–south through the islands. This landscape has been modified only in detail by glaciations; the largest changes occurred in the river valleys, which were broadened and straightened and whose sides were steepened. Subsequent submergence caused these valleys to become the straits of the archipelago (Pelletier, 1964; Fyles and Craig, 1965; Horn, 1967). At the close of the Wisconsin glaciation, the land surface was depressed, and the first marine invasion upon retreat of the ice shows a relative sea level commonly higher than at present. The highest recorded marine features are about 240 m above the present sea level.

The relative upper limit of marine submergence and the pattern of relative rebound vary widely throughout the Canadian Archipelago and arctic mainland, probably because of a combination of varied isostatic depression resulting from a nonuniform ice load, differences in crustal structure, and possibly active present-day tectonic forces (Craig and Fyles, 1960; Andrews, 1968). In the Hudson Bay region, for example, the relative rise of the land was at first very rapid (7.5 m per century, 8000 years ago), and then much slower (½ to 1 m per century in historical times) (Lee, 1962). The north coast of Devon Island underwent a slow rise during the period 16,000–9000 years ago, then a very rapid rise during the period 9000 to 7500 years ago, with a decreasing rate since that time (Müller and Barr, 1966). Evidence from east Greenland shows a very similar pattern, with the rapid rise persisting until 6000 years ago (Lasca, 1966). In central Ellesmere Island, however, the land continued to rise rapidly until 5000 years ago (Hattersley-Smith and Long, 1967). On the north coast of the island and the northeast coast of Baffin Island the relative rise of land was less rapid and more prolonged (Løken, 1965; Christie, 1967). In contrast, on western Victoria Island the sea level may not have changed more than 10 m in the past 9000 years.

The pattern of present-day changes in sea level confirms the local variability of vertical movements. On Cornwallis Island, successive Eskimo settlements have been moved to lower beach ridges as the land rose since human occupation, while on northern Devon Island, 300 km away, in an area where the land has been generally rising for the past 15,000 years, an Eskimo campsite that must have been occupied within the past ten centuries is now partly below sea level

(Fortier *et al.*, 1963). A further illustration of the complexity of Quaternary history is afforded by the presence of shallow-water sediments in cyclic layers, strongly resembling varves and apparently of glacial origin, in depressions of the sea floor in the western Queen Elizabeth Islands at present depths of 300 to 400 m. These deposits suggest that sea level was much lower during at least some stage of Pleistocene glaciation (Marlowe, 1964). From bathymetric and stratigraphic evidence and the presence of terrestrial organic matter on submerged terraces in the channels of the western Queen Elizabeth Islands, it seems reasonable to infer that the pre-Pleistocene or perhaps the "pre-Wisconsin" land surface in this area is still drowned by as much as 100 to 450 m (Marlowe, 1964; Pelletier, 1964; Horn, 1967). However, the average free-air gravity anomaly over the shield area to the south is +11.8 mgal; for the archipelago it is +7.3 mgal; and over the continental shelf +27.0 mgal, suggesting that the area is isostatically overcompensated, and that further submergence of up to 100 m would be required to restore equilibrium (Weber *et al.*, in press).

Details of the present subaerial landscape, and its development under an arctic periglacial climate, have been studied on a quantitative basis in very few places. Although there have been admirable studies of limited localities, the only extensive arctic periglacial area that has been mapped and classified in detail is Ellef Ringnes Island (Robitaille, 1961; Pissart, 1966, 1968; St.-Onge, 1965). Recent work has shown that many widely held concepts regarding the relative efficacy of frost action, mechanical and chemical weathering, and stream erosion in arctic regions need revision, and that the rate of development of distinctive arctic landforms or permafrost features may vary widely for reasons not fully understood (Lliboutry, 1965; Dunn and Hudek, 1966; St.-Onge, in preparation).

The geomorphology of arctic coastlines and the transport and deposition of modern arctic sediments are, in many respects, unique, due to the ephemeral nature of stream runoff and sediment transport in areas of permafrost and the distinctive behavior of the ubiquitous sea ice. Arctic coastlines cannot readily be classified in terms of available energy due to the alternately protective and violently erosive or disturbing effect of sea ice and to its erratic transporting power, whose capacity is unrelated to the quantity or size distribution of the sediment load. Local and offshore sediment distribution is related to wind-driven pack-ice movements as well as to ocean currents and distance from source of sediment. The modern sediments off the arctic coasts of North America show a distinctly yellow-brown near-surface layer containing abundant evidence of organisms; this is underlain along a sharp contact by dark gray mud with few or no organic remains (Marlowe, 1964; Horn, 1967). The change in sediment type does not reflect a single contemporaneous event, but appears to indicate a widespread, although locally varying, change in environment and conditions of deposition about 12,000 years ago. There has been much speculation about the cause and significance of the change, but no satisfactory explanation is known. In some areas, modern sediments contain a substantial proportion of material transported from a considerable distance by ice-rafting, suggesting that shorelines and glacier action, and the distribution of sea ice and icebergs, have been relatively constant long enough to have a significant geological effect on the land surface and the sea floor (Grant, 1965; Kranck, 1966).

Geophysical investigations to date permit a tentative reconstruction of the crustal structure beneath the Canadian Arctic Archipelago and mainland. Under the central stable region, the crust–mantle boundary lies at a depth of about 30 km; it maintains this depth under the exposed part of the Franklinian miogeosyncline, but under the Sverdrup Basin it becomes shallower, and the crust thins abruptly under the inner part of the present continental shelf (Gregory et al., 1961; Sander and Overton, 1965). A very large positive free-air gravity anomaly of 120 mgal, at least 600 km long, lies close to the edge of the continental shelf west of the Queen Elizabeth Islands (Weber, 1963). Magnetic and seismic evidence suggests that thick wedges or lenses of sedimentary material, perhaps somewhat similar to that found in the Sverdrup Basin but smaller, appear under the present continental shelf. The gravity anomaly may be due to a combination of thick sediments and thin crust or to an intrusion of nonmagnetic rocks. Beyond the continental slope the thickness of the crust is of the order of 20 km (Weber et al., in press).

The complicated late Tertiary history, the large vertical movements of both arctic Canada and Greenland in late Tertiary and Quaternary time, the rapid and differential rebound since the Pleistocene, and the apparent discrepancy between physiographic and gravity evidence all indicate that parts of arctic North America and Greenland are tectonically active (Roots, 1966). Critical regions of present-day tectonism are: (a) the area near Mould Bay and the "Prince Patrick horst" at the southwest corner of the Queen Elizabeth Islands, where flurries of small seismic shocks, anisotropic transmission of seismic energy, curious damping of the vertical fluctuations of the magnetic field, general crowding of geomagnetic lines of force into what has been called the "Great Arctic Magnetic Anomaly," and an erratic geothermal heat flow pattern have been observed; (b) the Baffin Bay–Nares Strait zone, a major lineament with many puzzling features including a region of markedly enhanced electromagnetic conductivity, a very large gravity gradient, and an over-all morphological pattern suggesting offset, which is belied by the adjacent stratigraphy and structure, although a major fracture has been confirmed; (c) the flexure zone along the east coast of Greenland, and (d) Iceland and the intersection of the Mid-Atlantic Ridge with the Brito-Arctic volcanic province (Wager, 1947; Hope,

1959; Berthelsen, 1961; Rikitake and Whitham, 1964; Whitham, 1964; Andersen, 1965; Paterson and Law, 1966; Kerr, 1967b; Haller, in press; Smith et al., in press). The relation of the activity of the midocean ridge at Iceland to the other active zones in the Arctic is complex (Demenitskaya and Karaskik, 1966; Demenitskaya and Dibner, 1966; Björnsson, 1967; Johnson and Heezen, 1967). There is some evidence that structures in Baffin Bay may have a connection with those in the Labrador Sea, which are in turn related to the Atlantic midocean ridge (Sykes, 1965; Godby et al., 1966; Kerr, 1967a).

SCIENTIFIC PROBLEMS

1. What are the historical and structural relationships between the Cordilleran geosyncline and the Franklinian geosyncline? What are the relations between the orogenies of the Cordillera in the Yukon and eastern Alaska, of the Brooks Range, and of the Innuitian system? Is the Innuitian system a feature truly marginal to the Arctic Ocean Basin, or is it a splayed offshoot of the Cordillera? Or is there no connection at all with the craton passing uninterrupted, except by fault steps, from the Canadian Shield to the Canada Basin?

Attempts at paleogeographic and paleotectonic correlation have been partly inconclusive because of the lack of reliable information on depth to basement and on facies and faunal transition and because critical areas "joining" the two systems are covered by younger rocks or the sea. The problem has considerable economic significance because the areas that are potentially favorable for the accumulation of petroleum in each region are in many respects similar, and it is important to know whether they are continuous. Subsurface investigations are now under way in the covered area. These efforts and careful stratigraphic, paleontologic, and structural comparisons now being made between the Innuitian and Cordilleran systems will do much to explain the tectonic framework of northern North America.

2. What is the age and nature of the Mackenzie River delta and its associated submarine canyon?

The old pre-Pleistocene delta now preserved mainly to the east of the present river has apparently suffered faulting and differential subsidence. The modern delta appears to be built in a graben-like depression that may still be subsiding. No reliable measurement of sediment thickness in the delta has been made, but scanty evidence suggests that it is very great, perhaps tens of thousands of meters. The geological similarity of the large deltas in the Gulf of Mexico and the Beaufort Sea, which lie at each end of the great sedimentary corridor through North America, may be oversimplified but may have potential economic value.

3. What is the reason for the marked difference in depth of the continental shelf off the north coast of Alaska and off the Canadian Archipelago?

North of Alaska the continental shelf is essentially continuous with that north of Siberia. It has an average depth up to 100 m and a lip at about 150 m at the edge of the continental slope. In contrast, the continental shelf west of the Queen Elizabeth Islands has an average depth of 400 to 600 m and a sharp straight lip to the continental slope at about 650 m. Morphologically, the two shelves are much alike; profiles and slopes are comparable, and surficial sediments are similar. The channels between the islands of the archipelago enter the Canadian shelf slightly below grade and rise to a low threshold at 400 to 450 m below sea level. Of those channels that have been surveyed, none has cut a valley in the outer shelf or down the continental slope. Physiographically, this continental shelf is typical despite its great depth. Bathymetric and geological evidence suggests a simple drowning of the Canadian shelf and adjacent glaciated channels; however, extensive regional gravity mapping shows that the area would have to be submerged still further to attain isostatic equilibrium.

4. What is the crustal structure, history, and nature of the current tectonism in the Mould Bay area at the southwest corner of the Queen Elizabeth Islands?

The anomalous geophysical and geological features of this region make it one of the most distinctive and critical areas of arctic North America. A full listing of the unusual features is beyond the scope of this report, but the following will illustrate the wide range of interrelated phenomena which have a bearing on regional problems: (a) The area lies at the end of the Sverdrup Basin, crossing its axis directly athwart the Innuitian fold structures. Rocks of the Franklinian geosyncline are truncated across their strike by the Eglinton graben which drops Mesozoic rocks of the Sverdrup Basin in their place. On the other side of the graben in the Prince Patrick horst, the Upper Devonian Franklinian formations recur without continuation of the Innuitian structures. (b) In comparison with the horizontal variations, vertical fluctuations of the magnetic field are strongly dampened over an area at least 60 by 100 km. (c) Seismic waves from sources to the east, received at Mould Bay by traveling beneath the crust and passing through or beneath the anomalous magnetic area and the graben, are attenuated by a factor of ten compared with energy received from comparable sources to the north, along a similar path, but skirting the anomalous magnetic area. However, waves traveling through the granitic layer arrive with about equal energy from each direction. (d) Local seismic activity is marked but sporadic and is concentrated within very restricted areas. Study of a recent flurry of microearthquakes shows that more than 2000 shocks originated within an ellipsoid 2 km in diameter, indicating remarkable concentration and localized release of strain. (e) High heat-flow might explain the magnetic anomaly and seismic anisotropy; however, geothermal measurements show anomalously low values to the south and normal values within and to the west of the area.

In addition to its crustal and tectonic features, this region is the type area for some of the major formations of the Sverdrup Basin. It has yielded plesiosaur remains with their implications for Mesozoic paleogeography.

5. What is the late Precambrian history of the shield, the relation between development of geosynclines within the shield area, and block movements that characterize its margins?

The arctic border of the shield offers well-exposed examples of block movements within the shield, often trending roughly perpendicular to its margin, in which repeated sedimentation and deformation serve to document the history. Particularly suitable for study are the Minto Arch on Victoria Island, where very fresh and unmetamorphosed sedimentary rocks underlie Paleozoic strata with good fossil control, and the Boothia uplift, which has been active since late Precambrian time and whose Paleozoic movements have influenced the Franklinian geosyncline. These questions are important to our understanding of the geology of North America as a whole.

6. What is the reason for concentration of distinctive ring intrusions of gabbro on Ellef Ringnes Island and of the gypsum anhydrite diapirs along the axis of the Sverdrup Basin? What is the mechanism and timing of their emplacement?

The two types of intrusions may not be related, but both are confined to the thicker parts of the Sverdrup Basin, where rock competency and the stress pattern allowed development of these unique pipe-like bodies. Recent careful stratigraphic study has yielded valuable information on the geological setting and the structural influence of these intrusions. Detailed petrological and geophysical investigations of selected bodies are now needed to fill out our understanding of these most spectacular and puzzling structures, whose occurrences may have a direct bearing on petroleum deposits in the area.

7. What are the relationships between the Alpha Cordillera and the Lomonosov Ridge, respectively, and the North American crustal platform with its Innuitian and related structures?

The weight of geophysical and morphological evidence suggests that the Alpha Cordillera is a remnant of, or a part of, a typical midocean ridge, whereas the Lomonosov Ridge has all the characteristics of an isolated strip of continental or shelf-type platform. An apparently logical explanation or reconstruction, compatible with present evidence, is that the Alpha Cordillera represents a former, and possibly still active, extension of the mid-Atlantic fracture zone and ridge whose connection with the ridge in the north Atlantic skirted the north coasts of Ellesmere Island and Greenland; and that the Lomonosov Ridge, at the time of the development of the Alpha Cordillera, was probably a part of the Siberian continental platform. Further widening of the Atlantic Ocean Basin appears to have developed a fracture into the Siberian continental platform, which, upon subsequent spreading, produced the Eurasia Basin and the Nansen Cordillera and which isolated the Lomonosov Ridge as a continental remnant, now a septum between two presently or formerly spreading ocean basins. This explanation accommodates the progressive lateral displacement resulting from the development and widening of the Atlantic rift into the Atlantic Ocean Basin in middle latitudes. At the northern end it also accounts for splaying of the rift into three branches and the successive and contemporaneous development of the Amerasia Basin of the Arctic Ocean with its median Alpha Cordillera, the Labrador Sea with its median ridge, and the Eurasia Basin of the Arctic Ocean with its median Nansen Cordillera. These branches of the Atlantic rift structure are separated by elongated masses of continental structure, namely, Greenland and the Lomonosov Ridge, respectively.

Evidence for the connection between the Alpha Cordillera and the known Mid-Atlantic Ridge, if it exists, will have to be sought at the edge of the continental shelf off the Queen Elizabeth Islands and the north coast of Greenland. Reconnaissance aeromagnetic surveys have extended only to the edge of the critical areas; they have produced information which, at present, is more tantalizing than illuminating. In the northernmost Canadian Archipelago, recent careful stratigraphic and structural mapping has added tremendously to our knowledge of the depositional environment and structural history of Paleozoic and younger rocks of the area. The pattern of tectonic evolution and influence is now established. Detailed gravity, magnetic, and seismic studies, with geothermal profile traverses, are urgently needed in the offshore area at the junction of the Alpha Cordillera, the Lomonosov Ridge, and the Canadian continental shelf to help explain this most important problem.

8. What is the relationship between the various belts of the Franklinian geosyncline and their contemporaneously developed equivalents in the northeast and east Greenland geosynclines and between the Sverdrup Basin and the Mesozoic-Tertiary geosynclines of west and east Greenland?

The consistent lack of faunal correspondence between the two sets of contemporaneous strata and the general European rather than North American affinities of the northeast Greenland deposits are significantly related to the timing and magnitude of the opening of various branches of the north Atlantic fracture system, to the relative displacement

of continental fragments, and to the comparative history of development of the Labrador Sea and the Eurasia Basin of the Arctic Ocean. Recent detailed studies on Ellesmere and Axel Heiberg Islands and in northwest Greenland are providing an illuminating and detailed picture of the nature and history of the Franklinian geosyncline. It would be of great interest and importance to the regional interpretation to compare these results with information from corresponding studies in northeast Greenland. Similarly, detailed comparative studies of the environment of deposition, source of sediment, and structural development and subsequent history of the Sverdrup Basin, the west Greenland (Disko) Mesozoic-Tertiary Basin, and the Mesozoic basins of east Greenland will, in turn, contribute directly to the interpretation of regional geologic and tectonic history.

9. What is the origin and history of Baffin Bay, and what is its relationship to the Labrador Sea?

Baffin Bay is one of the most puzzling of all geologic features in the Arctic. It has a great depth of more than 2500 m and an axial zone of high seismicity; judging from scanty earthquake data, it appears to be partly underlain by a thin crust. Across a sill which partly coincides with the Brito-Arctic transverse volcanic belt, it connects with the Labrador Sea and its median ridge, and it leads to or passes into a rift-valley-type fracture to the north—the Nares lineament. A thorough geophysical study would be most rewarding, for the Bay may represent an early stage in the postulated evolution of a rift valley into a true ocean basin. It is large enough to be the product of major crustal mechanisms yet small and accessible enough to make a thorough study practical and economically feasible. Moreover, it is bounded by a variety of rocks and structures that give good geologic control on the sequence of structural developments and their effect on the geologic environment of the adjacent continent.

10. What is the significance of the Nares lineament?

This major structural line separating Ellesmere Island and Greenland and joining Baffin Bay with the Lincoln Sea has been the object of much speculation. The remarkable enhancement of electromagnetic conductivity of the crust, as measured in an elongated zone just west of the north end of the lineament, is unique in North America and very rare throughout the world. It is not indicated by any known feature of the exposed geology, nor does it have any observed effect on the geomagnetic field. It does, however, coincide with a very steep gravity gradient. Careful geologic mapping has shown convincingly that the Nares lineament is a submarine rift valley, with only slight transcurrent displacement. It appears to have developed in stages since late Cretaceous time by crustal thinning which localized fracturing and rotational separation. Gravity surveys and seismic traverses would help to confirm the structural interpretation, and geothermal measurements are needed to test explanations of the conductivity anomaly. The extension of the lineament to the north, and its relation to the structures of the Morris Jesup Rise, the Lincoln Sea, and the Canadian end of the Lomonosov Ridge are as yet unknown. Hydrographic, aeromagnetic, and gravity surveys are the first requirement for study. Geophysical studies of the water-covered areas at the south end of the Nares lineament are also needed to investigate the relationship between the submarine rift valley, Baffin Bay, and the major fractures in the archipelago represented by Jones Sound and Parry Channel. The main geologic formations and structural trends appear to continue from Devon Island across Jones Sound to southern Ellesmere Island; however, recent gravity mapping has shown quite different gravity patterns on each island. Detailed geophysical information from the water-covered areas is not available; gravity, aeromagnetic, and seismic surveys are all necessary.

11. What is the late Tertiary and Quaternary history of Greenland?

Much of the rock surface beneath the Greenland ice cap is now near or below sea level, and gravity evidence suggests that the present saucer-shaped surface would rebound to a low undulating plateau were the ice removed. Very little is known of possible earlier Pleistocene glaciations, preglacial or interglacial marine invasions, or of changes of land level since the last glacial maximum, when the ice cap apparently covered most or all of the narrow continental shelf off the east and west coasts.

12. What is the deformational history of the northeast corner of Greenland?

The pattern of Paleozoic fold structures of northwest Greenland, northeast Greenland, and east Greenland is confusing. In northeast Greenland these deformations have overwhelmed and fragmented late Precambrian structures and appear to overlap one another with conflicting trends or to pass under younger strata or out to sea without apparent convergence or interference; forces from varying directions deformed geosynclinal material between the Atlantic and Arctic Basins and the Greenland craton. In the Northeast Foreland and in Peary Land, these structures are succeeded by Cenozoic structures, trending roughly parallel to the oceanic margin and characterized by moderate horizontal movements and large vertical displacements. These structural problems are clearly a part of the larger problems of the relations between the geosynclinal belts, the development of the Atlantic–arctic rift structures, and the fragmentation of the North American crustal block. Detailed stratigraphic and structural studies, with aeromagnetic surveys and bathymetry in the offshore area from the Morris Jesup Rise to the Belgica Bank, are badly needed.

13. What is the history and comparative consanguinity of the Brito-Arctic volcanic province? How does this relate to the development of the midocean ridge?

This province is the most completely developed, best exposed, and most accessible of all the volcanic complexes that lie transverse to the midocean ridges. It is exposed at Baffin Island, west Greenland, east Greenland, Iceland, the Faeroe Islands, and the British Isles, and these exposures are connected by conspicuous ocean-floor rises. The excellently exposed plateau basalts of east and west Greenland have been only sketchily studied but are known to contain intercalated sedimentary material which will aid dating. They should be compared with their lateral counterparts in the Faeroes and Britain and with the apparently contemporaneous flows in Iceland itself. Paleomagnetic studies can be useful and may aid in relating parts of the exposed volcanic assemblage to specific parts of the Atlantic Ocean floor. Gravity, magnetic, and heat-flow studies across the submarine sills joining the island outcrops would be most instructive.

14. What is the nature of the crust beneath Iceland?

Seismic surveys of the crust beneath Iceland have shown a series of layers of increasing seismic velocity. A substratum at the fairly shallow depth of from ½ to 5 km has a velocity of 6.3 km/sec, which is higher than normal velocities for plateau basalts and within the range of velocities for typical oceanic crusts. A similar section has been obtained from seismic work on the Faeroe Islands. The proximity of this layer to the surface warrants detailed study. Direct sampling of the layer by drilling appears feasible and economical and could be a valuable contribution to ocean-floor studies as a whole.

RECOMMENDATIONS

1. Continued and increased support should be provided for study by individual scientists of specific geologic problems in arctic Canada, Greenland, and the northernmost Atlantic Ocean Basin.

2. Detailed studies should be made of the geologic structure and history of Jan Mayen Island and the northern Mid-Atlantic Ridge.

3. Bathymetric and gravity surveys should be conducted, with adequate positioning control, to produce maps at 1:500,000 or larger scale of the continental shelf, continental slope, and Baffin Bay and maps at 1:250,000 of all inland waters.

4. Detailed geophysical surveys of Iceland should be conducted, along with a scientific drilling program.

5. Aeromagnetic surveys should be conducted, with adequate positioning control, to produce 1:250,000 maps of

all areas underlain by Phanerozoic rocks, including the continental shelves.

6. Geothermal heat-flow measurements should be obtained at typical sites within each geologic province.

7. Aeromagnetic profiles at 20- to 25-km spacing should be obtained over all the continental slopes and Baffin Bay.

ANTARCTICA

PHYSIOGRAPHY OF THE ANTARCTIC CONTINENT

Antarctica is commonly divided by the Greenwich meridian into East Antarctica and West Antarctica, though a more realistic division is made along the 30° W - 150° E meridian, with the wide mountainous belt of the Transantarctic Mountains lying generally along and on the Pacific side of this meridian.

The broad features of the stratigraphy, structure, and tectonic history of Antarctica are reasonably well known. In its simplest form the geology consists of an East Antarctic craton of older Precambrian age bordered by the Transantarctic geosynclinal, fold-mountain belt of latest Precambrian and early Paleozoic age, which is in turn bordered in West Antarctica by geosynclinal, fold-mountain, and volcanic belts of mainly Mesozoic and Cenozoic age (Ford, 1964; Harrington, 1965; Warren, 1965; Bakayev *et al.*, 1966). To a first approximation, the continental framework is similar to that of the other continents.

About 5 percent of the total area of the antarctic continent is exposed rock. In 1965, Soviet geologists estimated that more than half of this area had been geologically explored, but that reconnaissance geological maps at 1:250,000 to 1:1,000,000 covered only about 25 percent of the ice-free areas (Ravich, 1966). During 1969, the American Geographical Society, with contributions from seven countries, published a folio of 16 large-scale geologic maps, mostly at 1:1,000,000 scale. These maps cover the larger areas of rock outcrop in Antarctica, including considerably more than 50 percent of the total exposed rock. Much of this area, however, cannot be considered as systematically mapped at 1:1,000,000 scale.

Fortunately, most of the ice-free areas contain excellently exposed and but slightly weathered bedrock; however, the outcrops are mainly concentrated in relatively narrow linear belts along the Transantarctic Mountains and the coastal periphery of East Antarctica; thus in a broad analysis, only two dimensions of geology are seen—thickness and length. The Antarctic Ice Sheet offers a unique opportunity to test the influence of ice loading upon the earth's crust and ultimately to prove or disprove theories of crustal strength. In the future, tests may be made of the theories of phase transition at the crust–mantle boundary and of

subcrustal mass movement in response to isostatic adjustments resulting from changes of ice loading.

Geographically, the antarctic continent is antisymmetric to the Arctic Basin. We have yet to learn if deep earth forces and processes are different in polar areas than in lower latitudes. Because of possible continental drift or polar wandering, the continent may not have remained in a polar position long enough to show such differences in its rocks and structures. Much more detailed geologic investigations are needed to answer these questions.

A fundamental feature in the geologic and geophysical interpretation of any continent is the bedrock surface morphology. The bedrock surface beneath the Antarctic Ice Sheet in East Antarctica consists of large lowland plains bounded by several large interior mountainous regions and by a coastal fringe of partially exposed mountains. The Transantarctic Mountains form a great snow-capped orographic chain that transects the continent and rises from 2000 to 4000 m in elevation. The mountain chain is reasonably well exposed along its 4000 km of length. In contrast, West Antarctica would become a mountainous island archipelago if its ice cover were stripped away.

EAST ANTARCTICA

A relatively small exposed part of the craton is found along the coastal margin of East Antarctica and is thought to consist of a suite of high-grade metamorphic and plutonic rocks of heterogeneous structure with complicated early Precambrian tectonic history (Bakayev, 1966; Ravich, 1966). Although only a few radiometric dates approach 2000 m.y., the cratonic rocks are a distinctive suite whose age is probably early Precambrian (Archean) (Ravich, 1966). The cratonic suite consists of migmatized and "granitized" Ca–Mg-rich (pyroxene) and Al-rich (cordierite, sillimanite, garnet, biotite) gneisses and crystalline schists of the granulite facies. It also contains migmatized, dominantly retrogressively metamorphosed, amphibolite and biotite gneisses of the amphibolite facies. In places, deep fault zones consist of thoroughly retrograded low-grade schists (diaphthorites).

Charnockitic rocks, both metamorphic and plutonic, characterize the cratonic rock suite and hence are thought to be of diverse age within the early Precambrian (Klimov *et al.*, 1964). Abundant "rheomorphic" charnockite is probably derived from mobilized, "dry," multimetamorphic and ultrametamorphic rocks from deep within the crust. Plutonic charnockites of the coastal periphery form the largest charnockite province in the world.

Overlying the crystalline cratonic rocks in western Queen Maud Land and in the Denman Glacier area are subhorizontal homoclinal sedimentary rocks, dominantly quartz sandstone and graywacke, and volcanic rocks of late Precambrian and possibly early Paleozoic age (Ravich, 1966; Neethling, 1967). These rocks are slightly metamorphosed. In the Denman Glacier area, sedimentary rocks are underlain by chlorite–epidote schists of probable epicratonic origin (Klimov, 1964). In the Prince Charles Mountains, low-grade metasedimentary rocks, probably epicratonic, are intensely folded (Trail, 1964).

The youngest epicratonic rocks, flat-lying sandstones with minor coal beds and a Permian microflora, occur in the Prince Charles Mountains. *Glossopteris*-bearing sandstone erratics occur in nearby moraines (McLeod, 1964).

The original extent and thickness of the epicratonic deposits in East Antarctica are not known. At least locally, as in the Prince Charles and Denman areas, deposition probably was geosynclinal, and the lowest strata were subjected to low-grade dynamic metamorphism. This implies local orogenesis upon the craton during the late Precambrian. It is possible that the Gamburtsev-Vernadskiy Mountains and other inland ice-buried mountains might be intracratonic orogenic ranges that have been active and uplifted one or more times since the formation of the craton.

TRANSANTARCTIC MOUNTAINS

The Transantarctic Mountain chain extends from the Oates Coast to Coats Land and largely coincides with a late Precambrian–early Paleozoic geosynclinal and fold-mountain belt (Schmidt, 1966). The intensely folded, thick, flysch-type sedimentary rocks of probably late Precambrian age are unconformably overlain by folded archaeocyathid- and trilobite-bearing limestone and volcanic rocks of Cambrian age in the Pensacola Mountains and in the Nimrod Glacier area (Grindley *et al.*, 1964; Schmidt *et al.*, 1965). Similar geosynclinal sedimentary rocks occur in many places throughout the Transantarctic Mountains from the Shackleton Range to north Victoria Land, but age relations and correlations are not well established. In the dry valleys area of McMurdo Sound, intensely deformed metasedimentary schists, gneisses, and marble of the amphibolite facies are associated with pretectonic, syntectonic, and posttectonic granitic rocks. Previously, these rocks were considered to be cratonic basement; however, recent work shows that at least some of the rocks are metamorphic equivalents of the geosynclinal deposits of late Precambrian and early Paleozoic age (Blank *et al.*, 1963). The latest general orogeny was of early Paleozoic age. Granitic rocks similar to the McMurdo area suite occur throughout the Transantarctic Mountains. Such rocks and associated gneisses and schists could, in some places, be part of the East Antarctic craton, but age relationships from isotopic dating and other evidence are generally not well enough established to prove or disprove the existence of lower Precambrian rocks.

An absence of cratonic rocks beneath the Transantarctic Mountains would lend support to the hypothesis of continental growth by accretion of geosynclinal belts and would tend to contradict the hypothesis that the East Antarctic craton extends into central Marie Byrd Land (Ravich, 1966).

A flat-lying unmetamorphosed sedimentary succession, informally termed the Beacon rocks, unconformably overlies the folded geosynclinal and granitic rocks of the Transantarctic Mountains. Beacon rocks consist of sandstone and siltstone deposited in continental and coastal environments and range in age from Devonian to Jurassic (Grindley and Warren, 1964). The succession is commonly 2 to 3 km thick. Throughout much of the Transantarctic Mountains, Beacon rocks show a grossly similar lithologic sequence, i.e., Devonian quartz sandstone, lower Permian (?) glacial deposits, and glossopterid-bearing coal measures of Permian age.

The thick sequence of Beacon rocks in the Pensacola Mountains is moderately to intensely folded (Schmidt *et al.*, 1965). Apparently, the crust beneath this part of the Transantarctic Mountains remained mobile as late as Mesozoic time. The geology is structurally as well as lithologically similar to that of the Ellsworth Mountains, and this similarity suggests that the Ellsworth Mountain block may be allochthonous in West Antarctica (Craddock *et al.*, 1964a).

The Ferrar dolerites of Jurassic age intrude Beacon rocks and underlying basement in thick sills that aggregate in places more than 300 m (McDougall, 1963). Tholeiitic flood basalts, locally estimated as at least 2000 m thick, overlie Triassic sedimentary rocks in the Queen Alexandra Range and in north Victoria Land (Grindley, 1963; McGregor, 1965; Gair, 1967). In the northern Pensacola Mountains, a tabular body of stratiform gabbro at least 9500 km^2 in area and possibly 7 km thick may be of similar age (Ford and Boyd, in press).

A late Cenozoic volcanic province borders the Transantarctic Mountains along the Ross Sea from McMurdo Sound to Cape Adare. Isolated volcanics also occur in the Queen Maud Range of the Transantarctic Mountains and at Gaussberg on the Wilhelm II Coast of East Antarctica. The rocks are basaltic and trachytic. Many of these volcanic accumulations retain an initial depositional, constructional form, little modified by subsequent erosion. The larger volcanic piles are composite shield volcanoes. The largest volcano, Mt. Erebus, rises to 3743 m and still emits steam. In the dry valleys area of McMurdo, volcanic deposits are commonly interlayered with late Cenozoic moraines; cinder cones and lava flows with flow-crenulated tops have erupted on glacially sculptured valley sides. The large, late Cenozoic "volcanic" piles of Adare, Hallett, and Daniell Peninsulas as well as Coulman Island in northeastern Victoria Land consist of palagonitic and pillow breccias that formed during the intrusion of basaltic and trachytic lava into a thick ice cover. These palagonitic piles indicate that the antarctic ice cover was much thicker and more extensive in the past (Hamilton, 1967a).

WEST ANTARCTICA AND THE SCOTIA ARC

West Antarctica, that portion of the continent lying on the Pacific Ocean side of the Transantarctic Mountains, is a region with scattered nunataks and mountain groups widely separated by intervening ice. If the present ice cover were removed, West Antarctica would appear as a series of scattered islands, or group of islands, surrounding the submerged Byrd Basin, which would connect with the Ross Sea to the west, the Amundsen Sea to the north, and the Weddell Sea to the east. Complexities of the regional geology and the rather limited information available at present preclude any broad geological generalizations about the area.

Progress of geologic work in Antarctica during the period 1831-1962 has been well summarized (Anderson, 1965). Other reviews of current geologic knowledge have been published (Adie, 1962; Gunn, 1963; Ford, 1964; Harrington, 1965; Hamilton, 1967b), and the geology of the Antarctic Peninsula has been summarized separately (Adie, 1964a). The international Scientific Committee on Antarctic Research (SCAR) volume *Antarctic Geology* is very useful for an over-all view of current geologic activities on the continent (Adie, 1964b).

Marie Byrd Land and Ellsworth Land

The Ford Ranges and the peaks of Edward VII Peninsula in northwestern Marie Byrd Land have been studied recently (Wade, 1967). With possibly one exception, the oldest rocks present are a series of unfossiliferous metasedimentary strata consisting of quartzites, graywackes, and minor beds of quartzose shale. During a period of orogeny these rocks were intensely folded and intruded by large granitic plutons. Mafic dikes and irregular plutons cut these older rocks; Cenozoic olivine basalts and tuffs are present in the northern Ford Ranges. Major axes in the folded metasedimentary rocks plunge gently to the west-northwest. Radiometric ages from granite and biotite schist place the time of orogeny in the Cretaceous.

An anomalous and probably older block of gneisses and schists is found in the Fosdick Mountains. Two possible origins for these rocks have been suggested: they may represent a more highly metamorphosed and partially granitized portion of the lower grade metasedimentary rocks that are widespread in these ranges; or they may represent an older sequence of metamorphosed and granitized sedimentary rocks that has been elevated by block faulting and exposed by erosion of the overlying younger rocks (Wade, 1967).

Farther east along the Ruppert and Hobbs Coasts, between Mt. Shirley and Cape Burks, exposed rocks have been placed into a provisional sequence from oldest to youngest as follows: (1) gneisses and amphibolites; (2) metavolcanics; (3) granitic intrusives; and (4) mafic and felsic dikes (Sporli and Craddock, personal communication). Gneisses and amphibolites are not known to occur in the same outcrop as the metavolcanics; thus, their age relationship is speculative and based solely on the relative degree of their metamorphism. No definite conclusions have been made regarding correlation of any of these rocks with other units in West Antarctica.

The area between this northwestern portion of coastal Marie Byrd Land and the base of the Antarctic Peninsula is dominantly a volcanic province. All the exposed rock examined in the Hal Flood Range, the Ames Range, the Crary Mountains, the Toney Mountains, and Mt. Takahe is volcanic (Wade, personal communication). The Executive Committee Range is also part of this volcanic complex and has been described in some detail (Doumani, 1964). The large island, on which Mt. Siple is located, has not been visited but is presumed to be volcanic according to air photo interpretation. One age determination on an andesite from the Executive Committee Range suggests a late Tertiary (Pliocene) age for these volcanoes (Doumani, 1964).

Within this province, however, older rocks are exposed below the Cenozoic volcanics in several localities. Granodiorite is overlain unconformably by olivine basalts along the USAS Escarpment (Doumani and Ehlers, 1962). Metamorphic rocks occur below a volcanic sequence at Mt. Murphy, and both intrusive and metamorphic rocks underlie volcanics on Bear Island (Wade, personal communication). In the midst of this volcanic province lies the Kohler Range, which consists of exposed metasedimentary rocks, intrusive granitic rocks, granodiorites, and gneisses.

In the Jones Mountains, just south of Thurston Island, upper Tertiary olivine basalt volcanics lie unconformably on a basement complex of granite and andesitic volcanics cut by mafic and felsic dikes (Craddock *et al.*, 1964b). The granite, probably the oldest rock exposed, has an apparent K-Ar age of Triassic, and one of the youngest intrusives in the basement complex yields an apparent K-Ar age of Cretaceous. Whole rock K-Ar age determinations on flows of the overlying olivine basalt volcanics suggest eruption during the late Tertiary. Immediately to the south, in the Hudson Mountains, are similar olivine basalts that have been dated as Miocene by K-Ar whole rock analyses (Laudon and Bastien, in press).

Within the Jones Mountains there are some exposed rocks that may bear directly on the age of the Antarctic Ice Sheet. The diamictite that crops out intermittently on the unconformity between the basement rocks and the overlying volcanics is interpreted as a probable tillite (Rutford *et al.*, 1966, 1968). The possibility of contemporaneous volcanic and glacial activity in the Executive Committee Range has been suggested (Doumani, 1964). On Thurston Island, dioritic gneisses and interlayered schists are cut by mafic dikes (Craddock and Hubbard, 1961). Along the Eights Coast east of Thurston Island, quartz diorites contain inclusions of mafic rocks (Drake, 1962). These dioritic rocks are probably related. A single Rb-Sr date on biotite from quartz diorite gneiss from eastern Thurston Island suggests a late Paleozoic (Carboniferous) age (Craddock *et al.*, 1964c). Zircons from a quartz diorite collected at "Peeler's Pinnacle" to the east gave a lead-alpha age of middle Jurassic; a K–Ar age on biotite from the same sample yielded an early late Cretaceous age (Drake *et al.*, 1964).

The Ellsworth Mountains Fold Belt

The Ellsworth Mountains fold belt lies at the eastern edge of Marie Byrd Land (Craddock, 1966, in press). Its structural grain is transverse to the trend of both the Transantarctic Mountains to the south and the line of scattered exposures to the north along the coast of the Bellingshausen Sea. Available ice-thickness data suggest that there is a subsea-level trough at the northern end of this province and that a narrow trough may separate the southern end from the Transantarctic Mountains. The fold belt is dominated by the Ellsworth Mountains, a large mountain system containing the Sentinel Range and the Heritage Range. Vinson Massif, the highest known peak in Antarctica, is located in the southern portion of the Sentinel Range. To the south and southwest of the Ellsworth Mountains is a series of nunataks and small mountain groups.

Within the Ellsworth Mountains are found at least 13,000 m of mainly Paleozoic strata including fossiliferous Cambrian limestones, thick quartzites with Devonian brachiopods, a probably late Paleozoic glaciomarine unit, and an argillite unit bearing *Glossopteris* (Craddock *et al.*, 1965). Marbles and phyllites below the fossiliferous Cambrian limestones are considered upper Precambrian (?) to middle Cambrian. All these sedimentary rocks have been strongly folded in post-Permian time. Major structural trends swing from northwest in the southern Ellsworth Mountains to almost due north in the northern part; a major anticlinorium plunges gently to the north (Craddock *et al.*, 1964a). Scattered tabular mafic intrusives of unknown age occur in the southern Ellsworth Mountains.

Also included within the Ellsworth Mountains fold belt are the Pirrit Hills, Nash Hills, Martin Hills, Pagano Nunatak, and Hart Hills. This discontinuous series of outcrops forms the exposed eastern edge of the fold belt south of the Ellsworth Mountains. The Pirrit Hills consist of granite intruded into metasedimentary rocks, mainly slates and phyllites. The Nash Hills are predominantly clastic metasedimentary rocks that may correlate with the lower units of the Paleozoic sequence in the Ellsworth Mountains. These strata are also intruded by granitic rocks. Radiometric age determinations on the granitic rocks from both areas suggest emplacement during the early Mesozoic. Slightly metamorphosed sedimentary rocks, primarily carbonates, cut by intermediate plutons crop out in the Martin Hills.

Pagano Nunatak consists almost entirely of a gray, massive, medium- to coarse-grained granite of probably Mesozoic age. In the adjacent Hart Hills, an unfossiliferous metasedimentary sequence, from oldest to youngest, consists of gray to green quartz-mica phyllite, buff to gray subarkosic sandstone, and blocky thin-bedded carbonaceous phyllite with rare limestone beds in the upper part. Intruded into these rocks are large irregular masses of quartz gabbro. It is speculated that the sediments may have been derived from the lower Paleozoic granitic and metamorphic terrane in the Transantarctic Mountains (Webers, personal communication).

The exposed western edge of the Ellsworth Mountains fold belt is marked by a line of nunataks extending to the southwest, which includes Mt. Johns, Mt. Woollard, Mt. Moore, and the Whitmore Mountains. Mt. Johns is a solitary nunatak of massive, greenish quartzite, while Mt. Moore is made up of sandstones, quartzites, and schists (Anderson, 1960). In the Whitmore Mountains, a coarse-grained quartz monzonite makes up 95 percent of the exposed bedrock (Webers, personal communication). This monzonite is intruded into unfossiliferous metasedimentary rocks and is, in turn, cut by a younger, fine-grained granite in the Linck Nunataks. Both intrusive rocks are probably early Mesozoic in age.

Geophysical work in this part of West Antarctica strengthens the validity of the definition of the Ellsworth Mountains fold belt. This province may be isolated topographically from the surrounding areas (Bentley *et al.*, 1964). An abrupt change in the character of magnetic anomalies between Byrd Station and the Ellsworth Mountains suggests a well-defined line that may mark the western subglacial margin of the fold belt (Behrendt, 1964b).

The Antarctic Peninsula

The Antarctic Peninsula has been the object of geologic study since the turn of the century, but important problems of correlation of rock units between the various parts of the Peninsula remain. The general stratigraphy of the Peninsula has been summarized recently (Adie, 1964b).

The outcrops at the base of the Antarctic Peninsula closest to the Ellsworth Mountain fold belt and the coastal exposures of Marie Byrd Land have been studied and described (Laudon *et al.*, 1964, 1966; Halpern, 1967). The oldest rocks are pre-Jurassic dacites, but attempts to establish an Rb-Sr isochron age on these rocks have been unsuccessful (Halpern, 1967). Clastic sedimentary and metasedimentary rocks contain abundant Jurassic fossils (Laudon *et al.*, 1966). A plutonic intrusive suite ranging in composition from granodiorite to gabbro has been dated as mid-Cretaceous (Halpern, 1967). The youngest rocks known are Pliocene basaltic flows. On the basis of field relationships, geochronology, and geochemistry, the rocks of this eastern Ellsworth Land area have a closer affinity to the Antarctic Peninsula than to the Ellsworth Mountain fold belt (Halpern, 1967).

The Antarctic Peninsula proper is dominated by an axial core of the Andean Intrusive Suite (granite through gabbro) that makes up about 80 percent of the exposed rock. These intrusives have fragmented the older rocks, and the correlation of scattered patches of the variety of rocks exposed around the edges of the plutons is a difficult problem. The intrusive rocks of the Antarctic Peninsula generally are of Cretaceous age according to K-Ar and Rb-Sr dating (Halpern, 1967).

The oldest rocks known are those exposed in the vicinity of Marguerite Bay on the west side of the Peninsula. Here the "basement complex" of schists and gneisses has been considered probably Precambrian, possibly Paleozoic, and certainly pre-Jurassic (Nichols, 1955). Lower Paleozoic rocks, both plutonic and volcanic, may also occur along the Fallières Coast near Marguerite Bay. Both granites and andesites are present, and they have been assigned to the lower Paleozoic (Adie, 1954). Some of these rocks, however, have recently been determined to be of Cretaceous age by K-Ar dating methods (Grikurov, 1966).

The Trinity Peninsula Series, first described near Hope Bay and later extended southward to other parts of the Antarctic Peninsula, is probably of late Paleozoic age. This slate-graywacke sequence has been assigned to the Carboniferous on the basis of included plant fragments. The relationships between these rocks and the Cape Legoupil Formation, the Miers Point Series of Livingston Island, and the possibly Paleozoic strata of Alexander Island have not been established (Halpern, 1965).

At Hope Bay, the Jurassic Mt. Flora beds appear to lie unconformably on the Trinity Peninsula Series. The flora and fauna contained within these upper rocks have been definitely established as Jurassic; a similar fauna and flora is known from Alexander Island some 650 km to the south, although the environment of deposition there was apparently different. During the late Jurassic, the northern peninsula area seems to have been dominated by volcanic activity, while to the south, marine sedimentation continued, as indicated by the ammonite-bearing strata of Alexander Island (Howarth, 1958). Clastic sedimentary rocks from Alexander Island comprise the only known lower Cretaceous strata on the Antarctic Peninsula (Adie, 1958).

Upper Cretaceous marine sedimentary rocks are mainly confined to Seymour, Cockburn, Snow Hill, and James Ross Islands near the northeastern part of the peninsula. The Snow Hill Series is abundantly fossiliferous, and its age has been firmly established from paleontologic evidence. On Seymour and Cockburn Islands, lower Tertiary marine beds are also present.

The late Tertiary and Quaternary appears to have been a time of fairly widespread volcanic activity, particularly along the eastern edge of the peninsula. In the north, some upper Tertiary marine strata occur on Cockburn Island. The upper Pleistocene or lower Recent *Thracia* clays of James Ross Is-

land are apparently the youngest nonglacial sedimentary deposit known in the area. Volcanic activity apparently continued throughout the Pleistocene and Recent.

Available geochronologic, geochemical, stratigraphic, and structural information indicates that the Antarctic Peninsula has very close geologic affinity with the Andean system of southern South America. To the south this province may well trend westward through the Ellsworth Land nunataks into coastal Marie Byrd Land, where present age determinations indicate widespread orogenic activity during the late Mesozoic.

The Scotia Arc

The islands of the Scotia Arc mark a fairly well-defined submarine ridge that extends from the Antarctic Peninsula to the southern tip of South America. Although this arc is one of the most active tectonic regions in the world, it has received relatively little scientific study because of its inaccessibility and sparse population. Prominent tectonic features of the area include active volcanoes in the South Sandwich and South Shetland Islands, a deep-sea trench east of the South Sandwich Islands, belts of shallow and intermediate depth earthquakes west of this trench, and a zone of large gravity anomalies (Gutenberg and Richter, 1954; Heezen and Johnson, 1965). Many writers have mentioned the similarities between the Scotia Arc and the Caribbean Arc. Both arcs contain similar tectonic features at their eastern ends, and both appear to be bounded on their northern and southern limbs by major fault zones.

The Scotia Arc is of great geological and geophysical interest because of its location between South America and the Antarctic Peninsula and because of the possible continuity of structural features between the two continents. The islands of the Scotia ridge could represent fragments of either a disrupted or partially submerged landmass (Matthews, 1959). These islands could also have resulted from the fragmentation of a continental strip or landmass between the South American Andes and the geologically similar mountains of the Antarctic Peninsula (Hawkes, 1962). Some authors believe that the Scotia Arc is bounded on the north and south by large strike-slip faults along with displacements of hundreds of kilometers may have occurred (Heezen and Johnson, 1965; Wilson, 1966).

The geology of the Scotia Arc is complex and not well known. No definitely pre-Mesozoic rocks have been found, although some of the basement rocks may prove to be Paleozoic or older. The South Shetland Islands are separated from the Antarctic Peninsula by a trough (the Bransfield Strait), and the islands may represent a geanticlinal ridge parallel to the main elements of the peninsula. Supposedly Precambrian schists and phyllites form a basement complex on Elephant and Clarence Islands; a dunite–serpentine mass below the schists on Gibbs Island has been reported (Matthews, 1959).

The geology of the main group of islands is probably typified by the sequence on King George Island where a possibly Precambrian basement composed primarily of schists is overlain by Carboniferous (?) graywacke beds and Jurassic volcanics, intruded by early Tertiary Andean intrusives, and capped by Tertiary to Recent volcanics (Hawkes, 1961). Volcanism is active to the present day as is evidenced by two eruptions on Deception Island since 1967.

An exceedingly complex geologic history is indicated by the rocks of the South Orkney Islands. A high-grade metamorphic basement complex grades westward into rocks of a lower grade which resemble those of Elephant Island. Age determinations on micas from these rocks are grouped between Late Triassic and Middle Jurassic (Miller, 1960), but these dates are interpreted as indicating only the age of the folding of this unit and the overlying Graywacke-Shale Series. The Graywacke-Shale Series contains plant fragments which were orginally identified as Ordovician graptolites. Similarities exist between these strata, the Trinity Peninsula Series on the Antarctic Peninsula, and the Sandebugten Beds on South Georgia Island. Fossils thought to be Cretaceous have been collected from a thick conglomerate overlying the Graywacke-Shale Series. The only known igneous rocks on the islands are a few olivine dolerite dikes. Rocks of the South Orkneys appear to be continental in character, yet they lie at present along an oceanic arc (Matthews, 1959). The position and origin of these rocks are important clues to the tectonic history of the Scotia Arc.

South Georgia Island consists of a Precambrian (?) basement complex of schists overlain unconformably by the Sandebugten Series of possibly Carboniferous age. The Sandebugten quartzose graywackes are lithologically similar to the Trinity Peninsula Series of the Antarctic Peninsula and the Graywacke-Shale Series of the South Orkney Islands. The Cumberland Bay Series on South Georgia may be either a facies equivalent or a younger stratigraphic unit above the Sandebugten Series; however, the Cumberland Bay Series consists of tuffaceous graywackes and contains Lower Cretaceous fossils. Andean intrusives and Tertiary mafic dikes have been reported from the island. The presence of felsic intrusives marks South Georgia as an atypical oceanic island (Matthews, 1959).

The South Sandwich Islands consist of Cenozoic volcanic rocks overlying Paleozoic (?) mudstones and Precambrian (?) schists (Adie, 1962). Active volcanism still continues in the island group. The South Sandwich trench on the Atlantic side of these islands suggests that the Scotia Arc may be considered a true island arc system.

Recent investigations of the Scotia Arc include seismic refraction and reflection measurements by the Lamont-Doherty Geological Observatory; gravity, magnetic, and seismic refraction studies by the British Antarctic Survey and the Department of Geology, University of Birmingham, England; investigations of deep-sea sediments and bathymetry;

and various geologic investigations by the British Antarctic Survey, including paleomagnetic determinations, volcanological and petrological studies, and radiometric dating of rocks (Ewing and Ewing, 1959; Heezen and Johnson, 1965; Allen, 1966b; Griffiths et al., 1967a, 1967b; Heezen and Tharp, 1961; Ninkovich et al., 1964).

The South Sandwich Island arc and the South Sandwich trench seem to be very young tectonic features. These structures may lie to the east of an older arc that marks the site of a structural connection between the Andes and the Antarctic Peninsula ranges (Heezen and Johnson, 1965). The structure of the Scotia Sea appears to be very complex (Heezen and Tharp, 1961). Subcrustal velocities of about 7.5 km/sec have been reported for the eastern parts of the Scotia Sea, while more normal mantle velocities (8.1 km/sec) are found west of South Georgia and in the Drake Passage (Ewing and Ewing, 1959; Allen, 1966b). In these areas, the crustal thicknesses are more typical of those reported for ocean basins than of those found in continental regions. On the other hand, the crustal structure beneath the Falkland ridge, north of the Scotia Arc, appears to be more nearly of continental than oceanic type (Ewing et al., 1964; Allen, 1966a). The Falkland ridge may be a fragment of ancient Gondwanaland; accordingly, it is of considerable importance in evaluation of continental drift. Based on limited magnetic evidence, an ancient midocean ridge in the Drake Passage may have been involved in the drift of South America relative to Antarctica (Griffiths et al., 1967a). A transform fault of the ridge-arc type has been found between the southern termination of the Mid-Atlantic Ridge and the southern end of the South Sandwich trench. The existence of this transform fault may explain why the Andean seismic belt does not appear to continue into Antarctica.

ANTARCTIC GEOPHYSICS AND CRUSTAL STRUCTURE

The primary emphasis in antarctic geophysical exploration has been on the determination of subglacial topography from seismic reflections and gravity measurements. In addition, gravity, magnetic, seismic refraction, and surface-wave-dispersion studies have been carried out to investigate subglacial geology; paleomagnetic measurements have been made on a number of rock samples; and geophysical observations have been extended into surrounding oceans, primarily in the region of the Antarctic Peninsula and Scotia Arc. Although results are not extensive, they have shown that geophysical investigations can be of great value to future crustal studies.

Subglacial Topography

The general outlines of the continent beneath the ice are reasonably well known. East Antarctica is a true land area marked by a central mountain range completely buried by ice, with rough topography to the west having relief typically on the order of 1000 m and a large plain to the east. On the other hand, West Antarctica has a large central area which would be below sea level in the absence of the ice. The Ross Sea would connect with the Amundsen Sea and, almost surely, with the Weddell Sea around the north end of the Ellsworth Mountains. Marie Byrd Land, the Eights Coast, and the Antarctic Peninsula would each comprise one or more major islands and a number of smaller ones; the Ellsworth Mountains would probably become a peninsula.

Seismic Refraction Shooting

Because of logistic limitations, seismic refraction profiles in Antarctica have been limited to less than 30 km in length. They have thus been useful only in defining upper crustal layers. Most profiles on the ice have been unreversed, leaving some uncertainty in velocities and dips of interfaces deeper than the ice–bedrock boundary.

Refraction profiles on the ice have been completed on the West Antarctic plateau, on the Ross Ice Shelf, in Victoria Land, on the South Polar Plateau, and in southern Queen Maud Land (Woollard, 1962; Robinson, 1964). These show P-wave velocities in the upper crust between 5.8 and 6.4 km/sec, indicating the presence in both East and West Antarctica of typical continental crustal rocks. Above this basement, distinct regional differences have been found. Velocities (5.2 to 5.3 km/sec) and thicknesses (1 to 2 km) directly beneath the ice on the east flank of the Byrd Basin are similar to those near the Ellsworth Mountains, although the subglacial elevations in these two localities differ by some 2 km. In several profiles west of the Byrd Basin, on the other hand, the velocity in the upper subglacial layer is significantly lower (4.2 to 4.6 km/sec). The thickness of this layer decreases from 3 km near the Toney Mountains to 0.5 km under the Ross Ice Shelf. Profiles in East Antarctica indicate that the thick Paleozoic–Mesozoic sedimentary sequence found in the Transantarctic Mountains is absent or very much thinner in these regions. None of the refraction profiles has given any indication of a geosynclinal thickness of sedimentary rocks.

A set of five refraction lines has been surveyed in Bransfield Strait in water from 1 to 2 km deep. These show 1 to 4 km of probably sedimentary rock partly overlying rocks with typical continental crustal velocity and rock in which the wave velocity is about 7 km/sec. The latter can be associated with dunite-serpentine found on land nearby, but it may also represent oceanic crust which typically exhibits this high velocity near continents (Cox, 1964).

In the course of one reversed refraction profile near the Filchner Ice Shelf, where the rock surface is 1400 m below sea level, reflections, probably from the Mohorovičić discontinuity, were recorded (M. Hochstein, personal communica-

tion). This is a particularly significant finding in view of the difficulty which has been encountered elsewhere in the world in obtaining near-vertical reflections from this boundary, and it emphasizes the importance of further investigations of this sort. The measured mean compressional wave velocity in the crust was 6.0 km/sec, and the estimated Mohorovičić elevation was -25 km. This corresponds to a crustal thickness of 28 km for a sea-level column, which is in satisfactory agreement with gravity and surface-wave evidence for West Antarctica.

Magnetics

Because of lack of control for temporal variations in the magnetic field and wide station spacing (about 5 km), conclusions based on magnetic observations from oversnow traverses before 1960 are chiefly qualitative, indicating only the general nature of the subglacial rock. On more recent traverses, the use of proton precession magnetometers in pairs has made it possible to delineate anomalies of geologic origin. The sources of such anomalies found in Victoria Land, Queen Maud Land, and on the South Polar Plateau are estimated to lie 1 km or less beneath the ice (Robinson, 1964). This evidence supports the conclusion from seismic refraction shooting that only a thin sedimentary layer overlies the basement complex in these regions.

Airborne surveys provide continuous coverage and can be completed during periods known to be magnetically quiet; therefore, quantitative results have readily been obtained. These have indicated that the thickness of the sedimentary section lying between the ice and magnetic basement within and north of Byrd Basin averages about 1 km and probably increases to the southeast (Behrendt and Wold, 1963). Many anomalies occur in Marie Byrd Land, Ellsworth Land, and the southern Antarctic Peninsula, whereas, in the vicinity of the Ellsworth Mountains and for several hundred kilometers to the west, as well as in southern West Antarctica, very few anomalies are found. These data support the conclusion that the Byrd Basin defines a dividing line between the volcanic rocks of eastern Marie Byrd Land and the thick sedimentary sequences of the Transantarctic and Ellsworth Mountains and provide further evidence that the Ellsworth Mountains are not a simple continuation of the geology of the Antarctic Peninsula (Behrendt, 1964a).

Aeromagnetic surveys south of Queen Mary Coast have helped to define the trends of several basement horsts which uplift Precambrian rocks (Glebovskii, 1959a, 1959b). The mountains south of the Shackleton Ice Shelf and the subglacial Golitsyn Mountains near Pionerskaya appear to be part of a single structure or a series of parallel structures. Another ridge, also trending southwestward, probably extends from Mt. Brown, south of the West Ice Shelf, into the Davis Sea.

Fairly extensive shipboard magnetic surveys have been

conducted in the Bransfield Strait–South Shetland Islands region, revealing a strong regional positive anomaly associated with the South Shetland Islands (see the following section on Gravity Observations).

Magnetic anomalies support the assumption of the existence of a large batholith of the Andean Intrusive Suite in northeastern Trinity Peninsula. They also suggest the presence of southeast-trending faults which formed during emplacement of the batholith (Allen, 1966a). Surveys in several other places on the Antarctic Peninsula have been useful in solving local geological problems.

Gravity Observations

There are two serious problems involved in the study of geology from gravity anomalies measured on the Antarctic Ice Sheet. First, surface elevations, which are determined chiefly by altimetry, may be in error by 50 m or more, causing gravity anomalies to be incorrect by more than 20 mgal. Second, variations of subglacial topography have a predominant effect in determining the gravity anomaly at most points because of the large density difference between ice and rock. This effect can largely be accounted for in places where there are soundings of ice thickness, but these sites are widely spaced. Recently the advent of electromagnetic sounding has made it possible to determine subglacial topographic corrections without an exorbitant expenditure of time. However, reasonably accurate estimates of true *mean* gravity anomalies may be obtained by averaging observed values over wide areas; the effect of the rock topography may be either positive or negative, and the elevation error is reduced to about ±10 mgal.

Mean-free-air anomalies over the continent are close enough to zero to indicate over-all isostatic compensation for the ice sheet. However, it should be noted that only an imbalance corresponding to an ice thickness of several hundred meters could be detected with confidence (Bentley, 1964).

A mean-free-air anomaly of about –15 mgal exists over the Ross Ice Shelf, omitting stations which are close to the mountain front. Since elevations are more accurately determined on the floating ice shelf than elsewhere in Antarctica, this is a significant figure. If the assumption is made that the negative anomaly results from wastage of a grounded ice sheet which might earlier have covered the Ross Sea area, unloading must have occurred no more than 30,000 years ago. A figure of 10,000 years B.P. fits the data very well (Bennett, 1964).

Negative mean-free-air anomalies of several tens of milligals are also found throughout a large region extending from the Weddell Sea side of the South Pole all the way into Victoria Land. These anomalies cannot be explained in terms of recent thinning of the ice cover or as an expression of regional isostatic compensation for the Transantarctic Moun-

tains (Robinson, 1964). Seismic and magnetic evidence refute the possibility of a deep sedimentary basin. It is probable that the cause of this remarkable feature is to be found in the upper mantle.

There are also some smaller regions which are apparently out of isostatic balance, as indicated by a study of mean-free-air anomalies over squares 220 km on a side. In western Marie Byrd Land, inferred isostatic anomalies of –30 to –40 mgal are associated with, but not superimposed on, a subglacial trough cutting 2000 m below sea level. At the only point along the Amundsen Sea coast where observations have been made, there is an anomaly of –40 mgal, which probably cannot be explained solely on the basis of recent wastage of the ice. These anomalies both require much better definition if their geological significance is to be ascertained.

Gravity anomalies suggest a mean crustal thickness of about 30 km for West Antarctica and 4 km for East Antarctica (Woollard, 1962). These figures are surprisingly close to the results of surface-wave dispersion studies. A detailed analysis of the Bouguer gravity anomalies across the Transantarctic Mountains in the vicinity of McMurdo Sound indicates that the 10-km change in crustal thickness must occur very abruptly under the West Antarctic edge of these mountains (Robinson, 1964). This conclusion has been substantiated by observations in the Pensacola Mountains (Behrendt *et al.*, 1966). Robinson's suggestion of regional transcurrent faulting, however, was not supported by the latter study.

The results from gravity, seismic refraction, and magnetic observations in the South Shetland Islands and the Trinity Peninsula suggest that the South Shetlands are underlain at a depth of a few kilometers by very dense magnetic rocks having a high seismic velocity, thus indicating that they are probably of mafic or ultramafic composition. These rocks lie much deeper under Bransfield Strait and the Trinity Peninsula and are probably uplifted along a major fault on the southeastern margin of the South Shetland Islands (Griffiths *et al.*, 1964).

Surface-Wave Studies

Surface-wave dispersion studies in Antarctica are hampered by the unfortunate absence of any earthquakes on the antarctic continent, making it necessary to use wave paths which combine oceanic and continental segments. This introduces some uncertainty into the results, since the dispersion characteristics of most of the southern oceans have not been determined. Nevertheless, dispersion analyses are in agreement in indicating a mean crustal thickness of about 30 km in West Antarctica, and about 40 km in East Antarctica (Dewart and Toksöz, 1965). The dispersion data also show that group velocities across East Antarctica are much closer to those along average continental paths than to those across the Canadian shield. These results support other indications that central East Antarctica is not a simple crystalline shield.

Paleomagnetism

Determinations of pole positions in the geologic past have been made on several different groups of rocks. Agreement with the present pole position has been found for Cenozoic volcanics from Cape Hallett and also for Andean intrusive rocks of late Cretaceous to early Tertiary age (Turnbull, 1959; Blundell, 1962). Dolerite samples from three widely separated localities in the Transantarctic Mountains are in good agreement with each other in indicating a Jurassic pole position around 55° S, 140° W (Blundell, 1966). This position is widely different from the Jurassic pole positions found for the other southern hemisphere continents, thus supporting the theory of continental drift. The pole position corresponding to Precambrian gneiss from the Ongul Islands was near the present equator at approximately 110° W (Nagata, 1960). Strikingly different results have recently been obtained from Marie Byrd Land rocks. Late Jurassic-early Cretaceous granites yield a paleo-pole position of 30° S, 100° E, and younger basalts indicate a position of 60° S, 70° E. These positions agree neither with other antarctic data nor with observations from other continents. This suggests that Marie Byrd Land may have drifted relative to other continents and relative to other parts of Antarctica since Jurassic time.

Seismicity

Several seismograph stations have been in operation in Antarctica since the International Geophysical Year (IGY) in 1957–1958. Records from these stations have revealed that the whole antarctic continent appears to be devoid of earthquakes, except for very small shocks of magnitude <3.5 associated with local volcanic activity on Ross Island and some small events associated with the cracking of sea ice and shelf ice. Seismograph recordings at Byrd and Pole Stations and at various points on the periphery of Antarctica indicate that no earthquake of Gutenberg and Richter class d or larger (magnitude >5.3) has occurred in Antarctica since 1958 (Kogan *et al.*, 1965). This aseismicity is particularly surprising in the Antarctic Peninsula, which is believed to be a continuation of the seismically active Andean and Scotia Arc structures. It has been suggested that seismicity is inhibited by the thick Antarctic Ice Sheet. This is conceivable on the main part of the continent, but it is difficult to see how it could be so in the Antarctic Peninsula, where the ice cover is merely a confluence of mountain glaciers and is only a few tens of kilometers wide.

On the other hand, the stations within Antarctica have provided many important data for investigations of earthquakes along the midocean ridges surrounding Antarctica, in the Scotia Arc, in South America, in the Macquarie ridge–New Zealand region, and in other portions of the southern hemisphere. Before the installation of seismograph stations

in Antarctica, the calculated positions of earthquakes in many of these areas were uncertain by as much as several hundred kilometers. The stations in Antarctica now permit earthquake locations to be made with a precision of a few tens of kilometers or better. These locations of earthquake epicenters have been of considerable importance in investigations of the midoceanic ridge system that practically encircles Antarctica (Sykes, 1963, 1967; Stover, 1966). These stations will continue to be extremely valuable in future investigations of the southern hemisphere.

Earthquake mechanisms, the distribution of seismic activity, and magnetic anomalies on the midocean ridge system are now furnishing information about sea-floor spreading, continental drift, and continental reconstructions in the southern hemisphere. For this reason it is necessary to include the oceanic areas adjoining Antarctica in any national program for the geological and geophysical study of the continent.

From the distribution of earthquake epicenters, branches of the midoceanic ridge system appear to merge in two places in the vicinity of Antarctica. Two spreading ridges, the Mid-Indian Ridge and the East Pacific Rise, and a compressional feature, the Macquarie ridge, appear to meet near 60° S, 160° E (Sykes, 1967). Near 55° S, the Mid-Atlantic Ridge appears to intersect a seismically active feature (possibly a ridge or a fracture zone) that extends from the southern end of the South Sandwich trench to the central part of the Indian Ocean.

SCIENTIFIC PROBLEMS

1. What is the response of the earth's crust and mantle to the superimposed load of ice?

Gravity surveys to date have indicated that isostatic compensation for the superimposed load of the antarctic ice is at least three fourths complete, on a broad regional basis. By means of leveling for elevation determinations, and electromagnetic sounding for ice thickness measurements, much more accurate analyses of gravity data should be possible in the future. These should permit both the search for deviations of only a few percent from isostatic equilibrium over broad areas and the examination of more restricted areas. Glaciological data suggest that the thickness of the ice sheet may be changing in some places. Such areas, if they can be demonstrated to exist, would be of particular interest for the study of isostatic adjustment.

2. What is the geologic significance of the strong mean-free-air gravity anomalies which have been found in certain areas?

Several regions of strong mean-free-air gravity anomalies are already known in the Antarctic, and more will perhaps be discovered in the future. Some of these, at least, are too small in areal extent or exhibit gradients that are too sharp to permit reasonable explanation in terms of isostatic imbalance resulting from the presence (or recent removal) of the ice. It is more probable that these anomalies result from major geologic features of the crust or upper mantle. These areas are thus worthy of more concentrated investigation.

3. Why is the continental shelf of Antarctica depressed compared with those of other continents?

It has long been observed that the mean depth of the continental shelf of Antarctica is much greater than that of shelves surrounding other continents. Several suggestions for the cause of this depression have been made, but none has met with universal approval. Suggestions include depression by the weight of the present ice sheet, depression as a result of greater extent of grounded ice in the past, lowering due to glacial erosion, or some structural cause unrelated to past or present glaciation. To solve this problem it will be necessary to determine sedimentary thickness and age, crustal thickness, and degree of isostatic compensation, over a significantly extended segment of the continental shelf.

4. Is the present-day height (and appreciably greater potential rebound elevation) of the coastal periphery of East Antarctica and the Transantarctic Mountains entirely related to late Cenozoic block faulting caused only by ice loading, or is uplift largely related to older deep-seated crustal structures?

In terms of continental morphology, both the coastal periphery of East Antarctica and the Transantarctic Mountains are unusually high. Late Cenozoic uplift and block faulting related to ice loading are commonly emphasized as the cause, whereby in response to heavy ice loading, the lowland areas of the craton are suppressed and the highlands are uplifted, perhaps with a transfer of mantle material. However, some facts suggest that ice loading has only triggered latent forces related to old structures. For example, the present-day Transantarctic Mountains high overlies the roots of the later Precambrian–early Paleozoic fold-mountain belt, and the present height is likely related, in part at least, to this ancient mountain-building event.

The height of the coastal periphery is not so easily related to an old structural province. Epicratonic orogeny during the late Precambrian can be assumed only locally, as indicated by the greenschist rocks of the Prince Charles and Denman areas. Arguments for late Precambrian–early Paleozoic mountain building along the entire periphery are discounted in places by the unfolded epicratonic sedimentary rocks. On the other hand, the prevalent 400–500 m.y. isotopic dates may define some type of a unified peripheral structural province. The dates imply at least deep burial (a minimum of 3 km for argon loss) of the present-day surface rock during the early Paleozoic. Sufficient geologic facts to account for the peripheral uplift and fault-block mountains are not yet available but must be sought. If the coastal

periphery of East Antarctica did exist as a structural unit in the Paleozoic, then we must explain why such a Paleozoic structural unit in the presumed predrift continent of Gondwanaland became coincident with the post-Paleozoic breakup border of Antarctica.

The mountainous regions beneath the ice cover of East Antarctica, the Gamburtsev, Vernadskiy, and Golitsyn Mountains, are also considered to be Cenozoic fault-block mountains related to ice loading (Voronov, 1964; Kapitsa, 1966). But here, also, the present height may be more fundamentally related to older crustal and subcrustal activity. The hypothesis that the mountains of East Antarctica are a result of Cenozoic uplift related to ice loading least disrupts the notion of a stable craton, but more likely these mountains have deep and older roots that complicate the supposed simplicity of a broad early Precambrian shield.

5. Why is Antarctica aseismic?

The continent of Antarctica is unique among the continents of the world in its aseismicity. This is clearly a major problem of antarctic geophysics but one that is difficult to attack because of its negative nature. The first approach is probably to ascertain whether the earthquake belt of the Scotia Arc should be expected to extend into the Antarctic Peninsula. Geologic evidence is needed about whether regions of recent tectonic activity, where earthquakes might be expected, actually exist in Antarctica. Examination of the possible inhibiting effect of the Antarctic Ice Sheet is largely a theoretical problem.

6. What is the configuration of the bedrock surface in Antarctica?

The rock and ice surfaces of the coastal margin of East Antarctica, the Transantarctic Mountains, and the mountainous parts of West Antarctica are being depicted on topographic maps at about 1:250,000 scale and 200-m contour interval; aerial tricamera photography is now available for many of these areas. The large, completely ice-buried lowland plains and mountains of interior East Antarctica and the ice-covered basins, troughs, and ice shelves of West Antarctica have been located by geophysical–glaciological oversnow traverses during the past 12 years. However, the necessary details of the subglacial topography, which make meaningful structural interpretation possible, are lacking. Airborne electromagnetic sounding is a promising method for rapidly measuring ice thickness over large areas, but at the same time better ice-surface elevations are needed not only to determine rock-surface elevation accurately, but also to establish the ice load upon the bedrock and thereby to compute isostatic balances and, indirectly, crustal strength.

7. What are the crustal provinces within the continental area of East Antarctica and the region of marginal islands

which comprises West Antarctica? What is the nature of the boundary between the two parts of the continent?

A different mean crustal thickness between East and West Antarctica is fairly well established on the basis of earthquake surface-wave and gravity data. Very little is known, however, about variations within the two parts of the continent. It is highly probable, for example, that the crustal structure under the subglacial Gamburtsev Mountains in East Antarctica is quite different from that under the adjacent subglacial plains. Similarly, in West Antarctica, major differences are to be expected between the true land areas and the Byrd Subglacial Basin. All geophysical techniques would be useful in defining the composition and extent of the crustal provinces.

The abrupt difference between the crustal thickness of East and West Antarctica has been demonstrated in two localities on opposite sides of the continent. It is important for the understanding of regional tectonics to ascertain whether this abrupt change extends across the entire antarctic continent. Gravity traverses across the junction should provide the best attack on this problem. Evidence of strike-slip movement should also be sought.

8. What has been the geographic relationship of the different tectonic provinces of Antarctica to each other and to other continents in the geologic past?

Paleomagnetic and paleontologic data strongly suggest relative continental drift between Antarctica and other southern hemisphere continents. Since the phenomenon of continental drift is one of the major problems of geology throughout the world, it deserves careful study in Antarctica, as elsewhere. Particularly intriguing is the suggestion that at least parts of West Antarctica may have been widely separated from East Antarctica in the geologic past. It is, therefore, particularly important to obtain data from contemporaneous rocks collected in as many different antarctic localities as possible.

9. What is the nature of the lithologic and structural transition between the Transantarctic Mountains and East Antarctica?

Whether the Transantarctic geosyncline is epicratonic or is accretionary in the form of new continental crust, its structural boundary with East Antarctica is necessarily complex. Do the old geosynclinal rocks of the Transantarctic Mountains thin out against the East Antarctic craton, or do they merge with the epicratonic rocks of similar age in East Antarctica? Do the overlying epigeosynclinal rocks, the Beacon strata of the Transantarctic Mountains, extend far into East Antarctica? Or does an abrupt structural break preclude the continuation of any of these rocks into East Antarctica? The transition zone is partially exposed in northern Victoria Land and along Oates and George V Coasts, but the region involves complex structural and stratigraphic problems yet to be solved. For most of the length of the Transantarctic Mountains, the problem must be attacked by geophysical investigation beneath the ice-buried boundary of East Antarctica. On a long-term basis these geophysical interpretations should be tested by core drilling beneath the Antarctic Ice Sheet.

Most structural trends of the geosynclinal rocks of the Transantarctic Mountains approximately parallel the length of the modern mountain chain. However, in the Shackleton Range the structural grain is about perpendicular to the axis of the Transantarctic Mountains and trends toward the craton of East Antarctica (Stephenson, 1966). On the other hand, the Shackleton Range structural trends are more nearly parallel to those in the Ellsworth Mountains of West Antarctica.

10. What is the relationship between the circum-Pacific mobile belt, the Ellsworth Mountains fold belt, and the Transantarctic Mountains?

The Ellsworth Mountains fold belt is lithologically allied to the Transantarctic Mountains, but its structural style is closer to that of the circum-Pacific belt; the ages of its intrusive rocks appear to be mainly intermediate between those predominant in the other two areas. Geophysical exploration suggests that there may be no morphologic extension of the fold belt beyond the northern tip of the Sentinel Range, and the southern perimeter remains poorly defined. Recent work in the Pensacola Mountains has indicated that related folds may occur in that area. The geosynclinal sequence of the Ellsworth Mountains proper lies astride du Toit's projection of the Samfrau geosyncline in Antarctica, and the relationships between the various provinces of the antarctic continent bear directly on the larger questions of continental drift and the breakup of Gondwanaland.

11. Is the circum-Pacific mobile belt continuous through the Antarctic Peninsula, along coastal Marie Byrd Land, and thence toward New Zealand via the Macquarie Ridge, or does West Antarctica mark a major break in this belt?

The lack of seismic activity on the continent argues for the latter, but the poorly known regional geology suggests the former interpretation. A detailed examination of the young volcanic rocks of these areas would be of great value. The alkali olivine basalts of the Jones and Hudson Mountains are known to change westward to more continental-type volcanics in the Executive Committee Range. Preliminary study of the volcanic rocks of Peter I Island indicates an association common to orogenic volcanism but rare in oceanic provinces. Unusual volcanic suites are also known within the Antarctic Peninsula. A great deal more study of the petrogenesis, composition, association, and time relationships between the various volcanic terranes is needed. Combined with examination of the older rocks and an intensive geophysical program, such studies may define the mobile belt across West Antarctica or demonstrate that none exists.

12. What are the present and past relationships of the Scotia Arc to South America, the Antarctic Peninsula, and the Mid-Atlantic Ridge?

A number of tectonic features can be traced from the Andes of South America to the islands of the Scotia Arc and thence to the Antarctic Peninsula. Diverse geologic data such as age determinations, paleomagnetism, analysis of structural trends, and geophysical work in the Scotia Sea are all needed as a basis for understanding the role of the mid-ocean ridges, the Andean orogeny, and continental drift as they affect the development of the Scotia Arc.

13. What is the nature of the major fracture zones on the north and south limbs of the Scotia Arc?

These fracture zones are some of the largest distinctly linear features on earth. Their possible connection with similar zones on the East Pacific Rise and on the Mid-Atlantic Ridge is of special importance to the tectonic history of not only the Scotia Arc but also the entire southern hemisphere.

14. What factors account for the complex crustal and mantle structure in the Scotia Sea and below the Falkland ridge?

The abnormally low mantle velocities beneath the eastern half of the Scotia Arc, along with the normal velocities in the western half of the arc, are as yet unexplained. The existence of continental crustal structure beneath the Falkland ridge should be elucidated further, and the extent of this structure should be determined.

15. What is the nature of the junctures of major tectonic features near Macquarie Island and Bouvet Island?

Two spreading ridges, the Mid-Indian Ridge and the East Pacific Rise, and a compressional feature, the Macquarie ridge, appear to meet near 60° S, 160° E. The Mid-Atlantic Ridge seems to end in a seismically active feature, possibly a transform fault, near 55° S, 5° W. These junctures, along with the active ridges that nearly surround Antarctica, are of considerable interest to problems of sea-floor spreading, continental drift, and continental reconstruction in the southern hemisphere. These areas can be investigated by ships en route to Antarctica and by ships such as the USNS *Eltanin* that are assigned to antarctic waters.

16. What is the relationship of Cenozoic volcanism to tectonic elements in Antarctica and the Scotia Arc?

Unlike most of the circum-Pacific belt, the Pacific margin of Antarctica is not marked by present-day volcanic activity and seismicity. However, an active volcanic belt probably existed until quite recently. The reasons for this apparent reduction in volcanic activity may be related to the absence of earthquakes.

17. What is the geothermal flux in Antarctica?

The antarctic regions form a huge gap in the emerging picture of the global patterns of heat flow. As elsewhere in the world, regional patterns of heat flow can be useful in analyzing geologic structure and tectonics, particularly in areas of current activity. Reliable mean values of the geothermal flux are of particular significance underneath the Antarctic Ice Sheet, since it is this flux which largely determines the temperature at the base of the ice and, hence, the mode and speed of ice flow.

18. What is the early Precambrian history of the craton of East Antarctica, and specifically, what is the origin and significance of the prevalent charnockite?

The intrusive charnockites of the craton are associated with ultrametamorphosed and multiple-metamorphosed rocks of the granulite facies. These rocks are indicative of a dehydrating deep crustal environment. It seems unlikely that the surface rocks of the entire craton of East Antarctica could be so uniformly of such a deep source; therefore, as more is learned of the ice-buried interior part of the craton, perhaps younger, more hydrated cratonic rocks will be found. However, the coastal peripheral belt alone forms an unusually large region of granulite-facies rocks and charnockite that needs explanation. Why does this large peripheral belt expose such uniformly deep-seated rocks? Is the coastal periphery a structural unit in its own right, and if so, what events led to its present-day exposure? Are these events largely of Precambrian or Phanerozoic age?

19. Does the craton of East Antarctica underlie the upper Precambrian and younger geosynclinal strata of the Transantarctic Mountains?

Within the exposed rock areas of the Transantarctic Mountains, cratonic-like rocks are present but, on the basis of our limited knowledge, these rocks may just as well be high-grade regionally metamorphosed geosynclinal rocks of late Precambrian–early Paleozoic age. This question must be resolved through detailed geologic field mapping, petrology, and careful isotopic age determination.

20. What are the ages, compositions, and structural relationships of the basement rocks of West Antarctica, and are there any outcrops of Precambrian rocks in West Antarctica?

At least three exposed areas of possibly Paleozoic rocks are known in the Ford Ranges of coastal Marie Byrd Land, in the Kohler Range, and on Thurston Island. Only one of these has been dated as Paleozoic, and that by a single radiometric age determination. The supposedly Precambrian and Paleozoic rocks of the Antarctic Peninsula can only be said to be pre-Jurassic on paleontologic evidence. The oldest rocks of the Scotia Arc appear to be Triassic or older. The application of the isochron method of age determinations may shed further light on the age of these older rocks.

The sedimentary and metasedimentary sequences have not been subjected to any detailed study that might indicate direction of sediment transport, paleocurrent direction, or both. Only a few detailed structural analyses of folded rocks are available. Preliminary attempts at computer analysis of structural data from the Ellsworth Mountains suggest that this may be a most useful approach to the rather complex structural style in much of West Antarctica. The study of the basement rocks of West Antarctica provides a challenging area for the combined application of geology, geochemistry, geochronology, and geophysics.

21. What is the meaning of the prevalent 400–500 m.y. isotopic dates on rocks throughout the coastal periphery of East Antarctica and the Transantarctic Mountains?

More than 200 isotopic age dates on rocks from East Antarctica and more than 100 dates on rocks from the Transantarctic Mountains have been published. Most of these dates are K-Ar and Rb-Sr analyses on individual samples, and many are not supported by thorough field study (Picciotto and Coppez, 1963, 1964; Webb, 1962; Webb and Warren, 1965; Ravich and Krylov, 1964). The reliability of most of the dates for relating other than the youngest reset isotopic age is doubtful.

The most striking age relationship is a predominance of 400–500 m.y. isotopic dates throughout the coastal periphery of East Antarctica and the Transantarctic Mountains. In the Transantarctic Mountains this age agrees well with orogenesis and associated volcanism and plutonism of early Paleozoic age. However, few dates from the Transantarctic Mountains are older than 500 m.y., although the geologic history clearly indicates a mountain-building event of latest Precambrian age with which one would expect associated metamorphism, plutonism, and late Precambrian dates. At present only the Rb-Sr isochron work of Faure (in press) thoroughly supports the field evidence for such a late Precambrian event.

On the coastal periphery of East Antarctica, the abundant 400–500 m.y. dates are not related to any known major orogenic or plutonic event. A "Caledonian" fold belt has been suggested on the basis of these dates, as evidenced by several local remnants of folded greenschist facies rocks (Voronov, 1964). The limited occurrence of "Caledonian rocks" is attributed to widespread uplift and deep erosion. However, extensive plutonic rocks associated with such an orogeny have not been recognized, and the scattered remnants of unfolded upper Precambrian-lower Paleozoic sedimentary rocks argue against widespread orogeny younger than these rocks. Dates as old as 1800 m.y. are abundant eastward from the Amery Ice Shelf to Oates Coast, but no early Precambrian dates are recorded west of the Amery Ice

Shelf to Queen Maud Land. The lithologies and metamorphic structures of the crystalline gneisses and schists and charnockites are similar throughout the coastal peripheral zone, and these rocks are probably rightly considered early Precambrian (Ravich, 1966).

The apparent structural unity of the periphery of East Antarctica suggested by the abundant early Paleozoic dates is not understood.

22. What are the ages and correlations of stratified rocks within the Transantarctic Mountains and related rocks in adjacent areas, and what is the possibility of intercontinental correlation of these rocks?

Intensely metamorphosed equivalents of the geosynclinal rocks of late Precambrian and early Paleozoic age will be most difficult to date and correlate. The upper Precambrian graywacke suite is likewise difficult to date and correlate for lack of both fossils and lithologic and stratigraphic variation. The extensive Robertson Bay Group of northern Victoria Land is of questionable age, between late Precambrian and middle Paleozoic; hence, the whole structural continuity of the late Precambrian Transantarctic geosyncline into northern Victoria Land is debatable. The similar geosynclinal sequence of the Rockefeller Mountains and Ford Ranges of West Antarctica is yet to be either directly related to the Transantarctic geosyncline or divorced as a separate independent and probably younger geosyncline.

Within the Beacon rocks of the Transantarctic Mountains subtle horizontal and vertical lithologic changes and inconspicuous disconformities make both local and regional stratigraphic correlations difficult. A disconformity below the glacial unit separates Devonian and Permian rocks, and a probable disconformity between Permian and Triassic rocks can be demonstrated with plant fossils. Sparse megafossils in the Beacon rocks require that a concerted effort be made to find definitive paleontological material. The collection and study of pollen and spores has promise, as does careful searching for vertebrate remains. It is surprising that throughout such an extensive mountain chain no Ordovician, Silurian, or Carboniferous sedimentary rocks have yet been identified.

The Beacon succession has similarities with the Gondwana rocks of the other southern continents. However, many generalizations and suggested intercontinental correlations have been made without adequate knowledge of the rocks. As much effort must be made to study the contrasts of lithology as the similarities.

23. What was the paleogeography of Antarctica during the late Paleozoic and early Mesozoic?

A likely starting point in the difficult reconstruction of the paleogeography of the Transantarctic region is the late Paleozoic glacial deposits that are so widely exposed from the Pensacola Mountains to the McMurdo area as well as in the Ellsworth Mountains. Beacon strata above and below the glacial deposits are commonly interpreted as continental facies, but a nearshore marine depositional environment must also be considered.

Little is known of the detrital source or direction of sedimentary transport (Matz and Hayes, in press). The environment and mechanics of deposition as well as the form and type of sedimentary basins must be studied. Geologists using paleoclimatic and paleogeographic data must attempt to confirm or deny continental positions of Antarctica based on paleomagnetic data for the Beacon interval of time. Ultimately, such geologic information must agree with the geophysical interpretation before full confidence can be given to the hypothesis of continental drift. Many such problems can be resolved only by detailed mapping, section measuring, and the collection and analyses of paleontologic and paleogeographic data.

24. What is the relation of the extensive Jurassic igneous activity to continental and intercontinental structure?

The enormous intrusion and extrusion of gabbroic–basaltic rock during the Jurassic sets a definite younger limit to known sedimentation within the Transantarctic Mountains and East Antarctica. This igneous activity apparently marks a major event in the structural development of the largest part of Antarctica. The significance of these rocks with regard to lower crustal and subcrustal materials and to continental drift remains to be investigated.

25. What is the origin and distribution of the apparently unconsolidated material which lies beneath and in the basal layers of the ice sheet?

There is extensive seismic evidence of a considerable thickness of relatively unconsolidated sedimentary material under many parts of the Antarctic Ice Sheet. There is a strong suggestion also of morainal debris in the bottom few hundred meters of the ice itself. The evidence collected so far has come only as a by-product of the reconnaissance exploration. Although there is much information still to be culled from existing seismograms concerning the distribution of subglacial sedimentary layer thicknesses, more detailed investigations of the nature of this material are needed. This problem clearly has a direct bearing on the understanding of the processes of glacial erosion.

RECOMMENDATIONS

1. Emphasis should be shifted from reconnaissance geologic mapping to the study of specific problems, which will commonly require large-scale geologic mapping. Some problems of particular interest include (a) the origin and distribution of possible Tertiary tillites, (b) Beacon Group stratigraphy and paleogeography, (c) the age and correlation of the thick, unfossiliferous metasedimentary sequences of the Scotia Arc, the Antarctic Peninsula, Alexander Island, and the Edsel Ford Ranges, (d) the geologic history of the basement rocks in the Transantarctic Mountains, and (e) the origin and significance of the charnockites in East Antarctica.

2. Geologic mapping at 1:250,000 or larger scale of all areas of significant rock exposure should be completed at an early date. Areas in great need of attention include the lower Antarctic Peninsula, northern Victoria Land, and the adjacent Oates Coast.

3. A program of topographic mapping, with adequate positioning control, of the bedrock surface beneath the continental ice sheet by electromagnetic sounding methods should be initiated to define subglacial physiography and to identify sites for detailed geophysical surveys.

4. Systematic aeromagnetic profiles at about 50-km spacing should be obtained over the antarctic continent to establish structural trends and delineate tectonic provinces.

5. Paleomagnetic measurements should be extended in coverage, both in area and in geologic age, to assess past positions of various parts of the continent and to determine variations in the earth's magnetic field. Particularly recommended are studies of Jurassic diabase, Permo-Triassic volcanics, Permian varvites, and Cambrian rhyolites.

6. Seismic shooting, sounding, and coring of the deposits below grounded and floating ice should be undertaken to establish their composition and to aid in the interpretation of late Paleozoic and late Cenozoic sedimentary rocks in Antarctica. McMurdo Sound offers a convenient initial site.

7. Geophysical studies of the midocean ridges and other marine areas adjacent to Antarctica should be conducted, including especially measurements of the earth's magnetic field. Areas of particular interest include the junctures of ridges near Macquarie Island and Bouvet Island.

8. Geophysical studies of the antarctic continental shelf and slope should be conducted.

9. Additional long seismic refraction profiles should be attempted to define deep crustal and upper mantle structure.

10. At least one seismograph station should be established in the eastern Scotia Arc.

11. More extensive geophysical and geological studies should be conducted in the Scotia Arc and the adjoining Antarctic Peninsula.

12. Gravity surveys, combined with surface leveling and electromagnetic sounding of ice thickness, should be carried out wherever large regional imbalance in the glaciological regime occurs, wherever regional gravity anomalies are known to exist, in marginal areas where recent retreat or advance of ice is suspected, and in areas of special geologic interest.

13. A limited amount of deep drilling through the ice sheet into bedrock should be undertaken at selected localities to provide geologic information.

14. Geothermal heat-flow measurements should be obtained at typical sites within each geologic province.

15. Detailed seismic reflection profiles should be obtained in selected areas to examine subglacial layering, particularly the thickness and distribution of moraine near the base of the ice sheet.

16. Paleontologic studies should be continued to aid in the correlation of strata, to establish ancient environments, and to test the hypothesis of continental drift. The recent discovery of a Triassic tetrapod amphibian in the Transantarctic Mountains underscores the importance and potential of such work.

GENERAL RECOMMENDATIONS

The recommendations cited heretofore relate to special problems of research in specific geographic areas within the polar regions. The following general recommendations apply to all polar research. They are vital to the successful and efficient implementation of polar studies.

1. Many additional radiometric age determinations should be made on systematically collected rocks from the polar regions, with increased emphasis on the isochron method, which holds the greatest hope for establishing the time of original crystallization of many rocks.

2. Further studies of earthquake records should be carried out to establish the seismicity of the polar regions, to seek the mechanism of these earthquakes, and to define crustal structure by the analysis of surface-wave dispersion.

3. Regular station observations of earthquakes and of the earth's magnetic field should be continued.

4. A network of ocean-tide stations should be established along polar coasts to determine long-term changes in relative sea level.

5. Increased support should be provided for laboratory study of the extensive collections of polar rocks and scientific data now on hand.

6. Increased support should be provided for the preparation and publication of manuscripts on polar research already completed or nearing completion. It is especially important that provision exist for the publication of geologic and geophysical maps.

7. Support should be provided for the evaluation of promising new geophysical methods, such as portable high-frequency microearthquake recorders and magnetotelluric studies of crustal and mantle structure.

8. Support should be provided for experimental use in the polar regions of new mapping techniques such as color photography, orthophotography, infrared photography, and side-scanning radar.

9. Maps of 1:250,000 scale of West Antarctica and the Transantarctic Mountains should be completed as soon as possible.

10. Sketch maps of 1:500,000 scale from aerial photographs should continue to be provided to field parties in the absence of other modern maps.

11. Large-scale maps should be prepared of selected areas in Antarctica with extensive bedrock exposure.

12. A 1:1,000,000 base map of arctic Alaska should be compiled from existing 1:250,000 maps to supplement the Air Force 1:1,000,000 map, which is adequate for air navigation but obsolete for most other purposes.

13. A network of first-order horizontal and vertical control should be established throughout the Transantarctic Mountains.

14. A series of 1:1,000,000 maps of selected mountainous areas in Antarctica should be initiated.

15. A program should be initiated to acquire complete vertical aerial photographic coverage of rock outcrops in Antarctica.

16. Systematic aerial photography of Greenland should be completed as soon as possible.

17. A series of 1:1,000,000 contoured maps of the Antarctic Ice Sheet should be initiated.

18. Current efforts toward the improvement of logistic support should be continued and intensified in order to increase productivity of geological and geophysical field parties. Basic requirements for satisfactory operation include prompt delivery to and evacuation from the field, efficient transportation in the field, regular resupply or moving of base camp, and reliable communications.

19. Support and encouragement should be provided for the development of methods for rapid and accurate position determination in the polar regions. The lack of such methods poses a major obstacle for most systematic airborne, shipboard, and oversnow geophysical surveys.

20. Alternate or supplemental commercial support systems, responsible to the leaders of scientific field parties, should be developed.

21. Encouragement should be provided for the organization of international symposia on the geology and geophysics of each polar region at about ten-year intervals.

22. Increased support should be provided for the translation of foreign polar publications, particularly books and monographs.

23. An international agreement should be sought for the north polar region to promote a higher level of international cooperation in the scientific exploration of the Arctic. Provision should be made in such an agreement for joint programs, where mutually advantageous, and for exchange of scientific personnel.

REFERENCES

Adie, R. J., *The Petrology of Graham Land I, the Basement Complex and Early Paleozoic Plutonic and Volcanic Rocks.* Falkland Island Dependencies Survey Scientific Report No. 11 (1954).

Adie, R. J., "Geological Investigations in the Falkland Island Dependencies since 1940," *Polar Record*, 9, 3–17 (1958).

Adie, R. J., *The Geology of Antarctica.* Amer. Geophys. Union Geophys. Monograph 7, pp. 26–39 (1962).

Adie, R. J., "Geological History," in *Antarctic Research*. (R. E. Priestley, R. J. Adie, and G. de Q. Robin, eds.) pp. 118–162. Butterworths, London (1964a).

Adie, R. J., ed., *Antarctic Geology: Proceedings of the First International Symposium on Antarctic Geology*. North-Holland Publ. Co., Amsterdam (1964b).

Allen, A., *A Magnetic Survey of North-East Trinity Peninsula, Graham Land*. British Antarctic Survey Scientific Rep. No. 49 (1966a).

Allen, A., *Seismic Refraction Investigations in the Scotia Sea*. British Antarctic Survey Scientific Rep. No. 55, pp. 1–50 (1966b).

Anderson, J. J., "Bedrock Geology of Antarctica: A Summary of Exploration 1831–1962," in *Geology and Paleontology of the Antarctic*. (J. B. Hadley, ed.) Amer. Geophys. Union Antarctic Res. Series 6, pp. 1–70 (1965).

Anderson, V. H., *The Petrology of Some Rocks from Marie Byrd Land, Antarctica*. Ohio State U. Res. Found. Rep. No. 825-2, pt. 8 (1960).

Andrews, J. T., "Postglacial Rebound in Arctic Canada: Similarity and Prediction of Uplift Curves," *Can. J. Earth Sci., 5*, 39–47 (1968).

Arnold, K. C., "Aspects of the Glaciology of Meighen Island, Northwest Territories, Canada," *J. Glaciol. 5*, 399–410 (1965).

Backlund, H. G., and D. Malmquist, "Zur Geologie und Petrographie der Nordostgrönländischen Basaltformation," *Medd. Grønland, 87* (5) (1932).

Bakayev, V. G., *et al.*, eds., *Atlas of Antarctica*. USSR, Ministry of Geology, Moscow-Leningrad (1966).

Bearth, P., "On the Alkali Massif of the Werner Bjerge in East Greenland," *Medd. Grønland, 153* (4) (1959).

Behrendt, J. C., and R. J. Wold, "Depth of Magnetic 'Basement' in West Antarctica," *J. Geophys. Res., 68*, 1145–1153 (1963).

Behrendt, J., "Distribution of Narrow-Width Magnetic Anomalies in Antarctica," *Science, 144*, 993–999 (1964a).

Behrendt, J. C., "Crustal Geology of Ellsworth Land and the Southern Antarctic Peninsula from Gravity and Magnetic Anomalies," *J. Geophys. Res., 69*, 2047–2063 (1964b).

Behrendt, J. C., L. Meister, and J. R. Henderson, "Airborne Geophysical Study in the Pensacola Mountains, Antarctica," *Science, 153*, 1373–1376 (1966).

Bennett, H. F., *Gravity and Magnetic Survey of the Ross Ice Shelf Area*. U. Wisc. Geophys. and Polar Res. Center Rep. No. 64-3 (1964).

Bentley, C. R., "The Structure of Antarctica and its Ice Cover," in *Research in Geophysics, Vol. 2: Solid Earth and Interface Phenomena*. (H. Odishaw, ed.) MIT Press, Cambridge, Mass. pp. 335–389 (1964).

Bentley, C. R., R. L. Cameron, C. Bull, K. Kojima, and A. J. Gow, *Physical Characteristics of the Antarctic Ice Sheet*. Amer. Geog. Soc. Antarctic Map Folio Series No. 2, New York (1964).

Berquist, H. R., "Micropaleontology of the Mesozoic Rocks of Northern Alaska," U.S. Geological Survey Prof. Paper No. 302-D (1966).

Berthelsen, A., "Canada-Grønland, en geologisk sammenligning," *Medd. Dansk Geol. Foren., 14* (4), 363–373 (1961).

Björnsson, S., ed., "Iceland and Mid-Ocean Ridges; Report of a Symposium," *Rit Soc. Scientiarium Islandica, 38* (1967).

Blackadar, R. G., "Age of the Metamorphic Complex of Northernmost Ellesmere Island," *Arctic, 13*, 51 (1960).

Blake, W., Jr., "Preliminary Account of the Glacial History of Bathurst Island, Arctic Archipelago," Geol. Survey of Canada, Paper No. 64-30 (1964).

Blake, W., Jr., "End Moraines and Deglaciation Chronology in Northern Canada with Special Reference to Southern Baffin Island," Geol. Survey of Canada Paper No. 66-26 (1966).

Blank, H. R., Jr., R. A. Copper, R. H. Wheeler, and I. A. G. Willis, "Geology of the Koettlitz-Blue Glacier Region, Southern Vic-

toria Land, Antarctica," *N. Z. Roy. Soc. Trans., 2* (5), 79–100 (1963).

Blundell, D. J., *Paleomagnetic Investigations in the Falkland Islands Dependencies*, British Antarctic Survey Scientific Rep. No. 39 (1962).

Blundell, D. J., "Paleomagnetism of the Dolerite Intrusions, in Geology 1; Theron Mountains, Shackleton Range, and Whichaway Nunataks," *Trans-Antarctic Expedition 1955-58 Scientific Reports 8*, 61–67 (1966).

Bodvarsson, G., and G. P. L. Walker, "Crustal Drift in Iceland," *Geophys. J. Roy. Astron. Soc., 3*, 285–300 (1964).

Bowsher, A. L., and J. T. Dutro, Jr., "The Paleozoic Section in the Shainin Lake Area, Central Brooks Range, Alaska," U.S. Geol. Survey Professional Paper No. 303-A (1957).

Boyd, L. A., *The Coast of Northeast Greenland*. American Geographical Society, Special Publ. No. 30 (1948).

Brosgé, W. P., J. T. Dutro, Jr., M.D. Mangus, and H. N. Reiser, "Paleozoic Sequence in Eastern Brooks Range, Alaska," *Amer. Assoc. Petrol. Geol. Bull., 46*, 2174–2198 (1962).

Butler, H., "Das Old Red Gebiet am Muschusoksefjord, Attempt at a Correlation of the Series of Various Devonian Areas in Central East Greenland," *Medd. Grønland, 160* (5) (1959).

Callomon, J. H., "The Jurassic System of East Greenland," in *Geology of the Arctic*. (G. O. Raasch, ed.) Univ. of Toronto Press, pp. 258–268 (1961).

Campbell, R. H., "Areal Geology in the Vicinity of the Chariot Site, Lisburne Peninsula, Northwestern Alaska," U.S. Geol. Survey Professional Paper No. 395 (1967).

Carstens, H., "Cristobalite-Trachytes of Jan Mayen," *Norsk Polarinst. Skr., 121*, 1–10 (1961).

Christie, R. L., *Reconnaissance of the Surficial Geology of Northeastern Ellesmere Island, Arctic Archipelago*. Geol. Surv., Canada, Bull. No. 138 (1967).

Cobban, W. A. and G. Gryc, "New Species of Ammonites from the Seabee Formation, Northern Alaska," *J. Paleontol., 35*, 176–190 (1961).

Collins, F. R., and F. M. Robinson, *Subsurface Stratigraphic, Structural and Economic Geology, Northern Alaska*. U.S. Geological Survey Open File Rep. (1967).

Cox, M. J. G., "Seismic Refraction Measurements in Bransfield Strait," *Brit. Antarctic Survey Bull., 4*, 1–12 (1964).

Craddock, C., and H. A. Hubbard, "Preliminary Geologic Report on the 1960 U.S. Expedition to the Bellingshausen Sea, Antarctica," *Science, 133*, 886–887 (1961).

Craddock, C., J. J. Anderson, and G. F. Webers, "Geologic Outline of the Ellsworth Mountains," in *Antarctic Geology*. (R. J. Adie, ed.) North-Holland Publ. Co., Amsterdam, pp. 155–170 (1964a).

Craddock, C., T. W. Bastien, and R. H. Rutford, "Geology of the Jones Mountains Area," in *Antarctic Geology*. (R. J. Adie, ed.) North-Holland Publ. Co., Amsterdam, pp. 171–187 (1964b).

Craddock, C., P. W. Gast, G. N. Hanson, and H. Linder, "Rubidium-Strontium Ages from Antarctica," *Bull. Geol. Soc. Amer., 75*, 237–240 (1964c).

Craddock, C., T. W. Bastien, R. H. Rutford, and J. J. Anderson, "Glossopteris Discovered in West Antarctica," *Science, 148*, 634–637 (1965).

Craddock, C., "Ellsworth Mountains Fold Belt–A Link Between East and West Antarctica," Geol. Soc. Amer. Special Paper 87, pp. 37–38, 1966.

Craddock, C., "The Ellsworth Mountains Fold Belt," presented at 22nd International Geological Congress, New Delhi, 1964, Section 17 (in press).

Craig, B. G., and J. G. Fyles, "Pleistocene Geology of Arctic Canada," Geol. Survey of Canada, Paper No. 60-10, 1960. [Reprinted in *Geology of the Arctic*, Univ. of Toronto Press, pp. 403–420 (1961).]

Crary, A. P., "Arctic Ice Island and Ice Shelf Studies, Part II," *Arctic, 13*, 32 (1960).

Davies, W. E., "Glacial Geology of Northern Greenland," *Polarforsch., 5*, 94–103 (1961).

Demenitskaya, R. M., and V. D. Dibner, "Morphological Structure and the Earth's Crust of the North Atlantic Region," in *Continental Margins and Island Arcs*, Geological Survey of Canada, Paper No. 66-15, pp. 63–79 (1966).

Demenitskaya, R. M., and A. M. Karasik, "Magnetic Data Confirm That the Nansen-Amundsen Basin is of Normal Oceanic Type," in *Continental Margins and Island Arcs*, Geol. Survey of Canada, Paper No. 66-15, pp. 191–196 (1966).

Dewart, G., and M. N. Toksöz, "Crustal Structure in East Antarctica from Surface Wave Dispersion," *Geophys. J., 10*, 127–139 (1965).

Donovan, D. T., "The Jurassic and Cretaceous Systems in East Greenland," *Medd. Grønland, 155* (4) (1957).

Donovan, D. T., "Cretaceous of East Greenland," in *Geology of the Arctic* (G. O. Raasch, ed.) Univ. of Toronto Press, pp. 274–277 (1961).

Douglas, R. J. W., D. K. Norris, R. Thorsteinsson, and E. T. Tozer, "Geology and Petroleum Potentialities of Northern Canada," Geol. Survey of Canada, Paper No. 63-31 (1963).

Doumani, G. A., and E. G. Ehlers, "Petrography of Rocks from Mountains in Marie Byrd Land, West Antarctica," *Bull. Geol. Soc. Amer., 73*, 877–882 (1962).

Doumani, G. A., "Volcanoes of the Executive Committee Range, Marie Byrd Land," in *Antarctic Geology*. (R. J. Adie, ed.) North-Holland Publ. Co., Amsterdam, pp. 666–675 (1964).

Drake, A. A., "Preliminary Geologic Report on the 1961 U.S. Expedition to the Bellingshausen Sea, Antarctica," *Science, 135*, 671–672 (1962).

Drake, A. A., T. W. Stern, and H. H. Thomas, "Radiometric Ages of Zircon and Biotite in Quartz Diorite, Eights Coast, Antarctica," U.S. Geol. Survey Professional Paper No. 501-D (1964).

Dunbar, C. O., "Permian Invertebrate Faunas of Central East Greenland," in *Geology of the Arctic*. (G. O. Raasch, ed.), Univ. of Toronto Press, pp. 224–230 (1961).

Dunn, J. R., and P. P. Hudek, "Frost Deterioration: Ice or Ordered Water?" Geol. Soc. Amer. (Abstract), 1st Annual Meeting, Northeastern Section, p. 20 (1966).

Einarsson, T., "Upper Tertiary and Pleistocene Rocks in Iceland," *Rit Soc. Scientiarium Islandica, 36* (1962).

Einarsson, T., "Remarks on Crustal Structure in Iceland," *Geophys. J. Royal Astron. Soc., 10*, 283–288 (1965).

Ellitsgaard-Rasmussen, K., "Features of the Geology of the Folding Range of Peary Land, North Greenland," *Medd. Grønland, 127*, 7 (1955).

Ewing, J. I., and M. Ewing, *Seismic Refraction Measurements in the Scotia Sea and South Sandwich Island Arc*. International Oceanographic Congress, New York, preprints, pp. 22–23 (1959).

Ewing, M., W. J. Ludwig, and J. I. Ewing, "Sediment Distribution in the Oceans: the Argentine Basin," *J. Geophys. Res., 69*, 2003–2032 (1964).

Falconer, G., J. D. Ives, O. H. Løken, and J. T. Andrews, "Major End Moraines in Eastern and Central Arctic Canada," *Geog. Bull., 7*, 137–153 (1965).

Falconer, G., "Preservation of Vegetation and Patterned Ground under a Thin Body of Ice in Northern Baffin Island, NWT.," *Geog. Bull., 8*, 194–200 (1966).

Faure, G., J. G. Murtaugh, and R. J. E. Montigny, "Geology and Geochronology of the Basement Complex, Wisconsin Range, Transantarctic Mountain" (Abstract). Special Paper presented at Geol. Soc. Amer. Meeting, San Francisco, November 14–16, 1966 (in press).

Ford, A. B., "Review of Antarctic Geology," *Trans. Amer. Geophys. Union, 45*, 363–381 (1964).

Ford, A. B., and W. W. Boyd, Jr., "The Dufek Intrusion—A Stillwater-Like Stratiform Gabbro Body in the Pensacola Mountains, Antarctica" (Abstract). Special Paper presented at Geol. Soc. Amer. Meeting, Bozeman, May 1968 (in press).

Fortier, Y. O., R. G. Blackadar, B. F. Gelnister, H. R. Greiner, *et al.*, *Geology of the North-Central Part of the Arctic Archipelago, Northwest Territories (Operation Franklin)*. Geological Survey of Canada, Memoir No. 320 (1963).

Fraenkl, E., "Ei geologische Karte von Nord-Scoresby Land (NE-Grönland)," *Medd., Grønland, 113* (6) (1953).

Fraenkl, E., "Some General Remarks on the Caledonian Mountain Chain of East Greenland," *Medd. Grønland, 103* (11) (1956).

Frisch, T. O., "Plutonism and Metamorphism in Northernmost Ellesmere Island, Arctic Archipelago," unpublished PhD thesis, Univ. Calif., Santa Barbara (1967).

Fyles, J. G., "Surficial Geology of Victoria and Stefansson Islands, District of Franklin," *Geol. Surv. Canada Bull. 101* (1963).

Fyles, J. G., "Surficial Geology, Western Queen Elizabeth Islands," in *Report of Activities, May to October 1964*. Geological Survey of Canada, Paper No. 65-1, p. 3–5 (1965).

Fyles, J. G., and W. Blake, "Glaciation of the Northwestern Canadian Arctic Islands," in *Abstracts, International Association for Quaternary Research, VII International Congress*. p. 156 (1965).

Fyles, J. G., and B. G. Craig, "Quaternary of Arctic Canada, in Anthropogen Period in Arctic and Subarctic," *Trans. Sci. Res. Inst. Geol. of the Arctic*, State Geological Committee, U.S.S.R., *143*, 5–33 (1965).

Gair, H. S., "The Geology from the Upper Rennick Glacier to the Coast, Northern Victoria Land, Antarctica," *N. Z. J. Geol. Geophys., 10*, 309–344 (1967).

Gibson, I. L., "The Crustal Structure of Eastern Iceland," *Geophys. J., 12*, 99–102 (1966).

Glebovskii, Yu. S., "The Existence of a Subglacial Ridge in the Pionerskaya Area," *Bull. Sov. Antarctic Exped. (English trans.), 1*, 285–288 (1959a).

Glebovskii, Yu. S., "Subglacial Mt. Brown-Gaussberg Ridge," *Bull. Sov. Antarctic Exped. (English trans.), 1*, 381–385 (1959b).

Godby, E. A., R. C. Baker, M. E. Bower, and P. J. Hood, "Aeromagnetic Reconnaissance of the Labrador Sea," *J. Geophys. Res., 71*, 511–517 (1966).

Gordon, MacKenzie, Jr., "Mississippian Cephalopods of Northern and Eastern Alaska," U.S. Geol. Survey Professional Paper No. 283 (1957).

Grant, A. C., *Distributional Trends in the Recent Marine Sediments of Northern Baffin Bay*. Bedford Inst. Oceanography Rep. No. B.I.D. 65-9 (1965).

Gregory, A. F., M. E. Bower, and L. W. Morley, "Geological Interpretation of Aerial Magnetic and Radiometric Profiles, Arctic Archipelago, Northwest Territories," *Geol. Surv. Can. Bull. 73* (1961).

Griffiths, D. H., R. P. Riddihough, H. A. D. Cameron, and P. Kennett, *Geophysical Investigation of the Scotia Arc*. British Antarctic Survey Scientific Rep. No. 46 (1964).

Griffiths, D. H., W. A. Ashcroft, P. F. Barker, and L. E. Parkinson, "Geophysical Investigations in the Scotia Arc," in *Abstract of Papers IUGG 14th Gen. Assem., Zurich, 8*, 72 (1967a).

Griffiths, D. H., R. P. Riddihough, H. A. D. Cameron, and P. Kennett, *Geophysical Investigation of the Scotia Arc*. British Antarctic Survey, Scientific Rep. No. 58, pp. 1–43 (1967b).

Grikurov, G., "The Absolute Age of Some Rocks from the Region of Marguerite Bay, the Antarctic Peninsula," *Publ. Sov. Acad. Sci., 171* (6), 1399–1401 (1966) (in Russian).

Grindley, G. W., "The Geology of the Queen Alexandra Range, Beardmore Glacier, Ross Dependency, Antarctica; With Notes on the Correlation of the Gondwana Sequences," *N.Z. J. Geol. Geophys. 6* (3), 307–347 (1963).

Grindley, G. W., V. R. McGregor, and R. I. Walcott, "Outline of the Geology of the Nimrod-Beardmore-Axel Heiberg Glaciers Region," in *Antarctic Geology*. (R. J. Adie, ed.) North-Holland Publ. Co., Amsterdam, pp. 206–219 (1964).

Grindley, G. W., and G. Warren, "Stratigraphic Nomenclature and Correlation in the Western Ross Sea Region," in *Antarctic Geology*. (R. J. Adie, ed.) North-Holland Publ. Co., Amsterdam, pp. 314–333 (1964).

Gryc, G., J. T. Dutro, Jr., W. P. Brosgé, I. L. Tailleur, and M. Churkin, Jr., "The Devonian System in Alaska," *Alberta Soc. Petroleum Geol., Proc. Int. Symp. on the Devonian, 1* (in press).

Gunn, B. M., "Geological Structure and Stratigraphic Correlation in Antarctica," *N. Z. J. Geol. Geophys. 6*, 423–443 (1963).

Gutenberg, B., and C. Richter, *Seismicity of the Earth*, 2nd ed., Princeton Univ. Press, Princeton, N.J. (1954).

Haller, J., "Der 'Zentrale Metamorphe Komplex' von NE-gronland: Teil II, Die geologische Karte der Staunings Alper und des Forsblads Fjordes," *Medd. Grønland, 154* (3) (1958).

Haller, J., "The Carolinides: An Orogenic Belt of Late Precambrian Age in Northeast Greenland," in *Geology of the Arctic*. (G. O. Raasch, ed.) Univ. of Toronto Press, pp. 155–159 (1961a).

Haller, J., "Account of the Caledonian Orogeny in Greenland," in *Geology of the Arctic*. (G. O. Raasch, ed.) Univ. of Toronto Press, pp. 170–187 (1961b).

Haller, J., "The Geology of Northeast Greenland," *Medd. Grønland* (in press).

Halpern, M., "The Geology of the General Bernardo O'Higgins Area, Northwest Antarctic Peninsula," in *Geology and Paleontology of the Antarctic*. (J. B. Hadley, ed.) Amer. Geophys. Union, Antarctic Res. Series No. 6, pp. 177–209 (1965).

Halpern, M., "Rubidium-Strontium Age Measurements of Plutonic Igneous Rocks in Eastern Ellsworth Land and Northern Antarctic Peninsula," *J. Geophys. Res., 72*, 5133–5142 (1967).

Hamilton, W., "The Hallett Volcanic Province (Antarctica)," *Antarctic J. U.S., 2*, 177–178 (1967a).

Hamilton, W., "Tectonics of Antarctica," *Tectonophys., 4*, 555–568 (1967b).

Harrington, H. J., "Geology and Morphology of Antarctica," in *Biogeography and Ecology in Antarctica*. (J. van Mieghem, P. van Oye, and J. Schell eds.) Monographiae Biologicae, 15, W. Junk, The Hague, pp. 1–71 (1965).

Harris, T. M., "The Rhaeto-Liassic Flora of Scoresby Sounds, Central East Greenland," in *Geology of the Arctic*. (G. O. Raasch, ed.) Univ. of Toronto Press, pp. 269–273 (1961).

Hassan, Y. M., "Tertiary Faunas from Kap Brewster, East Greenland," *Medd. Grønland, 111*, 5 (1953).

Hattersley-Smith, G. F., "The Ice Cover of Northern Ellesmere Island," *Ann. N.Y. Acad. Sci., 95*, 282–289 (1961).

Hattersley-Smith, G., and A. Long, "Post-glacial Uplift at Tanquary Fiord, Northern Ellesmere Island, Northwest Territories," *Arctic, 20*, 255–260 (1967).

Hawkes, D. D., *The Geology of the South Shetland Islands I, The Petrology of King George Island*. Falkland Island Dependencies Survey Scientific Rep. No. 26 (1961).

Hawkes, D. D., "The Structure of the Scotia Arc," *Geol. Mag., 99*, 85–91 (1962).

Heezen, B. C., and G. L. Johnson, "The South Sandwich Trench," *Deep-Sea Res., 12*, 185–197 (1965).

Heezen, B. C., and M. Tharp, *The Physiographic Diagram of the South Atlantic, The Caribbean, the Scotia Sea, and the Eastern Margin of the South Pacific Ocean*, Geol. Soc. Amer., New York (1961).

Hills, L. V., "The Palynology of the Beaufort Formation on Ellef Ringnes Island, Arctic Canada." Geol. Survey of Canada paper (in preparation).

Hobson, G. D., and A. Overton, "A Seismic Section of the Sverdrup Basin, Canadian Arctic Islands," *Geophys.*, 550–562 (1966).

Hollick, A., "The Upper Cretaceous Flora of Alaska," U.S. Geol. Survey Prof. Paper No. 159 (1930).

Hope, E. R., "Geotectonics of the Arctic Ocean and the Great Arctic Magnetic Anomaly," *J. Geophys. Res., 64*, 407–427 (1959).

Horn, D. R., "Recent Marine Sediments and Submarine Topography, Sverdrup Islands, Canadian Arctic Archipelago," unpublished PhD thesis, University of Texas (1967).

Howarth, M. K., *Upper Jurassic and Cretaceous Ammonite Faunas of Alexander Island and Graham Land*. Falkland Island Dependencies Survey Scientific Rep. 21 (1958).

Imlay, R. W., "Characteristic Jurassic Mollusks from Northern Alaska," U.S. Geol. Survey Prof. Paper No. 274-D, pp. 69–96 (1955).

Imlay, R. W., "Succession and Speciation of the Pelecypod, Aucella," U.S. Geol. Survey Prof. Paper No. 314-G, pp. 155–169 (1959).

Imlay, R. W., "Characteristic Lower Cretaceous Megafossils from Northern Alaska," U.S. Geol. Survey Prof. Paper No. 335 (1961).

Ives, J. D., "Indications of Recent Extensive Glacierization in North-Central Baffin Island, Northwest Territories," *J. Glaciol., 4*, 197–206 (1962).

Jacobsen, N. K., ed. "Physical Geography of Greenland" (Rep. of Symp. SD2 of XIX Int. Geograph. Cong.), *Folia Geographica Danica, 9*, 234 (1961).

Johnson, G. L., and B. C. Heezen, "Morphology and Evolution of the Norwegian-Greenland Sea," *Deep-Sea Res., 14*, 755–772 (1967).

Jones, D. L., and G. Gryc, "Upper Cretaceous Pelecypods of the Genus Inoceramus from Northern Alaska," U.S. Geol. Survey Prof. Paper 334-E, pp. 149–165 (1960).

Jones, D. L., and A. Grantz, "Stratigraphic and Structural Significance of Cretaceous Fossils from Tiglukpuk Formation, Northern Alaska," *Bull. Amer. Ass. Petrol. Geol., 48*, 1462–1474 (1964).

Kapp, H., "Zur Petrologie der Subvulkane Zeischen Mesters Vig und Antarctics Havn (Ostgronland)," *Medd. Grønland, 153*, 2 (1960).

Kapitsa, A. P., "Glacial and Subglacial Relief of Antarctica," *Soviet Antarctic Expedition Information Bull., 6*, 143–150 (1966).

Kelly, M., *Quaternary Deposits in the Frederikshaab District, Southwest Greenland*. Grønlands Geologisk Undersokelse, Rep. No. 11, pp. 35–37 (1966).

Kerr, J. W., "Devonian of the Franklinian Miogeosyncline and Adjacent Central Stable Region, Arctic Canada," in *Proceedings of the International Symposium on the Devonian System*. (D. H. Oswald, ed.) *Alberta Soc. Petrol. Geol., 1*, 677–692 (1968).

Kerr, J. W., and R. L. Christie, "Tectonic History of Boothia Uplift and Cornwallis Fold Belt, Arctic Canada," *Bull. Amer. Ass. Petrol. Geol., 49*, 905–926 (1965).

Kerr, J. W., and P. G. Temple, "Stratigraphy and Structure of Bathurst Islands," in *Report of Activities, May to October 1964*. Geol. Survey of Canada Paper No. 65-1, pp. 5–8 (1965).

Kerr, J. W., "A Submerged Continental Remnant Beneath the Labrador Sea," *Earth Planet. Sci. Lett., 2* (4), 103–289 (1967a).

Kerr, J. W., "Nares Submarine Rift Valley and the Relative Rotation of North Greenland," *Bull. Canadian Petrol. Geol., 15*, 483–520 (1967b).

Kjartansson, G., *Geological Map of Iceland, Scale 1:250,000*. Published by the Cultural Fund, Reykjavik (1965).

Kjartansson, G., "Sur la récession glaciaire et des types volcaniques dans la region du Kjolur sur le plateau central de l'Islande," *Rév. Géomorph. Dynamique, 26*, 1 (1966).

Klimov, L. V., "Geology of the Antarctic Platform" in *Antarctic Geology*. (R. J. Adie, ed.) North-Holland Publ. Co., Amsterdam, pp. 681–691 (1964).

Klimov, L. V., M. G. Ravich, and D. S. Soloviev, "Charnockites of East Antarctica," in *Antarctic Geology*. (R. J. Adie, ed.) North-Holland Publ. Co., Amsterdam, pp. 455–462 (1964).

Koch, E. B., "Review of Fossil Floras and Non-Marine Deposits of West Greenland," *Geol. Soc. Amer. Bull.*, *75*, 535–548 (1964).

Koch, L., "Precambrian and Early Paleozoic Structural Elements and Sedimentation: North and East Greenland," in *Geology of the Arctic*. (G. O. Raasch, ed.) Univ. of Toronto Press, pp. 148–159 (1961).

Koerner, R. M., *A Petrofabric Analysis of a Core from the Meighan Icecap, Northwest Territories, Canada* (in press).

Kogan, S. D., I. P. Pasechnik, and D. D. Sultanov, "A Seismic Map of Antarctica," *Izv. Acad. Sci. USSR, Earth Phys. Ser., No. 2*, 81–83 (1965).

Kranck, K., "Sediments of Exeter Bay, Baffin Island, District of Franklin," Geol. Survey of Canada, Paper No. 66-8 (1966).

Kulp, J. L., R. Koligrov, J. Haller, and L. Koch, "Further Isotopic Measurements on Rock from Northeastern Greenland," *Nature, 196*, 160 (1962).

Lasca, N. P., "Postglacial Delevelling in Skeldas, Northeast Greenland," *Arctic, 19*, 349–353 (1966).

Lathram, E. H., *Preliminary Geologic Map of Northern Alaska*. U.S. Geol. Survey Open File Rep. (1965).

Lathram, E. H., and G. Gryc, "A New Look at the Geology and Petroleum Potential of Northern Alaska" (abstract), *Amer. Ass. Petrol. Geol. Bull. 50*, pt. I, 622 (1966).

Laudon, T. S., and T. W. Bastien, "Petrography and Petrology of the Hudson Mountains, Antarctica" (in press).

Laudon, T. S., J. C. Behrendt, and N. J. Christensen, "Petrology of Rocks Collected on the Antarctic Peninsula Traverse," *J. Sed. Petrol., 34*, 360–364 (1964).

Laudon, T. S., L. L. Lackey, and P. G. Quilty, "Geology of Eastern Ellsworth Land, Antarctica" (abstract), *Proc. 11th Pacific Sci. Congr., 4*, 29 (1966).

Lee, H. A., "Method of Deglaciation, Age of Submergence, and Rate of Uplift West and East of Hudson Bay, Canada," *Bull. Peryglacialny, 11*, 239–245 (1962).

Leffingwell, E. de K., "The Canning River Region, Northern Alaska," U.S. Geol. Survey Prof. Paper No. 109 (1919).

Lister, H., and P. J. Wyllie, "The Geomorphology of Dronning Louise Land," *Medd. Grønland, 158* (1), 73 (1958).

Lliboutry, L., "Le gel du sol," in *Traité de Glaciologie*, Masson et Cie, Paris, pp. 927–966 (1965).

Løken, O. H., "Postglacial Emergence at the South End of Inugsuin Fiord, Baffin Island, N.W.T." *Geog. Bull. No. 7*, 243–258 (1965).

Løken, O. H., "Baffin Island Refugia Older than 54,000 Years," *Science, 153*, 1378–1380 (1966).

Marlowe, J. I., *Marine Geology, Western Part of Prince Gustaf Adolf Sea, District of Franklin, Polar Continental Shelf Project*. Bedford Inst. Oceanography, Rep. No. 64-9 (1964).

Matthews, D. H., "Aspects of the Geology of the Scotia Arc," *Geol. Mag., 96*, 425–441 (1959).

Matz, D. B., and O. M. Hayes, "Sedimentary History of Devonian and Permian Rocks of Beacon Sandstone in Ross Sea Region, South Victoria Land, Antarctica" (abstract). Geol. Soc. Amer. Meeting, Boston, Mass., Mar. 16–18, 1967, Special Paper (in press).

Maync, W., "The Permian of Greenland," in *Geology of the Arctic*. (G. O. Raasch, ed.) Univ. of Toronto Press, pp. 214–223 (1961).

McDougall, I., "Potassium–Argon Age Measurements on Dolerites from Antarctica and South Africa," *J. Geophys. Res., 68*, 1535–1545 (1963).

McGregor, V. R., "Notes on the Geology of the Area between the Heads of the Beardmore and Shackleton Glaciers, Antarctica," *N.Z. J. Geol. Geophys., 8*, 278–291 (1965).

McLeod, I. R., "An Outline of the Geology of the Sector from Longitude 45° to 80°E, Antarctica," in *Antarctic Geology.*

(R. J. Adie, ed.) North-Holland Publ. Co., Amsterdam, pp. 237–247 (1964).

Miller, D. J., T. G. Payne, and G. Gryc, "Geology of Possible Petroleum Provinces in Alaska," *U.S. Geol. Survey Bull. No. 1094* (1959).

Miller, J. A., "K–Ar Ages of Some Rocks from the South Atlantic," *Nature, 187*, 1019–1020 (1960).

Moorbath, S., R. K. Webster, and J. W. Morgan, "Absolute Age Determinations in Southwest Greenland," *Medd. Grønland, 166* (9) (1960).

Morris, R. H., *Reconnaissance Study of the Marsh Anticline, Northern Alaska*. U.S. Geol. Survey Open File Rep. (1957).

Müller, F., and W. Barr, "Postglacial Isostatic Movement in Northeastern Devon Island, Canadian Arctic Archipelago," *Arctic, 19*, 263–269 (1966).

Nagata, T., and Y. Shimizu, "Paleomagnetic Studies on Precambrian Gneiss of Ongul Islands, Antarctica," *Antarctic Record, 10*, 1–8 (1960).

Neethling, D. C., "Pre-Gondwana Sedimentary Rocks of Western Queen Maud Land, Antarctica," in *Reemenes de trabajos presentados a las sesiones*, 1st Intern. Sym. Stratigraphy and Paleontology of the Gondwana, Mar del Plata, October 1–4, 1967. Associacion Geologica Argentina, Buenos Aires (1967).

Nicholls, G. D., "The Geology of Northeast Jan Mayen," *Geol. Mag., 92*, 127–140 (1955).

Nichols, R. L., *Bedrock Geology of Marguerite Bay Area, Palmer Peninsula, Antarctica*. Ronne Antarctic Res. Expedition Tech. Rep. No. 13, Office of Naval Research, Washington, D.C. (1955).

Ninkovich, D., B. C. Heezen, J. R. Conolly, and L. H. Burckle, "South Sandwich Tephra in Deep-Sea Sediments," *Deep-Sea Res., 11*, 605–619 (1964).

Overton, A., "Seismic Refraction Surveys, Western Queen Elizabeth Islands and Polar Continental Margin" (in preparation).

Palmasson, G., "Seismic Refraction Investigation of the Basalt Lavas in Northern and Eastern Iceland," *Jökull, 13*, 40–60 (1963).

Paterson, W. S. B., and L. K. Law, "Additional Heat Flow Determinations in the Area of Mould Bay, Arctic Canada," *Can. J. Earth Sci., 3*, 237–246 (1966).

Payne, T. G., *et al.*, "Geology of Arctic Slope of Alaska," *U.S. Geol. Survey Oil and Gas Inv. Map, No. OM-126* (1951).

Payne, T. G., "Mesozoic and Cenozoic Tectonic Elements of Alaska," *U.S. Geol. Surv. Misc. Geol. Inv. Map I-84* (1955).

Pelletier, B. R., *Development of Submarine Physiography in the Canadian Arctic and Its Relation to Crustal Movements*. Bedford Inst. Oceanography, Rep. No. 64-16 (1964).

Pessel, F., "Glacial Geology and Geomorphology of the Sortehjorne Area, East Greenland," *Arctic, 15*, 72–76 (1962).

Picciotto, E., and A. Coppez, "Bibliographie de mésures d'ages absolus en Antarctique," *Soc. Géol. Belg. Bull., 85*, 263–308 (1963).

Picciotto, E., and A. Coppez, "Bibliography of Absolute Age Determinations in Antarctica (Addendum)," in *Antarctic Geology*. (R. J. Adie, ed.) North-Holland Publ. Co., Amsterdam, pp. 563–569 (1964).

Pissart, A., "Etude de quelques pentes de l'Ile Prince Patrick," *Ann. Soc. Géol. Belg., 89*, Bull. 5-10, pp. B377–B402 (1966).

Pissart, A., "Les Polygones de Tundra de l'Ile Prince Patrick," *Mélanges de Géographie*, M. Omer Tulippe Memorial Vol., Univ. de Liège, I., pp. 151–163 (1968).

Porter, S. C., "Stratigraphy and Deformation of Paleozoic Section at Anaktuvuk Pass, Central Brooks Range, Alaska," *Amer. Ass. Petrol. Geol. Bull., 50*, 952–980 (1966).

Ravich, M. G., "Geological Structure of Antarctica," *Soviet Antarctic Expedition Information Bull., 6* (2), 85–93 (1966).

Ravich, M. G., and A. J. Krylov, "Absolute Ages of Rocks from East Antarctica," in *Antarctic Geology*. (R. J. Adie, ed.) North-Holland Publ. Co., Amsterdam, pp. 579–589 (1964).

Reed, B. L., "Geology of the Lake Peters Area, Northeastern Brooks Range, Alaska," *U.S. Geol. Survey Bull. No. 1236* (in press).

Reed, J. C., "Exploration of Naval Petroleum Reserve No. 4 and Adjacent Areas, Northern Alaska, 1944-53, Part I, History of the Exploration," U.S. Geol. Survey Prof. Paper No. 301, p. 192 (1958).

Reiser, H. N., M. A. Lanphere, and W. P. Brosgé, "Jurassic Age of a Mafic Igneous Complex, Christian Quadrangle, Alaska," U.S. Geol. Survey Prof. Paper No. 525-C, pp. C68–C71 (1965).

Rikitake, T., and K. Whitham, "Interpretation of the Alert Anomaly in Geomagnetic Variations," *Can. J. Earth Sci., 1* (1), 35–41 (1964).

Robinson, E. S., "Geological Structure of the Transantarctic Mountains and Adjacent Ice Covered Areas, Antarctica," PhD thesis, Univ. Wisc. (1964).

Robinson, F. M., and F. R. Collins, U.S. Geol. Survey Prof. Paper No. 305-A-L (1958-1964).

Robitaille, B., "Présentation d'une carte géomorphologique de la région de Mould Bay, Ile du Prince Patrick, Territoires du Nord-Ouest," *Can. Geog. 15*, 39–43 (1961).

Roots, E. F., "The Northern Margin of North America; a Progress Report on Investigations and Problems," in "Continental Margins and Island Arcs," Geol. Surv. of Canada Paper No. 66-15, pp. 188–190 (1966).

Rutford, R. H., C. Craddock, and T. W. Bastien, "Possible Late Tertiary Glaciation, Jones Mountains, Antarctica," Geol. Soc. Amer. Special Paper 87, pp. 144–145 (1966).

Rutford, R. H., C. Craddock, and T. W. Bastien, "Late Tertiary Glaciation and Sea-Level Changes in Antarctica," *Palaeog., Palaeoclimatol., Palaeoecol., 5*, 15–39 (1968).

Sable, E. G., *Geology of the Romanzof Mountains, Brooks Range, Northeastern Alaska*. U.S. Geol. Survey Open-File Rep. PhD thesis, U. of Michigan (1965).

Sable, E. G., and J. T. Dutro, Jr., "New Devonian and Mississippian Formations in De Long Mountains, Northern Alaska," *Amer. Ass. Petrol. Geol. Bull., 45*, 585–593 (1961).

Sander, G. W., and A. Overton, "Deep Seismic Refraction Investigations in the Canadian Arctic Archipelago," *Geophys., 30*, 87–96 (1965).

Savile, D. B. O., "The Botany of the Northwestern Queen Elizabeth Islands," *Can. J. Botany, 39*, 909–942 (1961).

Schmidt, D. L., "The Transantarctic Mountains (Antarctica)," *Geotimes, 11* (4), 15–17 (1966).

Schmidt, D. L., P. L. Williams, W. H. Nelson, and J. R. Ege, "Upper Precambrian and Paleozoic Stratigraphy and Structure of the Neptune Range, Antarctica," in *Geological Survey Research 1965*. U.S. Geol. Survey Prof. Paper No. 525-D, pp. D112–D119 (1965).

Schrader, F. C., "A Reconnaissance in Northern Alaska across the Rocky Mountains along Koyukuk, John, Anaktuvuk, and Colville Rivers and the Arctic Coast to Cape Lisburne, in 1901," U.S. Geol. Survey Prof. Paper No. 20 (1904).

Smiley, C. J., "Cretaceous Floras from the Kuk River Area, Alaska: Stratigraphic and Climatic Interpretations," *Geol. Soc. Amer. Bull., 77*, 1–14 (1966).

Smiley, C. J., "Paleoclimatic Interpretations of Some Mesozoic Floral Sequences," *Amer. Ass. Petrol. Geol. Bull., 51*, 849–863 (1967).

Smith, P. S., and J. B. Mertie, Jr., "Geology and Mineral Resources of Northwestern Alaska," *U.S. Geol. Survey Bull., 815* (1930).

Smith, W. E. T., K. Whitham, and W. T. Piche, "A Micro Earthquake Swarm in 1965 near Mould Bay, Northwest Territories, Canada," (in press).

Snelson, S., and I. L. Tailleur, "Large-Scale Thrusting and Migrating Cretaceous Foredeeps in the Western Brooks Range and Adjacent Regions of Northwestern Alaska" (abstract), *Proc. Amer. Ass. Petrol. Geol. Pac. Sec. Meeting, 1968*, Bakersfield, Calif. (1968).

Soen, O. I., "Geomorphological Observations on Sermersoq; a Contribution to the Geomorphology of South Greenland," *Grφnlands Geol. Undersφkelse Bull. No. 62* (1965).

Stephenson, P. J., *Geology, Theron Mountains, Shackleton Range, and Whichaway Nunataks: Transantarctic Expedition, 1955-1958*. Sci. Rep. No. 8, London, (1966).

Stockwell, C. H., "Fourth Report on Structural Provinces, Orogenies, and Time-Classification of Rocks of the Precambrian Canadian Shield," in Geol. Surv. of Canada, Paper No. 64-17, p. II (1964).

St.-Onge, D. A., "La Geomorphologie de l'Ile Ellef Ringnes," Geog. Branch (Canada), Geog. Paper No. 38 (1965).

St.-Onge, D. A., "Nivation Land Forms," in preparation for INQUA volume.

Stover, C. W., "Seismicity of the Indian Ocean," *J. Geophys. Res. 71*, 2575-2581 (1966).

Surtsey Research Society (S. Hermansson, Chairman): *Surtsey Research Progress Report I* (1965); *Surtsey Research Progress Report II* (1966); *Surtsey Research Progress Report III* (1967).

Swain, F. M., "Pleistocene Ostracoda from the Gubik Formation, Arctic Coastal Plain, Alaska," *J. Paleontol., 37* (4), 798–834 (1963).

Sykes, L. R., "Seismicity of the South Pacific Ocean," *J. Geophys. Res., 68*, 5999–6006 (1963).

Sykes, L. R., "Seismicity of the Arctic," *Bull. Seismol. Soc. Amer., 55*, 501–518 (1965).

Sykes, L. R., "Mechanism of Earthquakes and Nature of Faulting on the Mid-Oceanic Ridges," *J. Geophys. Res., 72*, 2131–2153 (1967).

Tailleur, I. L., and E. G. Sable, "Nuka Formation of Late Mississippian to Late Permian Age, a New Formation in Northern Alaska," *Amer. Ass. Petrol. Geol. Bull. 47*, 632–642 (1963).

Tailleur, I. L., and S. Snelson, "Large-Scale Flat Thrusts in the Brooks Range Orogen, Northern Alaska," (abstract), *Proc. Geol. Soc. Amer. Ann. Meeting*, San Francisco, Calif., Program, p. 217 (1966).

Tailleur, I. L., W. P. Brosgé, and H. N. Reiser, "Palinspastic Analysis of Devonian Rocks in Northwestern Alaska," *Alberta Soc. Petrol. Geol., Proc. Intern. Symp. on the Devonian System, 2* (in press).

Tailleur, I. L., and S. Snelson, "Large-Scale Thrusting in Northwestern Alaska Possible Relation to Rifting of Arctic Ocean" (abstract), approved for publ., Geol. Soc. Amer. Cordilleran Sec. Meeting, Tucson (1968).

Tappan, H., "Foraminifera from the Arctic Slope, General Introduction and Part I, Triassic Foraminifera," U.S. Geol. Survey Prof. Paper Nos. 236-A,B,C (1951), (1955), (1962).

Terasme, J. "Palaeobotanical Study of Buried Peat from the Mackenzie River Delta Area, Northwest Territories," *Can. J. Botany, 37*, 715–717 (1959).

Terasme, J., P. J. Webber, and J. T. Andrews, "A Study of Late-Quaternary Plantbearing Beds in North-Central Baffin Island, Canada," *Arctic, 19*, 296–318 (1966).

Thorarinsson, S., "The Median Zone of Iceland in the World Rift System; Report of a Symposium," Geol. Surv. of Canada Paper No. 66-14, pp. 187–211 (1966).

Thorarinsson, S., "The Surtsey Eruption and Related Scientific Work," *Polar Rec., 13*, 571–578 (1967).

Thorsteinsson, R., and E. T. Tozer, "Summary Account of the Structural History of the Canadian Arctic Archipelago since Precambrian Time," Geol. Surv. of Canada Paper No. 60-7 (1960).

Thorsteinsson, R., and E. T. Tozer, *Banks, Victoria, and Stefansson*

Islands, Arctic Archipelago. Geol. Surv. Can. Memoir No. 330 (1962).

Todd, R., "Foraminifera from Carter Creek, Northwestern Alaska," U.S. Geol. Survey Prof. Paper No. 294-F, pp. 223–235 (1957).

Tozer, E. T., "Geological Reconnaissance, Prince Patrick, Eglinton and Melville Islands, Arctic Archipelago, Northwest Territories," Geol. Surv. of Canada Paper No. 55-5 (1956).

Tozer, E. T., "Summary Account of Mesozoic and Tertiary Stratigraphy, Canadian Arctic Archipelago," in *Geology of the Arctic.* (G. O. Raasch, ed.) Univ. of Toronto Press, pp. 381–402 (1961).

Tozer, E. T., and R. Thorsteinsson, *Western Queen Elizabeth Islands, Arctic Archipelago.* Geol. Surv. of Canada Memoir 332 (1964).

Trail, D. S., "Schist and Granite in the Southern Prince Charles Mountains," in *Antarctic Geology.* (R. J. Adie, ed.) North-Holland Publ. Co., Amsterdam, pp. 492–497 (1964).

Trettin, H. P., "Pre-Mississippian Rocks of the Nansen Sound Area, District of Franklin," Geol. Surv. of Canada Paper No. 64-26 (1964).

Trettin, H. P., "Precambrian to Carboniferous Rocks of M'Clintock Inlet Region Northeastern Ellesmere Island," in *Report of Activities, May to October, 1965.* Geol. Surv. of Canada Paper No. 66-1, pp. 7–11 (1966).

Trettin, H. P., "Geology of Pre-Mississippian 'Eugeosynclinal' Rocks in Selected Areas of Northern Ellesmere Island," in *Report of Activities, May to October, 1966.* Geol. Surv. of Canada Paper No. 67-1, pp. 13–18 (1967).

Trettin, H. P., "Devonian of the Franklinian Eugeosyncline," in *Proceedings of the International Symposium on the Devonian System.* (D. H. Oswald, ed.) *Alberta Soc. Petrol. Geol., 1,* 693–701 (1968a).

Trettin, H. P., "Pre-Mississippian Geology of Hazen Plateau and United States Range, Northern Ellesmere Island, in Report of Activities, May to October 1967. Geol. Surv. of Canada Paper 68-1, part A, pp. 212–219 (1968b).

Trettin, H. P., *M'Clintock Inlet, North Coast of Ellesmere Island: Relationships between Franklinian Geosyncline and Arctic Ocean Crust.* Geol. Surv. of Canada (Bulletin in press).

Troelsen, J. C., "Contributions to the Geology of Northwest Greenland, Ellesmere Island, and Axel Heiberg Island," *Medd. Grønland, 149* (7) (1950).

Trümpy, R., "Triassic of East Greenland," in *Geology of the Arctic.* (G. O. Raasch, ed.) Univ. of Toronto Press, pp. 248–254 (1961).

Turnbull, G., "Some Paleomagnetic Measurements in Antarctica," *Arctic, 12,* 151–157 (1959).

Voronov, P. S., "Tectonics and Neotectonics of Antarctica," in *Antarctic Geology.* (R. J. Adie, ed.) North-Holland Publ. Co., Amsterdam, pp. 692–702 (1964).

Wade, F. A., "Geology of the Marie Byrd Land Coastal Sector of West Antarctica," *Antarctic J. U.S., 2,* 93–94 (1967).

Wager, L. R., "Geological Investigations in East Greenland: I, Gen-

eral Geology from Angmagsalik to Kap Dalton," *Medd. Grønland, 105* (2) (1934).

Wager, L. R., "Geological Investigations in East Greenland: IV, The Stratigraphy and Tectonics of Knud Rasmussens Land and the Kangerdlugssuak Region," *Medd. Grønland, 134* (5) (1947).

Wager, L. R., and W. A. Deer, "Geological Investigations in East Greenland: III, The Petrology of the Skaergaard Intrusion, Kangerdlugssuak," *Medd. Grønland, 105* (4) (1939).

Wahrhaftig, C., "Physiographic Divisions of Alaska," U.S. Geol. Surv. Prof. Paper 482, p. 52 (1966).

Walker, G. P. L., "Geological Investigations in Eastern Iceland," *Bull. Volcanologique, 27* (1964).

Wanless, R. K., R. D. Stevens, G. R. Lachance, and D. C. M. Edmonds, "Age Determinations and Geological Studies; K-Ar Isotopic Ages," Geol. Surv. of Canada, Paper No. 66-17, p. 49 (1967).

Warren, G., "Geology of Antarctica," in *Antarctica.* (T. Hatherton, ed.) Praeger, New York, pp. 279–320 (1965).

Washburn, A. L., and M. Stuiver, "Radiocarbon-Dated Postglacial Delevelling in Northeast Greenland and its Implications," *Arctic, 15* (1), 66–73 (1962).

Webb, P. N., "Isotope Dating of Antarctic Rocks, A Summary – I," *N.Z. J. Geol. Geophys., 5,* 790–796 (1962).

Webb, P. N., and G. Warren, "Isotope Dating of Antarctic Rocks, a Summary – II," *N.Z. J. Geol. Geophys., 8* (2), 221–230 (1965).

Weber, J. R., "Gravity Anomalies over the Polar Continental Shelf," *Contrib. Dominion Observatory, 5* (17) (1963).

Weber, J. R., L. W. Sobczak, and E. F. Roots, *Geophysical Investigations over the Arctic Continental Margin* (in press).

Wenk, E., "Tertiary of Greenland," in *Geology of the Arctic.* (G. O. Raasch, ed.) Univ. of Toronto Press, pp. 278–284 (1961).

Whitham, K., "Anomalies in Geomagnetic Variations in the Arctic Archipelago of Canada," *J. Geomag. Geoelec. 15,* 227–240 (1964).

Whitham, K., and F. Andersen, "Magnetotelluric Experiments in Northern Ellesmere Island," *Geophys. J. Roy. Astron. Soc., 10,* 317–345 (1965).

Wilimovsky, N. J., and J. N. Wolfe, *Environment of the Cape Thompson Region, Alaska,* USAEC Division of Technical Information, Oak Ridge, Tenn. (1966).

Wilson, J. T., "Are the Structures of the Caribbean and Scotia Arc Regions Analogous to Ice Rafting?" *Earth Planet. Sci. Lett., 1,* 335–338 (1966).

Woollard, G. P., "Crustal Structure in Antarctica," *AGU Monograph No. 7: Antarctic Research,* pp. 53–73 (1962).

Woolson, J. R., *et al.,* Seismic and Gravity Survey of Naval Petroleum Reserve No. 4 and Adjoining Areas, Alaska," U.S. Geol. Survey Prof. Paper 304-A, p. 25 (1962).

Yochelson, E. L., and J. T. Dutro, Jr., "Late Paleozoic Gastropoda from Northern Alaska," U.S. Geol. Survey Prof. Paper No. 334-D, pp. 111–147 (1960).

3

The Polar Oceans

A significant change is taking place in polar oceanographic research. The era of scientific reconnaissance is coming to a close, as the broad features of the polar environment become known; it is now necessary to examine past research as a basis for pointing out critical areas for investigation. Future work should be focused on the solution of significant problems. The purpose of this chapter is to outline present knowledge of the Arctic and Antarctic Oceans and to propose a U.S. national program of research in the polar oceans.

The answer to certain significant questions about the global environment, particularly climatic changes, can be found in the polar oceans. To begin with, the polar regions are the heat sinks for the ocean just as they are for the atmosphere. Deep circulations of the world ocean are driven by temperature differences between the equatorial and polar regions. Cold waters formed in high latitudes sink to the ocean floor and spread outward to form the deep and bottom waters of the Pacific, Indian, and Atlantic Oceans. To understand the global circulation of the oceans, the nature of these cold-water sources must be known. In addition, the ice cover of the Arctic Ocean is believed to be a key factor in the climate of the northern hemisphere; removal of the sea ice by natural or artificial means might produce radical changes in weather conditions. However, not enough is yet known about atmospheric and oceanic circulation and their interaction to predict either the future of the ice cover or the changes to be expected if it is removed. An adequate model to explain air–ice–water circulation does not now exist. Finally, the crustal structure of the earth beneath the polar oceans is only partially understood. Although these areas evidently have textures and structure analogous to those found in other oceans, their detailed physical relief and geophysical characteristics must be known in order to integrate them into the global tectonic pattern. Recent hypotheses of sea-floor spreading and continental drift, which

are now providing a great stimulus to the earth sciences, need to be tested in the polar regions. This chapter treats in sequence the topography, sediments, and structure of the floor of the polar seas; formation of polar water masses and their circulations; sea-ice cover and its influence on air–sea interaction; the chemistry of the polar seas; and concludes by proposing some challenging scientific problems for investigations.

THE FLOOR AND UNDERLYING CRUST OF THE ARCTIC OCEAN AND ITS BORDERING SEAS

TOPOGRAPHY AND SEDIMENTS

Little progress was made on our knowledge of the Arctic Ocean floor between the time of Nansen's initial discovery of the arctic abyssal basin and the beginning of more detailed explorations by drifting ice stations and aircraft landings on sea ice following World War II. At the turn of the century, Nansen published a bathymetric map of the Arctic Ocean which showed a single, elongate basin with depths between 3 and 4 km. When, in 1949, Emery reviewed all 156 soundings available from the Arctic Basin, he compiled a map that was little different from Nansen's. In contrast, the past decade has seen a tremendous increase in our knowledge of the Arctic Basin. The Soviet Union conducted a massive arctic program on drifting ice stations, using aircraft, helicopters, and drifting automatic radiometeorological stations (DARMS). The United States has also conducted drifting ice station programs and has carried out 40,000 km of under-ice reconnaissance with nuclear submarines. A physiographic diagram of the floor of the Arctic Ocean, using all available drift station soundings plus seven million soundings taken by nuclear submarines, and the names of the major geographic features, are shown in Figure 1.

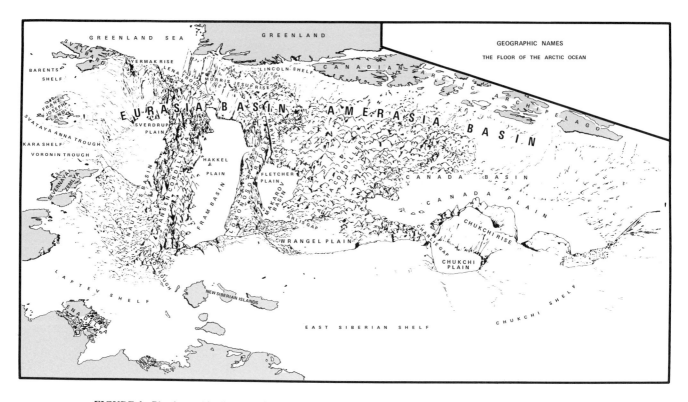

FIGURE 1 Physiographic diagram of the floor of the Arctic Ocean showing geographic names (Beal, 1966).

The deep basin of the Arctic Ocean includes an area of about 3.6 million km². More than seven million soundings have been collected in the basin; two soundings for each square kilometer. Unfortunately, soundings are concentrated along the tracks made by drift stations and nuclear submarines, leaving large gaps in the coverage of the basin. Soundings are especially needed on the lower continental slopes and the adjacent margins of the basin where three submarine mountain ranges intersect the continental blocks of America and Eurasia. Nuclear submarine reconnaissance (Figure 2) has provided some echograms in these interesting areas, but more intensive surveys are still needed.

The Arctic Ocean is unique in that two thirds of its area is underlain by continental shelves. The continental shelf north of Eurasia is the widest in the world, with widths of 850 km in the Barents Sea, while the part of the shelf north of Europe is cut by deep re-entrants. The best known of these cuts are the Svataya Anna and Voronin Troughs, which show depths of 500 m well into the Kara Sea. The shelf break north of Europe ranges between 350 and 500 m and is thus deeper than the world average. North of Asia, the shelf break is closer to the usual 200 m and appears to be unmarked by troughs, although canyons occur on the outer rim. North of Alaska and the Chukchi Sea, the continental shelf narrows from 25 to 40 km in width, with a shelf break at a depth of about 200 m. At least three submarine canyons are found on this shelf; two of these lead into the Chukchi

Plain, while the third, Barrow Canyon, leads into the Canada Basin. The shelf north of Canada is characterized by deep passages, 500 to 1000 m deep, between the islands of the Archipelago. Some of these are straths separated from the Arctic Basin by structural highs.

The central Arctic Ocean is divided by three mountain ranges into four separate basins, each nearly 4 km deep. There are also two plains at intermediate depth and three marginal plateaus. These major features are illustrated in Figure 1. For some purposes, it is convenient simply to define two basins, the Eurasia and Amerasia Basins, separated by the Lomonosov Ridge.

The Alpha Cordillera is the dominant feature of the Amerasia Basin. It is arcuate in cross section and varies in width from 400 km to nearly 1000 km. The Cordillera is marked by sea mounts and by scarps ranging from 100 to 800 m in height. The general relief is some 2 km above the 4-km-deep Canada and Fletcher Plains. The highest sea mounts on the crest rise to about 1200 m below sea level.

The Lomonosov Ridge, discovered by Soviet researchers, does not resemble any other mountain ridge on the floor of the ocean. It is only about 40 km wide at its narrowest point but becomes somewhat broader where it intersects the Alpha Cordillera and the continental slopes of Eurasia and Greenland. The crest depth of the Ridge is between 850 and 1200 m, giving it a relief of some 3000 m above the adjacent plains. In cross section, the slopes are gently convex, leading

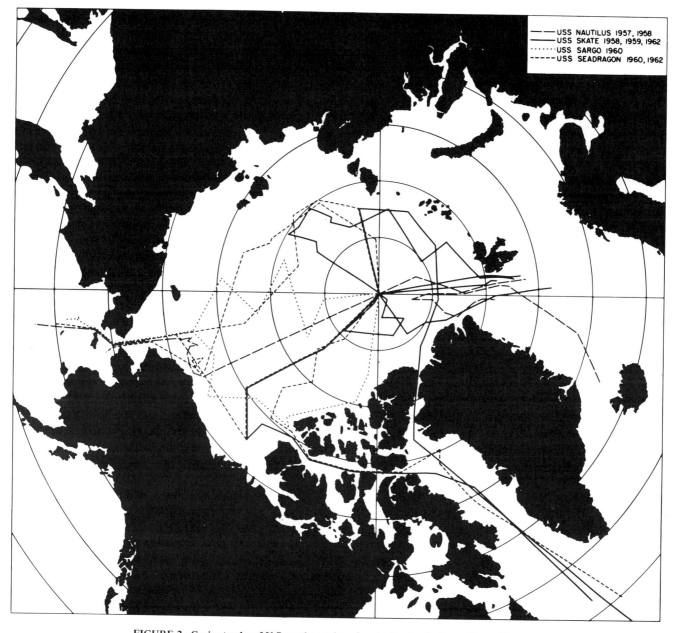

FIGURE 2   Cruise tracks of U.S. nuclear submarines in the Arctic Ocean (Beal, 1968).

to a smoothly rounded crest. Recent evidence suggests that the Ridge is a fragment of the former Eurasian continental shelf which "split" away from the continental block when the basin was formed.

The Nansen Cordillera or Arctic Mid-Oceanic Ridge is the extension of the Mid-Atlantic Ridge across the Eurasia Basin. Although the physiography of the Cordillera differs somewhat from the Mid-Atlantic Ridge, the associated earthquake belt is continuous. Earthquake epicenters in the Arctic Ocean all fall in a narrow band across the Eurasia Basin, which coincides with the Nansen Cordillera.

From the Arctic Entrance between Greenland and Sval-

bard to the Eurasian Shelf north of the Lena Delta, the Nansen Cordillera is remarkably straight and narrow. A great circle between these points falls entirely within the Cordillera. Its width is about 200 km over the entire length. The Nansen Cordillera is made up of peaks, ridges, and deep rifts. Relief above the adjacent plains is from 1000 to 1500 m. Three of the echograms collected by submarine showed rifts with depths between 5000 and 5500 m below sea level. Thus the maximum relief of the Nansen Cordillera is more than 3000 m, but half of this is relief below the level of the plains. There is no detectable sedimentary fill in the rifts.

The Nansen Cordillera or Arctic Mid-Oceanic Ridge intersects the lower continental slope of Eurasia at the point where the continental margin shows a sharp change in direction. The slope above the Cordillera is broken and irregular, and the continental shelf is incised by the Sadko Trough. The belt of earthquakes continues across the shelf and into the valley of the Lena River but becomes diffuse and then vanishes in the continent.

There are three rises on the margins of the Arctic Basin: the Chukchi Rise north of the Chukchi Sea, the Morris Jesup Rise north of Greenland, and the Yermak Rise north of Svalbard (Figure 1). Each of these appears to be an extension, or fragment, of the continental blocks.

In general, the topography of the ocean floor can be divided into a smooth realm in which the underlying features predominate and a rough realm in which tectonic and volcanic constructions dominate the sea floor. The more obvious problems of the smooth realm relate to morphologic activities of currents, both steady and catastrophic, both downslope and along slope. Although sedimentary processes clearly control the form of the smooth floor, the nature of this relationship is poorly understood and is one of the more promising areas in need of investigation. Abyssal plains which occupy the deepest portions of the Arctic Basin were formed by ponded sediment apparently carried to abyssal depths by downslope flow, while the aprons of sediment which stretch out from the continental slope have been shaped in part by these downslope movements but probably to a greater extent by the waters involved in the deep thermohaline circulation.

The rough realm appears to have been created by a steady evolution of the ocean basins involving the replacement of mantle derivatives in a continuously widening rift valley. This process is still going on and is marked by the belt of shallow epicenters. The active Arctic Mid-Oceanic Ridge is curiously asymmetric with respect to outlines of the arctic continental slopes, and in this way it has a decidedly different pattern from that displayed by the adjacent Atlantic Mid-Oceanic Ridge. The Arctic Mid-Oceanic Ridge is cut by fracture zones which appear to mark the course followed by the continents which have fled in opposite directions from the expanding ridge. Such fractures provided important information for the reconstruction of the Atlantic and Norwegian-Greenland Sea but to date have only been tentatively revealed in the Arctic Basin. The reconstruction of the predrift continental masses is an important problem which is now receiving much attention, but much more must be learned, particularly in critical areas such as the central Arctic, before a reliable reconstruction can be completed.

Since, in most respects, the sea floor of the polar seas differs very little from the sea floors at lower latitudes, it seems appropriate that sea-floor research in polar regions should lay greatest emphasis on those special problems unique to high latitudes.

The changing patterns of glaciation on the adjacent land may be traced through the fluctuations in ice rafting recorded in the history book of marine sediments. Changing patterns of productivity and surface currents are recorded by the entombed tests of pelagic organisms. Thus, a study of long deep-sea cores allows the reconstruction of a Late Tertiary history of the oceans. Such a reconstruction may also be of interest not only to the geologist but to the physical oceanographer in identifying the pertinent oceanographic factors governing the modern distributions. To this end, much longer cores from the Arctic and Antarctic are badly needed. In the Arctic, it is necessary to obtain only the 10- to 20-m penetration now routine in oceanographic research in order to make real progress (present lengths are only 1 to 4m). Such cores should reach well back into the Late Tertiary.

The Greenland and Norwegian Seas are the "northernmost North Atlantic." Most of the region can be studied by large research vessels during the summer. The exception is the ice-covered sea off western Greenland, which is occupied by the East Greenland Current at all seasons. However, even the region of the northern East Greenland Current can usually be penetrated by heavy icebreaker in summer.

The topography of the Greenland and Norwegian Seas is dominated by the Mid-Atlantic Ridge, which is continuous with the Nansen Cordillera in the Arctic Basin through the Lena Trough. The continental shelves of Greenland and Svalbard are deeper than most shelves; shelf breaks occur at 450 m or more, and the shelf off Greenland is wide and rough. Soundings and magnetic data from icebreakers and other research vessels, as well as aeromagnetic profiles, have added much new data in this region. The drift of ice station Arlis II contributed valuable information on the western Greenland Sea. Heat flow of 2.6 cal cm^{-2} sec^{-1} (twice "normal") was found on the Greenland continental slope at 68°50′ N – 20°40′ W, decreasing to 1.3 cal cm^{-2} sec^{-1} some 100 km to the southeast and farther from the Mid-Oceanic Ridge.

CRUSTAL STRUCTURES

In contrast to bathymetric data, geophysical data required for an understanding of the crustal structure of the Arctic are much less satisfactory. Many types of geophysical measurements are not available, and those that have been taken do not provide adequate spatial coverage.

Magnetic Anomaly Patterns

The existing aeromagnetic profiles suggest that the Alpha Cordillera, the Nansen Cordillera, and adjacent plains are marked by "banded" anomalies parallel to the mountain ranges. The anomalies are much larger in the Amerasia Basin.

These findings, if confirmed, suggest sea-floor spreading from the Cordilleras and offer a hypothesis for, and a means of dating, the formation of the Arctic Basin.

Heat Flow through the Ocean Floor

About 90 percent of all measurements of the flux of heat from the earth's interior at the surface have been made in the ocean floor beneath a kilometer or more of water. Such measurements are now easily accomplished from a ship in the open ocean. Heat-flow measurements in the Arctic Basin can best be taken from well-chosen ice-drift stations. The drift rate of ice in the Arctic Ocean is generally only a few kilometers per day—an order of magnitude less than that of a vessel in the open sea. Daily observations from a drift station yield very closely spaced measurements, which permit an analysis of such small-scale variations in the heat flow as might be caused by lateral inhomogeneities in the earth's crust and upper mantle. Comparable station densities are not economically feasible on a routine basis with research vessels. Considering the diverse topography of the major features in the Arctic Basin, intensive heat-flow study in the Basin may well lead to knowledge having general application to the solid earth.

Distribution of approximately 150 heat-flow observations in the Arctic as of the end of 1967 is summarized in Figure 3. The observations at a were made by the Soviets, at k, m, r, and q by the Canadians, and the remainder by the United States. As all three countries have active programs, the number of observations can be expected to increase. Figure 3 represents about 3 percent of the surface of the earth and the heat-flow measurements within it—probably about the same percentage of the total number of heat-flow observations on earth. The uneven distribution also is typical of the status of observations for the earth as a whole. Only in the Alaskan quadrant does the station density approach the required number for a regional interpretation. There the good coverage is a consequence of the local ice-drift pattern—a closed gyral with a period of about 5 years centered over the Canada Basin. The most significant finding of earth heat-flow studies to date is the equality of the heat flow on land and sea. Beyond this, the interpretative problems can be viewed in the following categories:

1. Problems of large regions (linear dimensions of 10^3 to 10^4 km) in which the anomaly exceeds the uncertainty in individual determinations

2. Local problems (linear dimensions of 10^2 km) in which the anomaly exceeds the uncertainty of individual determinations

3. Problems of large regions (linear dimensions of 10^3 to 10^4 km) in which the anomaly does not exceed the uncertainty of individual determination

4. Problems relating to the thermal environment of the sea bottom which, in addition to their pertinence to heat flow, are important to other oceanographic and marine geologic investigations.

In category 1, the most significant finding from the world's major oceans had been the discovery of a tendency toward high heat flow near the seismic axis of the mid-oceanic ridge system. From the distribution of observations, it is clear that the heat flow in the vicinity of the seismic axis in the Arctic is essentially unknown. High heat flow from the ridge is confirmed only locally from land observations on Iceland and from oceanic observations nearby (t, Figure 3).

In category 2, three sites have provided useful results relative to local problems. At site e, a systematic drop in the heat flow by 40 percent over a horizontal distance of a few tens of kilometers has suggested a sharp contrast in crustal properties at the boundary of the Canada Basin. The sense of the contrast is opposite to that expected from the horst or basin-foundering theories of the Alpha Cordillera but may be consistent with the Alpha Cordillera viewed as an extinct midoceanic ridge. At site t, the negative correlation between heat flow and distance from the Mid-Oceanic Ridge was confirmed. The heat flow falls on the order of 1 μcal cm^{-2} sec^{-1} per 100 km. At sites k, l, and m, low to normal heat flow precludes a thermal explanation of anomalous attenuation of the magnetic field observed locally.

Results in category 3 require much time and effort to obtain, but they may in the long run provide some of the most useful constraints on geophysical models of lateral variations in the crust and upper mantle. For example, preliminary results from sites b, c, e, g, h, and i yield a mean heat flow of 1.37 cal cm^{-2} sec^{-1} with a standard error of 1 percent for the Canada Abyssal Plain and a mean of 1.16 with a standard error of 2 percent for the highlands to the west and north (Marshall and Lachenbruch, 1968). This difference of only 0.2 μcal cm^{-2} sec^{-1} is equivalent to the steady heat generation of 3 or 4 km of typical granite or 10 to 15 km of typical basalt. Inasmuch as the higher heat flow occurs in the deep basin where the structure is believed to be oceanic, the difference could hardly be accounted for in the crust. Thus the data strongly suggest marked differences in the upper mantle beneath the Canada Abyssal Plain and the neighboring highlands to the west and north.

Problems in category 4 are receiving increasing attention from heat-flow investigators because of the sensitivity of their results to the assumption that the sediments are in a thermal steady state. Although movement of bottom water would not necessarily result in significant changes in bottom temperature with time, if such changes are observed, they almost certainly imply that significant movements occur. These changes can be detected either by long-range tempera-

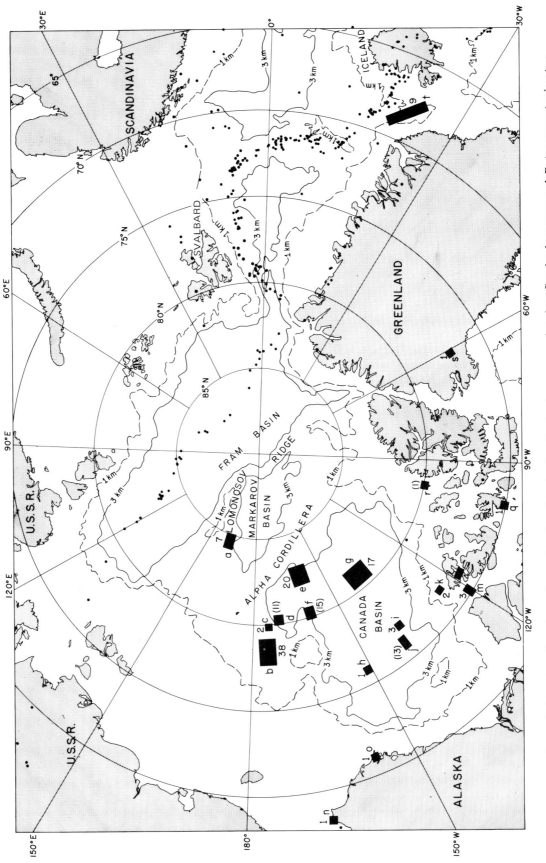

FIGURE 3   Arctic Ocean heat flow observations and earthquake epicenters. Rectangles are areas where heat flow has been measured. Dots represent epicenters.

ture observations at fixed points at and near the ocean bottom or more simply, though less precisely, by careful measurements of the temperature as a function of depth in the bottom sediments. In the latter case, heat-conduction theory is used to reconstruct the temperature history of the sea bottom. This method was applied at site t to demonstrate rapid fluctuations of sea-bottom temperature on the order of 0.1° C. They were evidently associated with systematic motions of near-bottom isothermal water layers over distances on the order of 200 km.

An additional finding from Arctic Ocean studies is that empirical relations between water content and thermal conductivity of sediments used in other oceans do not generally apply to Arctic Ocean sediments.

Seismic Profiling and Reflection Shooting

Continuous soundings of sediment thickness are an essential part of any marine geophysical program. Profiles have been obtained in the Arctic Ocean from drifting stations using various sound sources. Results from explosions gave a sediment thickness of over 3.5 km beneath the Wrangel Abyssal Plain. The most recent results with spark sources on drift station T-3 have provided insight into sedimentary structures not possible with any other tool. More of this type of data is required, particularly in the Eurasia Basin. However, the currents there do not carry a drift station on a desirable course perpendicular to the major structural trends. For this reason, seismic profiling in that interesting area will have to be conducted from submarines or powerful icebreakers.

Gravity Data

A complete gravity survey over the polar regions is necessary to complete the worldwide net of observations used to establish a reference surface for mapping the earth. A detailed gravity survey of the entire Arctic Ocean should provide a good check on the best value for polar flattening, independent of satellite data. On the other hand, observed gravity is influenced by geological structure; gravity data are one of the fundamental tools for studying the earth's structure as a function of mass distribution.

Gravity measurements have been taken from U.S. drifting stations and by use of light aircraft landing on the sea ice. To date, about 700 locations have been sampled over the Arctic Basin, the shelves, and adjacent coastal areas. Unfortunately, most of these data are from the Canada Basin, concentrated near Alaska and Canada. Some results have been published, and certain generalizations are possible. The Canada Basin appears to be in isostatic equilibrium, and indications point toward a negative free-air anomaly existing on the outer continental shelf from Alaska to the Canadian Archipelago. The structure of the Brooks Range of arctic Alaska can be traced across the Chukchi Sea to Siberia. The line of gravity stations available across the Arctic Basin shows a Bouguer anomaly, which suggests a deficiency of mass under the Alpha Cordillera.

More adequate coverage is needed in the Arctic Ocean. Planners of future work should pay particular attention to the location of gravity stations. Gravity data are degraded when positioning is poor; satellite navigation may be a solution to this need.

Refraction Seismology

Data on seismic velocities in the crust and mantle of the Arctic Ocean are almost completely lacking. Refraction seismology requires two stations whose spacing can be changed. Meeting this requirement is very difficult and expensive in an ice-covered ocean. The paucity of seismic velocities is one of the most serious drawbacks to an understanding of the crustal structure of the Arctic Basin.

The few explosion seismology studies that have been made were all in the Canada Basin. Early short refraction profiles on the southern flank of the Alpha Cordillera showed a few hundred meters of sediment; 2.8 km of material of 4.70 km sec^{-1} velocity was shown to overlay the "oceanic layer" of undetermined thickness with a velocity of 6.44 km sec^{-1}. This appears to be the usual oceanic crust, although mantle velocity was not attained. A recent unreversed refraction profile on the Alaskan continental rise showed 3.8 km of water and 2.5 km of sediment overlaying an 8.68-km-thick layer of 4.40 km sec^{-1} velocity, and mantle velocity was ascribed to the dip of the Mohorovičić (Moho) discontinuity downward toward the continent. This appears to be the only determination of crustal thickness in the Arctic Basin. The normally encountered oceanic layer was not present.

Several refraction measurements of crustal thickness have been reported for the continental shelves in the Chukchi Sea and in the Canadian Archipelago. These studies gave a depth of 30 km to the Moho discontinuity. The Chukchi Sea study showed an anomalously low mantle velocity of 7.56 km sec.$^{-1}$.

Earthquake Seismology

Studies of epicenter distribution, surface-wave dispersion, and first-motion studies of earthquakes have provided useful information about arctic structure. The advantage of this technique is that data are obtained without the expense and effort of manning stations in the ice pack. Improved epicenter locations using computers have shown that essentially all earthquakes in the Arctic Basin occur in a narrow band in the Eurasia Basin, along the arctic extension of the worldwide ocean rift system. Focal mechanism study indicates extension perpendicular to the ridge axis, i.e., the crust is opening along the epicenter belt. None of the surface-wave dispersion analyses have suggested continental crustal thickness, but several point to thickness intermediate between continental and oceanic. The most recent of the studies used records from Resolute Bay in the Canadian Archipelago and therefore obtained the shortest path lengths. Rayleigh and Love wave dispersion showed oceanic crustal thickness in the deep basins.

All the dispersion studies are limited by the facts that the epicenters are only found along the Mid-Oceanic Ridge and seismometers are located far from the deep basin. Any propagation path will include a large percentage of continental crust. As can be seen from Figure 1, the physiography of the basin is complex, yet the earthquake propagation paths from the Nansen Cordillera will cross either only a part of the Eurasia Basin or nearly all the major features. Bottom-mounted seismometers could be located to provide better paths to detail the crustal structure of the major physiographic provinces.

THEORIES ON THE ORIGIN OF THE ARCTIC OCEAN FLOOR

The review of the present state of knowledge of the physiography, sediments, and structural elements of the Arctic Basin given above shows that much remains to be done. This review would not be complete without mention of working hypotheses formulated recently to interpret the features on the floor of the Arctic Basin.

Following Nansen's famous drift in the *Fram* (1893–1896), which laid to rest the concept that the Arctic Ocean was everywhere shallow and dotted with islands, students of the earth were left with four possibilities to explain the existence of the Arctic Ocean: (1) it has existed since the earth's formation; (2) it formed during drift of continental blocks; (3) it formed by subsidence of continental blocks; or (4) it exists because of some combination of these mechanisms. The second mechanism, horizontal movement of the earth's crust, also called sea-floor spreading or continental drift, has recently become attractive to many researchers as a result of recent paleomagnetic studies on polar wandering and reversals of the earth's field, magnetic data from the sea floor indicating reversely magnetized crustal blocks, and magnetic and topographic profiles of the midoceanic ridges. The various data all point to the formation of oceanic crust along the axes of the ridges as the continents spread apart. These ideas seem to provide a coherent framework for observations and will stimulate future work in the polar regions as elsewhere. Sea-floor spreading from the crest of the Nansen Cordillera is believed to explain the origin of the Eurasia Basin. The Nansen Cordillera is an active midoceanic ridge. Recently, it has been suggested that the Alpha Cordillera is also a midoceanic ridge which was a locus of spreading in the past. Both magnetic and bathymetric data have been used to support this concept of the Alpha Cordillera as a "fossil" midoceanic ridge. Additional geophysical data

with better geographical distribution will be required to evaluate sea-floor spreading in the Arctic Ocean. The Arctic Basin offers an opportunity to study parallel midoceanic ridges, both youthful and ancient, which are possibly related to a shift of a convection cell in the mantle.

RECOMMENDATIONS

1. The climatic history of the Arctic Ocean should be reconstructed in detail. This can be done with a sufficient number of long piston cores from the ocean floor. Efforts should be made to install heavy winches and coring apparatus on the ice stations so that cores of at least 15 m can be successfully raised. The implications of such data for our understanding of world climate give this project a high priority.

2. A new aeromagnetic survey of the Arctic Ocean should be undertaken, largely to test the sea-floor-spreading hypothesis. Previous aeromagnetic data were not obtained with this theory in mind. The need is for as many flight lines as possible flown at right angles to the ridge axis. This will allow correlation of anomalies and a check for symmetry about the axis.

3. Seismic refraction experiments should be conducted to determine crustal thickness in the major basins and on the rises. Despite many plans and attempts in the past, no suitable refraction data have been obtained in the central Arctic Ocean. The mobility required for refraction profiles can be obtained by icebreakers or helicopters in combination with a drifting ice station. Crustal structures of major features, such as the Arctic Mid-Oceanic Ridge, Lomonosov Ridge, and the Alpha Cordillera, should be measured. In view of hypotheses that consider the Alpha Cordillera to be an extinct area of rifting, structural comparisons between the Cordillera and Arctic Mid-Oceanic Ridge will be of great interest. Similarly, the concept of the Lomonosov Ridge as a broken segment of the Eurasian Shelf stimulates acquisition of seismic information comparing the ridge and shelf.

4. The collection of geophysical data from the drifting ice stations would be greatly accelerated by the use of aircraft at the station to extend the area of coverage. Helicopters or light planes would allow measurements to be made out to a range of 100 miles or more on each side of the station as it drifts along. Instead of a line of data, the result would be a band of data. With the aid of these aircraft, temporary stations of a few weeks' duration could be established for obtaining cores, heat flow, and other geophysical data.

TOPOGRAPHY AND CRUSTAL STRUCTURE OF THE SEAS SURROUNDING ANTARCTICA

The ocean floor surrounding Antarctica has only recently begun to be explored. Over the past four years the USNS

Eltanin has conducted studies in these areas using magnetic, seismic profiling, and precision depth recording (PDR) instruments; a sea gravimeter was installed in 1967. The *Eltanin* has operated almost exclusively in high southern latitudes of the Pacific Ocean during this time. The results of this work will provide a valuable addition to our knowledge, since practically no previous geophysical work has been done in the high southern latitudes of the Pacific Ocean.

OCEAN FLOOR SURROUNDING ANTARCTICA

The antarctic continent is almost completely surrounded by the Mid-Oceanic Ridge. The ring is incomplete only in the sector between the Drake Passage and the middle of the Atlantic. Between the Ridge and Antarctica, there are deep basins floored by extensive abyssal plains and a wide, smooth continental rise. Recent hypotheses of continental drift and sea-floor spreading require extensive data on the entire Mid-Oceanic Ridge for verification. The orientation of major fracture zones cutting the Ridge are well known only in the South Pacific. Lack of information on this fundamental fabric is a serious hindrance to understanding of the origin and evolution of the antarctic portions of the Atlantic and Indian Oceans.

Magnetics

Total magnetic intensity profiles from the oceans bordering the antarctic continent, taken mostly by the USNS *Eltanin,* have revealed a magnetic anomaly pattern parallel to and bilaterally symmetric about the Pacific Antarctic Ridge and the Indian Antarctic Ridge. The anomaly pattern of both these ridges is the same as that found to be associated with many other portions of the midoceanic ridge system. The linearity and symmetric nature of the pattern is as predicted by the sea-floor-spreading hypothesis. The implication is that much of the ocean floor has been formed by the sea-floor-spreading process and that the axis of the midoceanic ridge system has been the locus of the process.

The fact that the magnetic anomaly pattern is the same for many sections of the midoceanic ridge system indicates the contemporaneous nature of these areas. Heirtzler *et al.* (1968) have extrapolated a time scale for the anomaly patterns, suggesting that these portions of the midoceanic ridge system have been developing continuously throughout the Cenozoic. Figure 4 is an isochron map giving the age in millions of years for the basement rock as revealed by the magnetic patterns.

The implications regarding continental drift have been elaborated elsewhere (Heirtzler *et al.*, 1968). Of fundamental importance to this problem is the history of motion of Antarctica. The study of magnetic lineation in the oceanic areas bordering Antarctica affords a unique opportunity for synthesizing this history. The entire region from longitude

150° E, west to 15° W and south of 50° S latitude is almost devoid of systematic survey. It is understood that the long-range plans for the National Science Foundation's USNS *Eltanin* include coverage of this region. It is hoped that this program will be realized, particularly in the difficult and inaccessible region of the South Indian Ocean.

The study of the paleomagnetism of long cores from seas around Antarctica has provided important data concerning the climatic history of Antarctica (Opdyke *et al.*, 1966). These studies have shown that the glaciation of Antarctica began before 4 million years ago, since ice-rafted detritus of this age has been identified in oceanic cores. Paleomagnetic studies of oceanic cores have also provided much useful information concerning the rate of sediment accumulation around Antarctica. The paleomagnetic study of Antarctic cores is certain to be of great assistance in unraveling the Late Tertiary and Pleistocene history of the seas surrounding Antarctica and perhaps the climatic history of Antarctica itself. There is a need for longer piston cores; an increase from the present 10 to 20 m to lengths of 50 to 60 m is attainable with only some modification to existing equipment. Such cores should reach well back into the Tertiary.

RECOMMENDATIONS

1. A greater number of shipborne studies on topography and crustal structure of the seas surrounding Antarctica should be undertaken, employing standard geophysical techniques, especially in the virtually unexplored sector which extends from the Scotia Arc halfway around the world to Macquarie Ridge south of New Zealand.

2. More investigations should be made beneath the ice-covered areas of the Weddell Sea by ice stations, aircraft landings, and submersibles.

3. The history of motion of Antarctica and its implications regarding continental drift and sea-floor spreading should be studied in greater detail, especially by investigating magnetic anomalies and lineation in the oceanic areas bordering Antarctica, including the difficult and inaccessible region of the South Indian Ocean.

4. Long cores, 50 to 60 m in length, should be taken from the sea floor around Antarctica for paleomagnetic, sedimentation, and other studies on the climate history of Antarctica.

WATERS OF THE ARCTIC OCEAN AND SUBARCTIC SEAS

CIRCULATION OF THE ARCTIC OCEAN

The Arctic Ocean proper is an ice-covered northern extension of the Atlantic Ocean. Convective circulation in the Arctic Ocean can be represented in primitive fashion by a two-

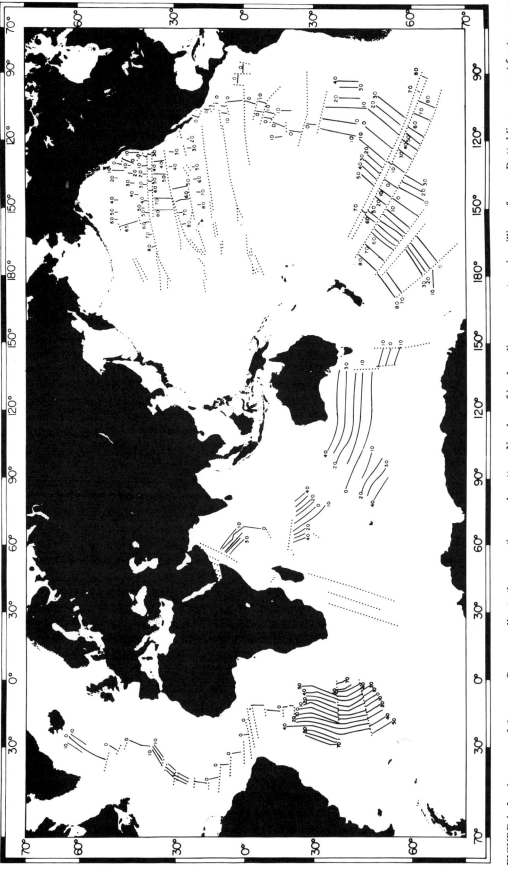

FIGURE 4 Isochron map of the ocean floor according to the magnetic anomaly pattern. Numbers of isochron lines represent age in millions of years. Dotted lines represent fracture zones.

layered estuarine model. Warm saline water, originating in southern latitudes, enters the Arctic Basin west of Svalbard, where it sinks below the surface and then spreads throughout the basin at intermediate and deep levels. Fresh cold water, from river inflow and from an excess of precipitation over evaporation, is added to the ocean at the surface. The surface water is formed by a mixing of this fresh water with the underlying Atlantic water, particularly around the margins of the basin. The resulting arctic surface water, cold and low in salinity, flows out of the Arctic Ocean as the East Greenland Current, completing the cycle of inflow at depth, upward mixing, and outflow at the surface. The prevailing winds aid in driving this flow. In the western part of the Arctic Ocean there is, in addition, a wind-driven gyre. There the prevailing winds of the polar high drive the surface currents in a clockwise motion.

A real understanding of currents in the Arctic Ocean and their driving forces will exist when it is possible to predict how the circulation would be altered by changes in winds, ice cover, precipitation, and entrance size. An ability to predict seems to lie far ahead. A proper model of any type—analytical, numerical, descriptive, or analogue—is still lacking.

Water and Ice Exchange through the Entrances to the Arctic Ocean

The balance method is a first approach to understanding an isolated sea. Steady circulation is assumed, and all available data are used to check the balance between inflow and outflow of such quantities as water and ice. This oceanographic accounting quickly shows the poor state of knowledge for the Arctic Ocean.

Water and ice in the Arctic Ocean are exchanged with: (1) the Atlantic Ocean through the Greenland Sea and Canadian Archipelago, (2) the Pacific through the Bering Strait, (3) the atmosphere through precipitation and evaporation, and (4) the continents through river discharge.

Although the largest volumes of water enter and leave the Arctic Ocean between Greenland and Svalbard, this transport is the least understood of all. The inflow from the Atlantic takes place on the eastern side of the Greenland-Svalbard passage. The amount of water actually entering the Arctic Ocean by this route has, in recent years, been estimated to be from 1.5×10^6 to 6.0×10^6 m^3 sec^{-1} by different authors. Nearly all the data available are from the summer season. The outflow in the East Greenland Current can only be indirectly estimated, as no complete set of direct measurements exists. Recent figures are 4.9×10^6 m^3 sec^{-1} for water and 0.1×10^6 m^3 sec^{-1} for ice discharge. Although the volume of ice that leaves is small in relation to that of water, it is of considerable importance to the Arctic Ocean heat balance. The flow of water out of the Arctic Ocean through the Canadian Archipelago is about 1.0×10^6 to 1.2×10^6 m^3 sec^{-1}. The amount of ice lost through the

Canadian Archipelago is apparently negligible when compared with the loss to the Greenland Sea.

The volume of water entering by way of the Bering Strait is approximately 1.2×10^6 m^3 sec^{-1}, a number which is more confidently known than the Atlantic exchange values. The Bering Strait value is based on work with current meters during summer and long-term measurements with electrodes on the eastern side of the strait.

The amount of fresh water entering the Arctic Ocean by river discharge is about 0.1×10^6 m^3 sec^{-1}, and the excess of precipitation over evaporation is about one tenth of that. These volumes are trivial in comparison with seawater exchanged between the Arctic and Atlantic Oceans.

Attempts have been made to establish the balance between these various flows, but the results are not satisfactory. The most pressing need is for better information on the ice and seawater exchange between the Arctic and Atlantic Oceans, which takes place between Greenland and Svalbard.

Surface and Subsurface Currents

The drift of ice research stations has outlined many of the features of ice movements and currents in the upper layers. T-3, for example, has been tracked for twenty years, making three orbits around the anticyclonic gyre in that period of time. However, the behavior of the ice and water over an extended area is not known. An array of markers on the ice must be tracked to determine the pattern of ice motion. The vector-velocity field of the ice which is thus determined may be divided into a rotational or vortical part and a divergent part. Vorticity of the pack can be related to the downward flux of water just beneath the Ekman layer, a fundamental quantity in circulation. Divergence is required in heat and mass balance studies of the pack ice.

Subsurface circulation is almost unmeasured. Continuous current observations over long periods of time will be necessary to separate the general circulation pattern from the fluctuating flow. There is even dispute about the sense of movement of the Atlantic water around the western part of the basin. Does it travel clockwise or counterclockwise? The course of the deep and bottom waters is no clearer.

Current Fluctuations

The general circulation is only a statistical mean. The ice and waters fluctuate continually in space and time. The motions range in scale from molecular to geological, and energy is supplied to the circulation in certain scales of space and time and withdrawn at other scales. A dynamical description requires attempts at measuring the motions. A beginning has been made at Fletcher's Ice Island (T-3), where a satellite navigation system gives detailed ice motion and a vertical string of meters below the ice measures ocean currents. The time scales associated with the inertial period (about 12 hours) and cyclonic systems (several days) seem to be especially important. The ice and upper layers respond quickly to the wind, reflecting the passage of atmospheric pressure systems.

Internal waves with shorter periods are also observed, but an understanding of the transient response of ice and water to wind and pressure changes requires three-dimensional coverage not yet available.

Mixing Processes

In the estuarine arctic model, vertical mixing links the inflow at depth with the surface outflow. Yet, as in other oceans, the identity of the process that produces the mixing is not clear. Shear instability and penetrative convection have both been suggested as important in the Arctic Ocean, but critical experiments have not been made. Other processes, such as localized convective mixing along the edges of the continental shelf, may also be important and should be investigated.

Relation of Wind-Driven and Density-Driven Currents

Since arctic currents are driven partly by winds and partly by salinity differences, there is the problem of the relation between these two modes of circulation. How are the two modes coupled? Is the motion stable? This is the combined wind- and thermohaline-driven current problem. Investigations in this restricted sea may provide insights that can be extrapolated and applied to the world ocean. Only narrow entrances and exits join the Arctic Ocean and the other oceans. This relatively closed basin should be a productive focus of investigation.

CIRCULATION OF SUBARCTIC SEAS

Norwegian Sea

Formation of Arctic Bottom Water and North Atlantic Deep Water The bottom water in the Pacific and Indian Oceans is all of antarctic origin, but the Atlantic Ocean contains water from both arctic and antarctic sources. There has been general agreement among oceanographers that the principal antarctic source of bottom water is the Weddell Sea. Concerning the northern sources, there has been more disagreement. Early theories considered that the main northern source of deep and bottom waters was the surface of the Labrador Sea between Labrador and Greenland. It was concluded that late winter atmospheric conditions in this region were sufficiently severe to cause vertical convection from the surface to the bottom. More recent investigations have made it clear that the major source of deep and bottom waters is the Norwegian Sea, and that at the present time vertical convection in the Labrador Sea does not extend to depths greater than 1500 m. The specific proposals for future

oceanographic work on this matter have accordingly been focused on the Weddell and Norwegian Seas.

The term "Arctic Mediterranean Sea" has been used by Sverdrup *et al.* (1942) to describe, collectively, all the waters to the north of the Greenland–Iceland Ridge, the Faeroes-Iceland Ridge, and the Faeroes-Scotland or Wyville Thomson Ridge. Thus the Arctic Mediterranean includes the Greenland and Norwegian Seas, as well as the Arctic Ocean proper. It is a convenient term in the discussion of bottom-water formation.

The densest water in the world oceans is all formed in Mediterranean Seas—the Mediterranean itself, the Red Sea, and the Arctic Mediterranean Sea. What these seas have in common is a relatively shallow sill which separates their deepest waters from the outside ocean and a local climate which results in the production of water denser than that of the outside ocean. In each case, this results in an inflow of surface water from the outside ocean and an outflow of dense water over the sill into the outside ocean. In the case of the Mediterranean and Red Seas, it is the excess of evaporation over precipitation which produces dense, highly saline water; but in the case of the Arctic Mediterranean Sea, the conditions imposed by the arctic climate are different. There the precipitation exceeds evaporation, and it is the cooling of the surface water by the atmosphere which produces water of high density. As a result, the denser outflow is less saline and very much colder than the inflow.

In Sverdrup's water budget for the Arctic Mediterranean Sea, the role of the dense outflows was ignored, because at the time the budget was prepared (1942) these outflows were not known to exist; the saline inflow past Scotland (3 million m^3 sec^{-1}) was added to by the inflow through the Bering Strait and the excess precipitation and runoff within the sea, and the resultant outflow (3.55 million m^3 sec^{-1}) was allotted wholly to the shallow East Greenland Current. Since that time, it has become clear through the work of a number of investigators that these dense outflows are almost certainly in excess of 3 million m^3 sec^{-1} exclusive of the East Greenland Current, pointing to the need to revise the water, salt, and heat budgets for the Arctic Mediterranean Sea.

In order to do this properly, the following steps are necessary:

1. Monitor the inflowing water in the Faeroes-Scotland Channel, using direct measurements and oceanographic stations. This must be carried out during at least one entire winter. There is evidence that the inflow is stronger in winter, and it must follow that the outflows are also stronger in winter.

2. Monitor the outflow through the Iceland–Faeroes Channel and the Faeroe Bank Channel.

3. Monitor the dense outflow through the Greenland-Iceland Channel. An attempt to do this with moored current

meters in the 1966–1967 winter failed, apparently because the velocity of the outflow water was too high. Probably shipborne current meters will have to be used.

4. At least one synoptic oceanographic survey of the Norwegian Sea will have to be undertaken, preferably toward the end of winter. The water masses within the Norwegian Sea have only been observed in coarse scale. A fine-scale volumetric oxygen–salinity (O/S) diagram is needed for this sea.

5. There must be a rigorous program of meteorological observations throughout the Norwegian Sea survey. This program should be conducted in close collaboration with the program of water and ice exchange measurements for the Arctic Ocean proper. The outflows from the Norwegian Sea constitute the major northern source of deep and bottom water for the world ocean and a reliable estimate of the amount of this distribution would be of the greatest value.

Bering Sea

The Bering Sea, having an area of 23×10^6 km^2, is the second largest of the seas adjacent to the world ocean, the largest being the Mediterranean. It is composed of a deep basin on the southwest and a large resource-rich continental shelf on the east and north and has been subjected to relatively little concerted oceanographic effort.

Some surface waters of the North Pacific reach the Bering through passes in the Aleutian Chain. Temperature and salinity data indicate that water down to depths of 100 m may be brought to the surface in the vicinity of the Aleutian Passes. This nutrient-rich water supports some of the most productive biotic communities found on earth.

A large part of water flow into the Bering Sea apparently occurs at longitude 170° E, where the stream converges with water moving northward in the Western Subarctic Gyre, resulting in the formation of a cyclonic eddy over the Aleutian Basin and an anticyclonic eddy in the vicinity of the North Rat Island Ridge. The main flow continues northward around the Ridge and turns eastward, establishing the general cyclonic circulation over the deep basin. In the eastern part, cyclonic and anticyclonic eddies are created as the current turns northward adjacent to the continental shelf; and, in the northern part, the current diverges, sending one branch northward through the Bering Strait and the other southwestward along the shores of Kamchatka, where it eventually becomes the East Kamchatka Current and discharges back into the north Pacific Ocean. Currents over the continental shelf of the Alaska coast are chiefly tidal, except adjacent to the coastline where runoff from Alaska rivers flows northward and is discharged through the Bering Strait. This flow varies with seasons but supplies about 20 percent of the inflow to the Arctic Ocean. The quality of this water is not well defined. In the extreme western part of the strait a southward-flowing current, or "polar" current is occasion-

ally observed. Flow through the Bering Strait has been under investigation for a number of years by a group from the USN Arctic Submarine Research Laboratory using continuous electromagnetic methods and other techniques. Currents at depth are presently being investigated by the University of Washington group headed by Dr. L. K. Coachman.

Oceanography of the Aleutian Passes Calloway (1963) presents temperature and salinity data in the vicinity of the Aleutian Islands and passes. He concludes that the geostrophic assumption is not a close approximation near the islands, since the pressure gradient is not vanishing at depth. He also concludes that east of Amchitka Pass the steric level north of the Aleutian Islands is greater than on the Pacific Ocean side. Major water exchange is through Amchitka Pass and between Attu and Kiska Islands, with the direction of flow being into the Bering Sea. In the upper 50 to 100 m, the isotherms and isohalines, respectively, approach the surface near the Islands. Below these depths, the isotherms and isohaline surfaces bend down. The surface-temperature chart pictures the Islands as lying in cold water, the result of tidal mixing in the passes and around the Islands.

During the summers of 1965 and 1966, hydrographic and primary productivity studies were made by personnel of the University of Alaska from the *Acona* in the region of Unimak Pass. Salinity distribution at the surface showed that a salinity boundary occurs inside the pass as well as to the north. A surprising feature was the presence of high-salinity water to the east, resulting in a region of minimum salinity in the middle of the pass. Four water types were indicated. The effect of Unimak Pass is to prevent the northward transport of the nearly isohaline water occurring below the sill depth, which is about 50 m. Deeper water is either mixed upward or prevented from entering the pass by the sill. Eastward-flowing water that flows along the north side of the Aleutian Islands appears to mix with waters flowing north through the passes in such a way as to bring deep nutrient-rich water to the surface and may provide part of a basis for the highly productive waters found there and in Bristol Bay. Further studies of this interesting phenomenon are needed to delineate the mechanism, extent, source, and importance of this upwelling to the biological economy of the Bering Sea.

The oceanographic processes occurring in the Bering Sea during the late fall, winter, and early spring months are almost totally unexamined. The deep water of the Bering Sea appears to come from the north Pacific; however, it is not known whether this deep water may be modified by processes in the Bering Sea due to cooling during the winter. Obviously, all oceanographic processes of the Bering Sea are profoundly influenced during the months of late fall, winter, and early spring and need to be studied in greater detail during these periods. A group from the University of Washington is beginning to compile historical and atmospheric-pressure data preparatory to a study of Bering Sea circulation.

OPPORTUNITIES FOR RESEARCH

Sea Ice and Climatic Change

There are compelling reasons for a better knowledge of Arctic Ocean circulation. The Arctic Ocean is considered to be an important and possibly a key factor in the climate of the northern hemisphere. The sea ice covering this ocean has a great influence on the radiation balance and, hence, a great influence on the atmospheric circulation. Removal of the ice cover will have significant effects on global weather. The arctic ice cover lies on the boundary separating the circulations of air and water. Its maintenance or disappearance depends on the complex interaction of these two circulations. In the future, efforts to influence climate by removing the ice cover will receive serious attention. Such schemes as sprinkling lampblack on the ice to change the radiation balance or damming the Bering Strait to change ocean circulation have been proposed. Quantitative answers on the relationships of sea, air, and ice cover will be needed to assess such proposals.

Unique Stable Platform Afforded by Drifting Ice

Some of the unresolved problems of arctic circulation are not limited to the Arctic Basin but are related to fundamental problems of physical oceanography in all oceans. The role of current fluctuations, the nature of the mixing process, and the combined wind-driven and thermohaline-driven current are universal problems. At first, it might be thought that such questions could best be solved in other oceans. However, it is possible that answers may be found more easily in the Arctic. The drifting ice cover provides a unique stable platform for detailed oceanographic research. Such a platform, floating in deep water free of wave motion and manned all year, is not yet available in open oceans. Ships are uneconomical to keep on a station for long periods and suffer from wave motion. Buoys remain stationary at one location but lack a human presence to guide experiments intelligently while they are in progress. Also, basic problems, involving delicate oceanographic measurements of long duration, may best be answered in the Arctic. This has been true in the past, and it is reasonable to assume that such basic oceanographic discoveries as the Ekman drift current, internal waves, and adiabatic effects, all of which were discovered and first studied during the pioneering phase of arctic exploration, may continue with modern instruments and logistic support. In 1928, Nansen expressed the hope that "From the drifting ice all movements of the water—the horizontal currents as well as . . . vertical oscillations of the layers may be continually and carefully studied at all depths in an ideal manner which is not possible in the open ocean; and many of the greatest problems of oceanography may thus be solved." This statement applies as well today as when it was written.

Deep-Water and Bottom-Water Formation

The north and south polar regions are the source of all the deep, cold bottom water found throughout the world ocean. This deep water is formed by atmospheric cooling at the sea surface in late winter, increasing the density of the surface water sufficiently for it to sink to the bottom of the ocean and spread to lower latitudes. Roughly three quarters of all the water in the oceans has come from the polar regions. This has been known in principle for many years, but there is considerable question about how much is formed each winter and to what extent the production of bottom water depends on long- and short-term climatic fluctuations.

RECOMMENDATIONS

Since so many aspects of the circulation are interrelated with each other and with meteorological effects, a unified approach is necessary. A concentrated field effort over a limited period is recommended; perhaps one of 18 months' duration would cover one seasonal cycle with sufficient overlap. The goal would be to collect a body of data adequate for constructing a model of Arctic Ocean circulation. Winds and currents within the ocean basin would be measured from a net of drifting ice stations, three manned and several more unmanned. Water transport through the entrances and exits would be monitored by permanent installations and by icebreaker expeditions, while nuclear-powered submarines would be employed for seasonal hydrographic surveys.

1. Water transport in entrances to the Arctic Ocean should be measured. Measurement of water transport anywhere in the ocean is time-consuming, difficult, and expensive, but measurements such as these will be especially difficult because of poor weather and sea ice. Studies to date indicate that the transport will vary on time scales of days, months, and years, not only in the shallow, narrow passages, such as the Bering Strait and the Canadian Archipelago, but also in the Greenland–Svalbard entrance. Therefore, any measuring systems used must allow for repetitive measurements over all seasons of the year for several years at least.

The three principal methods of measuring water transport are (a) dynamical calculations based on temperatures and salinities, (b) direct current measurements by drogues, floats, or current meters, and (c) by the electromagnetic method. The geostrophic flow method is not suitable in the arctic entrances for two reasons: first, it assumes steady-state flow and no friction, though these assumptions would certainly not be valid in the shallow passages or perhaps even in the Greenland–Svalbard entrance; second, ships are required to take hydrographic stations across the current flow. This would not be possible in winter in the Archipelago or in the East Greenland Current, even by icebreaker.

Current measurement by drogues or floats is not feasible in the drifting ice, although current meters and subsurface floats will be possible and valuable during the summer months. However, any method requiring ships in the winter ice pack cannot be considered. Consideration can be given to current meters which could be placed in summer, powered to operate for a year or longer, and recovered during some later summer. These will be expensive because each meter, or string of meters, will require a long-life submersible power source and data-logging system. Recovery will be difficult, because surface floats cannot be used in the ice. This consideration also precludes the use of radio telemetry for data transmission. Each system will need an acoustic locator device, and precision navigation will be necessary in planting the units. Minimum instrumentation in the Greenland–Svalbard passage (about 600 km wide with maximum depths of over 3000 m) might well require 50 to 100 individual current meters and the use of ships and icebreakers to plant them. This sort of system is certainly possible, but considerable development will be required. The problems associated with placing strings of instruments in the open ocean for later recovery are by no means solved at this time.

Alternatively, the electromagnetic method of measuring water transport in the entrances to the Arctic Ocean appears to be one of the most feasible of the available systems. Seawater moving in the earth's magnetic field generates an electrical potential which can be detected with suitable electrodes. In theory, the electrical potential produced by seawater of known resistivity moving through the earth's magnetic field could be computed for various water speeds through a given cross-sectional area to provide a calibration for an electrode system. In practice, an empirical calibration is required because the electrical conductivity of the sea floor has an effect and cannot be computed.

A possible system for use in the Greenland–Svalbard entrance was investigated recently and discussed with a cable manufacturer and a cable-laying company. The proposed system called for seven electrodes to be laid on the bottom between West Svalbard and the shelf off northeastern Greenland. The sea cable could be of a simple type, because it carries only the dc voltage detected by the electrodes—no power need be sent down the cable. The estimated cost of 700 km of cable and laying is between $1 million and $1.5 million. The seven electrodes would provide 21 pairs which could be sequenced to allow assessment of water transport through as many segments of the passage. Digital recording and computer processing would be required to handle the data.

Problems inherent in the electromagnetic method are the need for calibration and changes in the magnetic field, both of which present serious problems in the arctic regions. Calibration requires measurement of water transport in the channel by an independent method at least once. In the arctic entrances, the calibration would be accomplished by a multiship operation during summer. Variations in the earth's magnetic field are perhaps the most serious problem associated

with the electrode system. The Atlantic–Arctic Ocean passage is north of the main auroral belt, but magnetic storms will be troublesome. It appears likely that a filtering system could be devised which would pass the dc signal from the electrodes while rejecting the earth current signals caused by magnetic storms. The time scale of interest in the water-transport study is variations over periods of days, while the magnetic fluctuations are in minutes. If this were not possible, data taken during magnetic disturbances would have to be rejected; this could amount to some 10 to 30 percent of the total. The great advantage of the electrode system is that once it is placed and calibrated, data can be collected at low cost for the life of the cable, and all instrumental complexities are centered in the shore-based recording system.

Similar systems could be used in the Bering Strait and the Canadian Archipelago, but burial of the sea cable at the shoreline to protect it from ice damage would be an added expense. (For example, in the Bering Strait, burial of a cable 6 to 7 m into the sea floor out to a 40-m water depth would cost about $750,000.)

Measurement of ice export from the Arctic will be greatly improved by better knowledge of water speeds in the East Greenland Current and by more reliable ice-thickness measurements from nuclear submarine data. The area of the current covered by ice can be judged by aerial reconnaissance, by visual observations in summer and radar in winter. It is hoped that, satellite imagery will be available for this purpose also. Better data on ice velocities could be obtained by marking suitable floes and tracking them as they move south in the East Greenland Current. This could be done by placing on the floes radar transponders which could be interrogated by ice reconnaissance aircraft. Absolute locations would be no better than the aircraft navigation, but positions of the markers relative to each other would be quite good. This technique could, of course, be used to study ice drift in any of the arctic entrances.

Finally, one can picture the "grand experiment" where electrodes are spaced across the Bering Strait, the Greenland–Svalbard entrance, the Svalbard–North Cape (Norway) entrance, and Baffin Bay to monitor all water transport through the entrances to the Arctic Ocean. Based on experience in the Bering Strait and cost estimates for the Greenland–Svalbard cable mentioned above, the instrumentation would cost at least $5 million. Ship operating costs and other items would raise that total estimate to a substantial part of the annual budget for oceanography in the United States. However, considering the knowledge that could be gained about the workings of the North Atlantic and the heat balance of the Arctic Ocean, this might well be the most significant experiment on a national scale that oceanography could accomplish in the 1970–1979 decade.

2. Continuous ocean-current temperature and salinity observations should be made and data obtained at as many depths as possible from the ice-drifting stations to deter-

mine the large-scale motions of ice and water. Surface ob-servations of wind and atmospheric pressure should also be recorded. Extremely accurate navigation is required, since the velocity of the ice station must be subtracted from the measurements to obtain true ocean currents. The Navy satellite navigation system has proved adequate for the pur-pose on T-3 and might serve other stations. This network of observations would give a three-dimensional array of the fields of motion and mass. If the spacing of instruments in the horizontal and vertical dimensions is chosen properly, it will produce a set of data on the steady as well as time-dependent motions in the upper layers of the Arctic Ocean. This program should be integrated with the network of ice stations proposed separately by the Panel on Glaciology for the study of ice divergence.

Strings of current meters hanging below the ice will be adequate only for upper and intermediate layers. When the strings are too long, cable motions give undesired and un-known biases to the data. Deeper currents will require dif-ferent techniques. The "abyssal whistle" now under develop-ment at Woods Hole Oceanographic Institution may be useful for deep currents. This employs a neutrally buoyant float carrying an acoustic pinger which emits a sound at pre-scribed intervals. The range and direction of the float would be determined with a hydrophone array at an ice station.

Bottom currents can be studied with a variety of presently available meters for short periods of measurement. Bottom photographs have also proved useful in determining direc-tions of bottom currents. However, continuous time series studies of deep and bottom currents may prove difficult. Pop-up or telemetering instruments implanted by an ice-breaker may be useful.

3. Smaller scales of motion which are important to mix-ing processes should be measured with small arrays at a single ice station or from icebreakers.

Reliable criteria to discriminate between the different mixing processes should be selected. For example, penetra-tive convection in "salt fingers" might be studied by intro-ducing dye beneath the ice and photographing the flow pat-tern. Shear instability involves a high rate of vertical shear in relation to the vertical-density profile. Detailed current and salinity observations would need to be made. Sonic flowmeters have properties of rapid response which should make them useful for this work.

The possibility of local mixing along the edge of the basin would require an icebreaker expedition. Several detailed hydrographic profiles should extend across the shelf and out into the deep basin. These could be conveniently done north of the Chukchi Sea and Alaska.

4. Field investigation should be interwoven with theoret-ical arctic studies. The goal here is a model of Arctic Ocean circulation capable of prediction. No type of model should be overlooked. Numerical models involving digital computers will be central to much of this work. However, rotating tank models provide visual evidence and are particularly appropri-ate for polar oceans. Their use in modeling polar oceans is attractive. First, the effect of the variation of the Coriolis parameter with latitude may be unimportant, permitting layered models to be used. Second, the polar oceans are approximately circular in outline and relatively easy to re-produce. Analytical models usually involve simplified as-sumptions but, in many cases, provide more insight than do other types of models.

Eventually it will be possible to construct a combined numerical model of air, water, and ice circulation to serve as a basis for experiments on climate modification. This Arctic Ocean circulation model could then be integrated with atmosphere models.

ANTARCTIC WATER MASSES AND CURRENTS

The unique position of the Antarctic Ocean makes it an es-sential element in the understanding of world ocean condi-tions. The Antarctic Ocean encompasses the southern parts of the Atlantic, Pacific, and Indian Oceans; their circulations cannot be studied without reference to the Antarctic circu-lation. It contains the only complete zonal flow in the oceans, linking the three oceans together.

Data from cruises of the British ship HMRV *Discovery* provided the basis of modern knowledge on the water masses and currents of this region. Expeditions of the Soviet ship *Ob* and of the USNS *Eltanin* have supplemented these data.

ANTARCTIC CIRCUMPOLAR CURRENT

The volume transport of the Antarctic Circumpolar Current is not well known, although it is one of the largest of ocean currents. Estimates range from $45-90 \times 10^6$ m^3 sec^{-1} (Osta-poff, 1961) to 200×10^6 m^3 sec^{-1} (Gordon, 1967). These estimates are based on the geostrophic method and point up the need for direct observations of current velocity. Prelimi-nary measurements have been made in the Drake Passage, but more extensive work is needed.

Several methods show promise for direct current measure-ments in this area. Of these, Swallow floats are probably the best choice. About six floats could be dropped across the Drake Passage and tended by one research vessel, such as the USNS *Eltanin*, passing back and forth between them for a period of several weeks. The AN/SRN-9 Satellite Navigation Receiver would provide the required accurate positioning. Parachute drogues could also be employed and tracked by a surface vessel or, in a more extensive program, by satellite positioning. If any array of drogues is to be tracked over a considerable time span, satellite tracking might be the more economical method. An IRLS (Interrogation, Recording, and Location System) platform would be attached to the surface buoy and its position determined during each satellite pass. Another technique, as yet untried, would be the placement of a tiltmeter on an iceberg to measure directly the tilt of the sea surface. Such a tiltmeter might have an output telemetered to a ship or shore station. The swift currents should produce easily measurable tilts which would provide a reference level for geostrophic current determinations.

ANTARCTIC CONVERGENCE

The Antarctic Convergence, or polar-front zone, is not well understood. The nature of the converging or diverging process is in question, and meager data are available pertaining to time variation of both position and structure of the front. A polar-front study could be patterned after the multiship studies of the Gulf Stream. An excellent opportunity for such an operation exists when the USNS *Eltanin* is operating in antarctic waters south of New Zealand and Australia. During this time, ships of these countries may cooperate, along with ships of other nations that have already made numerous contributions to our understanding of antarctic waters.

The instrumentation on each ship should be of continuously *in situ* type. One of the most useful instruments would be the 700-m expendable bathythermograph (BT) probes now available aboard the *Eltanin*. The salinity–temperature–depth recorder (STD) is required to obtain the necessary data.

The form of the survey should be a detailed study along a wide section of the front, of the order of hundreds of kilometers for a period of weeks. More extensive studies can be planned after the results of the first survey become known. Future surveys may be designed to study the front seasonally and at different locations over such formations as ridges and basins.

FORMATION OF ANTARCTIC BOTTOM WATER

The question of how much antarctic bottom water is formed is of great importance, since far more than half of the bottom waters of the world ocean are of antarctic origin. The rate of production of this water has been estimated to be as high as 29 million m^3 sec^{-1}, but it can be argued from the distribution of variables in the waters surrounding Antarctica that virtually no renewal is taking place at the present time. Those who favor large production of Antarctic water argue that the salt released by the freezing process during winter is sufficient to raise the density of the surface waters along the periphery of the continent to a value greater than that of the resident deep water. However, the observations made during the drift of the German ship *Deutschland* across the Weddell Sea in the winter of 1912 show a negligible increase in the salinity of the surface layer. The density of this layer never approaches that of the deep water.

Antarctic bottom water is also of importance to marine geology. The circulation of these waters is the principal factor governing the distribution of materials that constitute the great sediment drifts of the continental margins. A concerted effort must be made to obtain a better understanding of these currents and of their nature, particularly near the points of origin, so that their modern characteristics can be more clearly defined and so that we may better interpret the history of fluctuations contained in the stratified bottom deposits.

The drifts of the *Deutschland* and the British ship *Endurance* are illustrated in Figure 5. These represent the only real penetration into the Weddell Sea in the winter. If the drift of the *Endurance* could be duplicated by a modern ice station, it is possible that this question could be resolved for practical purposes, since this drift encompasses the entire area in which bottom water may be formed.

Such a drifting station should be instrumented for conventional water-sampling equipment and also for continuous direct current measurements. A strong complementary meteorological program should also be undertaken concurrently to assess the heat exchange between the water and the atmosphere, since bottom water cannot be formed in the absence of such an exchange.

Barges have been proposed for polar research, to act as drifting stations similar to those on ice floes and ice islands but with greater safety and comfort. As envisioned, they would be constructed according to the design principles used in the Norwegian ship *Fram* to render them crushproof. They would have center walls through which instruments could be lowered and would be fully equipped with such things as living quarters, laboratories, and generators. A Norwegian shipyard has estimated that the *Fram* could be built again for less than a million dollars. A recent design study calls for a much more elaborate barge which was considered too costly for the U.S. antarctic program.

RECOMMENDATIONS

1. Studies should be made on the volume transport of the Antarctic Circumpolar Current using presently available tools and techniques.

2. All-year studies should be made on the converging and diverging processes of the Antarctic Convergence (polar-front zone) to include time variations of both the position and structure of the front.

3. Studies should be made on the formation of antarctic bottom water to cover the amount, rate of production, and processes, especially in the Weddell Sea; also, a new design study of a barge for the Weddell Sea should be made. While

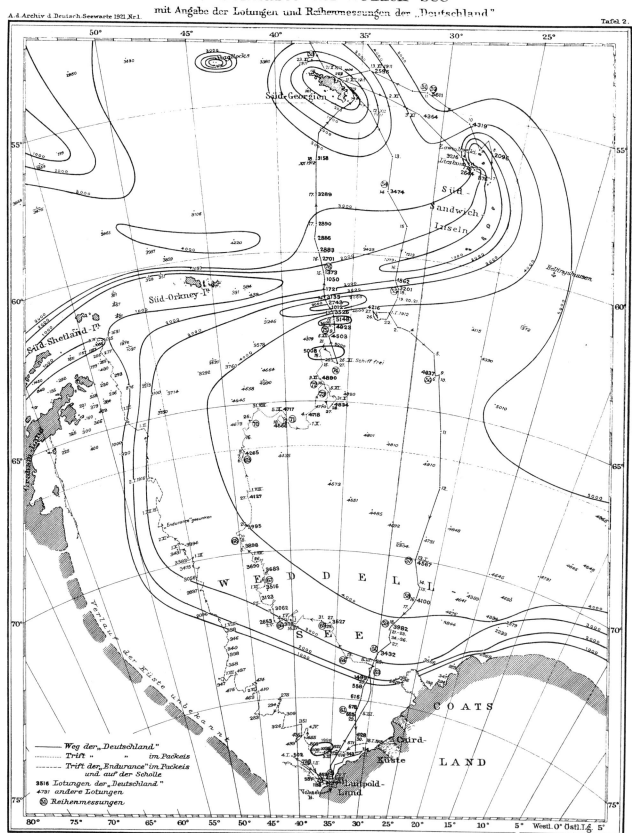

FIGURE 5   Drift tracks of the "Deutschland" and "Endurance" in the pack ice of the Weddell Sea.

the barge concept appears to be most practical at this time, alternatives such as the *Alpha* ice floe station used in the Arctic during the IGY should also be investigated. The importance of this problem may very well justify a thorough study seeking the best method of approach to its solution.

AIR–SEA INTERACTION IN POLAR OCEANS

The most important aspect of sea–air interaction in the polar regions is whether the surface is covered by sea ice, which serves as an effective barrier to the exchange of heat between ocean and atmosphere. Sea-ice cover suppresses wind stress and wind mixing, reflects a large proportion of the incoming shortwave radiation, imposes an upper limit on the surface temperature, and impedes evaporation. Its changes of phase are heat buffers, and the transfer of heat is essentially reduced to molecular conduction. On the other hand, the heat-transfer processes over open water in the vicinity of large ice masses are greatly enhanced, particularly during the winter season. Wind and water stresses keep the sea ice in almost continuous motion, causing the formation of open leads, polynya, and pressure ridges.

The contrast in behavior of arctic and antarctic sea ice is primarily determined by geographic location. The Arctic Ocean remains essentially ice-covered throughout the year, and its annual variation of ice extent is no greater than 30 percent, whereas at the end of summer antarctic sea ice is reduced to about 20 percent of its maximum winter extent (see Table 1).

TABLE 1 Estimated Mass Budget of Arctic and Antarctic Sea Ice

	Mean Thickness (m)	Area at End of Summer (km^2)	Area at End of Winter (km^2)	Annual Variation of Volume (km^3)
Arctic	3–4	9×10^6	12×10^6	9×10^3
Antarctic	1	4×10^6	20×10^6	23×10^3

Mean total mass of sea ice on earth: $4–5 \times 10^4$ km^3
Total amount freezing (and melting) each year: 3×10^4 km^3

BASIC SCIENTIFIC PROBLEMS

When the energy received by both upper and lower surfaces of sea ice is known, its mass budget (including complete disappearance) can be computed. However, the transition from ice-free to ice-covered conditions is not fully understood. A special problem in this context is the freezing of open leads during the cold season. The instability of the ocean boundary layer caused by the expulsion of brine during rapid ice formation has not been adequately studied.

In Chapter 4, Polar Glaciology, the over-all stability of large sheets of sea ice is identified as one of the most important problems to be solved. Due to logistical limitations, most of our knowledge about the energy budget of sea ice comes from regions with a perennial, continuous ice cover (Central Arctic). The critical processes, however, can only be studied where the ice cover is seasonal and probably sensitive to small fluctuations in the atmosphere and in the ocean.

The dynamic interactions are exceedingly complex among the three media: air, ice, and ocean. Only the steady-state wind-driven circulation in the Arctic Ocean has been studied. Some time-dependent solutions are presently under investigation. However, very little is known about the internal ice stress associated with divergence or shear of the flow. All model computations will remain unsatisfactory until the appropriate stress and flow observations have been made.

Interesting and possibly important dynamic phenomena may be occurring in the zone of transition from ice-covered to ice-free ocean where the boundary-layer stresses vary rapidly and where differential heating may introduce strong baroclinity.

In comparison with arctic sea ice, even less is known about the various aspects of antarctic sea ice, including distribution and state, movement, and heat exchange.

In the coastal regions of both Antarctica and Greenland, strong katabatic winds are common. It is not known to what extent these winds influence the energy budget of the sea surface. If they can cause the ice to drift away from shore, the open water will be subjected to an extreme rate of heat loss.

The Canadian Archipelago offers an opportunity to study the interaction of small land masses with small bodies of water. Within short distances one may find seasonal and perennial snow covers as well as ice covers, which are suitable for the study of mesoscale processes.

RECOMMENDATIONS

1. Maximum use should be made of numerical and analogue models of the oceans surrounding Antarctica. Most likely the oceanographic observations necessary to compute advection in the southern ocean will not become available in the near future. To test such models, it may be expedient to develop a numerical model for the Arctic Ocean, whose circulation is better known and whose boundary conditions are easier to specify. The most important unknown quantity in this case is the magnitude of the water transport through the Greenland Sea.

2. Field and laboratory experiments should be conducted on the initial phases of freezing of seawater, aimed at evaluating the structure and depth of convection in the water and the fluxes of salt and heat and their possible connection with

the formation of bottom water. Field experiments should be made in the middle of open leads. A stationary platform (ship or buoy) should be placed in an area where the ice cover is seasonal and pertinent oceanographic and atmospheric parameters may be observed before, during, and after the formation of sea ice. A suitable area for such an experiment is the Bering Sea. A theoretical model should be developed representing conditions in the first few hundred meters of an open Arctic Ocean. The model should contain the effects of radiation, evaporation, admixture of fresh water from the continents, and vertical mixing in the water column. (For recommendations concerning the over-all stability of large sheets of sea ice, refer to Chapter 4.)

3. Experiments should be conducted to establish internal stresses of sea-ice sheets. This can be done by correlating the observed field of wind and water stress with the resulting divergence and shear of the ice flow field. At the same time, a method of modeling an asymmetric rheology of sea ice should be developed. (See Chapter 4.) Full use should be made of satellite observations to monitor the extent of antarctic sea ice and its variations. Special attention should be given to the number and size of open leads, particularly near the coast of Antarctica.

CHEMICAL OCEANOGRAPHY IN POLAR REGIONS

New chemical concepts and techniques have resulted in many recent advances in marine chemistry and chemical oceanography. The improvement of methods in elemental and isotopic analyses of minor constituents and trace elements have allowed much better definition of the detailed composition of seawater. Development of sensitive procedures such as neutron activation analysis, isotopic dilution techniques used in the mass spectrometer, atomic absorption, x-ray fluorescence, gas chromatography, and thin-layer column chromatography with molecular-weight-dividing capabilities have provided means not only to estimate total quantities of elements but also to determine their contributing chemical forms as well as individual isotopes.

SCIENTIFIC PROBLEMS

Chemical Fingerprinting of Water Masses

The introduction of radioisotopes in the ocean from tests of atomic devices and the development of sensitive techniques for measuring these radioisotopes in very low concentrations in both water and organisms have provided powerful tools for studying processes in the ocean. More recently, methods of isolating dissolved organic material in seawater and characterizing its many constituents open up entirely new ways of understanding the biological cycle of the sea, transfer pro-

cesses within water masses, and air–sea interactions. In the Arctic Ocean, particularly in the Canada Basin, four fairly easily definable horizontally stratified water masses have been identified by conventional oceanographic techniques. These water masses have different origins and different circulation patterns and must be constantly interacting with each other. In addition, the existence of a fine structure of thin water masses or lenses is not easily detectable by conventional techniques.

The technology of chemistry is now capable of "fingerprinting" techniques and can significantly enhance our knowledge of this complex oceanographic system. Detailed studies in the trace metal composition should be undertaken to define the concentrations of total elements present and the contributing chemical forms.

The large number of dissolved organic compounds present in ocean water may also prove to be useful as tracers. The quantitative analytical work of specific organic tracers has been worked out, and techniques have been developed to obtain large samples of dissolved organic matter for carbon-14 dating, used in studying large-scale residence times in the ocean. Contributions to the organic pool from terrestrial or marine sources can be easily identified from the dissolved organic matter by determination of the $^{13}C/^{12}C$ ratios. The organic fingerprinting technique for studying water masses has not been advanced to the point where good examples can be drawn as is done with the trace metals. However, it seems inevitable that water conditioned under vastly different environments would have considerable variation in its organic content and composition. These differences may serve to fingerprint water masses.

Ice–Water Interaction

Studies of interface phenomena of air–sea interaction, sediment–water interaction, freshwater–seawater interaction need to be extended into the study of the ice–water interface. Consideration must be given to ionic gradients beneath the ice surface, the mechanism of ice formation in open water, such as leads, and the effect of these on vertical mixing and water-mass formation. Studies on ice–water interaction are important to biological activity at the interface which profoundly influences the biological economy of ice-covered seas. Recent work in the open seas of the south Pacific, southeast Alaska, and elsewhere have shown gradients in ionic components that are statistically significant, particularly of the microconstituents between the surface and the first half meter of depth. Similar gradients are now being found at other depths in the ocean, and it is quite possible that these gradients can be used to determine the rate of transfer between water masses in a microstructure system. Sampling techniques and the development of high-precision analytical procedures are extremely important in these studies. Salinity and temperature gradients alone are not sufficient, because under these conditions the concept of constancy of composition of seawater is probably not valid, thus making sigma-t relationships questionable. Rigorous chemical methods of sampling and studying the important elements affected by freezing and thawing can lead to a better understanding of the ice–water interface.

Carbon Dioxide Flux

Studies on the general problem of the world's budget of CO_2 and its distribution between the air and the sea have not included the Arctic and subarctic in adequate detail. Implications for world climate make this an important area for research. The partial pressure of carbon dioxide in the water and atmosphere has been measured in detail in other oceans, but few analyses have been made in high latitudes. A few investigations have recently been started, particularly near Barrow, Alaska, although these are confined largely to locations readily accessible from shore.

The classical concept of CO_2 transfer between the oceans and the atmosphere shows CO_2 invading the oceans largely in high latitudes and leaving the oceans in the tropics. However, experimental data have shown that, in much of the tropical and subtropical seas, the CO_2 pressure of the water is lower than that in the atmosphere, indicating a gradient into the sea. It was observed (Hood *et al.*, 1963) that large quantities of CO_2 escaped from the oceans in the areas of upwelling near the South American coast. At all stations in the upwelling zone, the partial pressure was very high with respect to that of the air.

Our understanding of the dynamics of CO_2 exchange in the ocean is limited. The rate of exchange between air and sea and the dependence on environmental conditions is far from understood. The influence of ice cover and surface temperature on the CO_2 problem needs further detailed study.

Geochemical Traverses from Pole to Pole

Most of the deep water of the world ocean comes from the polar regions. Oceanographers have drawn up north–south profiles of such properties as temperature, salinity, density, and dissolved oxygen in order to delineate the spreading of the deep water and its probable paths of flow. These interpretations are limited in two important ways: (1) the available data have been sparse and taken from scattered separate expeditions often separated by many years; and (2) the data are limited to the standard basic properties such as temperature, salinity, and dissolved oxygen. It is impossible to draw up even composite profiles of important geochemical properties because of the scarcity of measurements. The USNS *Eltanin* is capable of obtaining two perfect reference profiles extending from Arctic to Antarctic in both the Pacific and Atlantic Oceans. The station network could be dense

with all stations extending to the bottom, much as was done in *Eltanin* cruises 28 and 29. With its processing laboratories and storage capacity for large samples, the *Eltanin* could obtain dense samples for study of certain important geochemical properties. Data could be obtained on the distribution of radiocarbon, which has proved to be a valuable indicator of the time scale of oceanic circulation but which still has not been sampled in any great quantity in the ocean. A panel of leading geochemists could be called on to determine which types of analyses should be made and which properties should be measured and to set up procedures for carrying out the analyses, as well as to guide the scientific program.

RECOMMENDATIONS

1. Further studies should be made on chemical fingerprinting, especially on organic techniques, in order to enhance knowledge of the complex oceanographic system, including the biological cycle of the sea, transfer processes within water masses, and air–sea interactions.

2. Greater attention should be given to studying ice-water interaction phenomena, especially ionic gradients beneath the ice surface. The mechanism of ice formation in open water, such as leads, and the effect of these on vertical mixing and water-mass formation, sampling techniques, and development of precision analytical procedures are especially critical to this study.

3. Investigations should be encouraged on CO_2 transfer between the Arctic and subarctic oceans and the atmosphere as contributions to the general problem of the earth's CO_2 budget with its implications for world climate.

4. Geochemical traverses should be made from the Arctic to the Antarctic in both the Atlantic and Pacific Oceans in order to better delineate the paths of flow and spreading of deep water.

LOGISTICS

To be worthwhile, scientific programs need continuity and support at adequate levels. This is particularly true in high latitudes where cold, ice, and isolation present severe challenges. Vehicles are required to transport investigators to and from remote sites, and platforms are needed at the sites to support field parties. A vehicle or platform may serve as a base for several different types of investigations; rarely, if ever, does a particular vehicle or platform satisfy all field research programs.

In the Arctic Ocean, we recommend:

1. A semipermanent drifting ice station should be established. This role has been taken by the ice island T-3 in the past; however, a number of additional facilities must be

added to make it a useful research base for the research as recommended.

(a) Improved aircraft support from Point Barrow should be provided for safety and efficiency. A modern, long-range airplane is needed for scientific and cargo flights. The C-130 "Hercules" is ideal for this purpose and could not only support the station but also conduct aeromagnetic and other surveys.

(b) The ice station should be permanently equipped with light aircraft and turbine helicopters. This would allow additional observations to be made on all sides of the station out to a few hundred miles along its drift-path and would result in measurements along a broad swath rather than along a narrow corridor as is now being done.

(c) Adequate power should be provided on the station. Power generators should be installed in such a manner that they can be properly balanced and switched automatically, thus providing even and continuous power. Frequency for scientific instruments should be controlled carefully by means of a special regulator.

(d) Radio communications with the ice stations should be of highest quality so that principal investigators at their home station can speak directly to their assistants on the station through a telephone patch or some such network. The radio facilities should be professionally installed and maintained.

2. Temporary satellite substations should be established on ice floes. T-3 is an anomalously thick piece of ice in comparison with most other ice in the Arctic Ocean and is of freshwater origin. Many oceanographic and biological measurements should be made from a more typical slab of sea ice. Two temporary stations in addition to the semipermanent station would give a triangular array for measurements of ice deformation and ocean currents. These stations should be located about 100 miles from the base station and could be serviced by helicopters.

3. Icebreakers should complement the drift stations and are essential where synoptic oceanographic measurements are required. The U.S. Coast Guard is presently extending the life of the Wind-Class icebreakers and planning for construction of larger, more powerful ships. These efforts are commendable and should be fully supported. Present icebreakers are inadequate for work in the central polar basin. A ship capable of operating in heavy ice throughout the year is necessary for significant geophysical and oceanographic progress. The scientific community should exercise a strong voice in the design of research facilities on new icebreakers.

4. Nuclear-propelled submarines should be used for the collection of bathymetric and some types of geophysical data; they are unrivaled for this purpose in the Arctic Ocean. A few months of cruises by a properly instrumented submarine could accomplish a complete survey of the Arctic Ocean. Submarines can also be used for synoptic hydrographic surveys in ice-covered waters.

5. Shore-based stations to monitor currents should be established at the entrances and exits of the Arctic Ocean. The Cape Prince of Wales, Alaska, station maintained by the Naval Undersea Warfare Center is a valuable national asset and should be maintained and improved. A similar monitoring station is needed for the East Greenland Current. A location at or near Nord in northeast Greenland would be desirable as a base for current observations.

6. Manned ice stations should be supplemented with automatic unmanned stations whenever possible. For routine weather and oceanographic data collection, a network of such stations should be installed on the ice pack. The IRLS (Interrogation, Recording, Location System) is recommended for transmitting data from the station to the continental receiving station. This satellite station has the advantage of providing the geographical coordinates of the station, which is essential in the ever-drifting ice pack.

For the oceans surrounding Antarctica, the Panel recommends:

1. A drifting platform should be established in the Weddell Sea to study the formation of bottom water in the winter. This could be a one-year project. The suitability of drifting barges, ice stations, and obsolete icebreakers as platforms should be examined. The drift would provide opportunity for other oceanographic, geophysical, and biological investigations. Adequate instrumentation should be installed on the platform for measuring atmospheric parameters connected with heat flux which might influence bottom-water formation. A thorough aerial photographic survey of ice in the Weddell Sea in different seasons should be a first step in this project. Both visible and infrared photography should also be considered.

2. The USNS *Eltanin* should continue to be used to its maximum capability. Planning should be flexible to allow for new instruments and changing oceanographic problems; for example, sono-buoys would make seismic refraction work possible from a single ship. A systematic geophysical survey around Antarctica in the almost unexplored sector from 150° E longitude west to 15° W longitude, can contribute significantly to antarctic research.

INTERNATIONAL COOPERATION

Oceanography is truly an international science, largely because the oceans are open to researchers of all nations. Cooperation and exchanges of ideas between countries are necessary for the growth of polar and global oceanography. In Antarctica, exchanges of scientists between nations have been highly successful and rewarding. Unfortunately, such exchanges have not taken place in the Arctic Ocean on the same scale; such international collaboration in Arctic Ocean research is highly desirable.

1. Steps should be taken to explore the possibilities of initiating international cooperative research programs

(a) between the Soviet Union and the United States in the Chukchi Sea;

(b) between Canada, Denmark, and the United States in Baffin Bay; and

(c) between Denmark, Norway, the United States, and perhaps others aimed at monitoring exchanges of water between the Greenland Sea and the Arctic Ocean and supported from research stations at Nord (Greenland) and in Svalbard.

REFERENCES

Calloway, R. J., "Ocean Conditions in the Vicinity of the Aleutian Islands, Summer 1957," *Intern. N. Pacific Fisheries Comm. Bull.* No. 11, pp. 1–29 (1963).

Gordon, A. L., "Geostrophic Transport through the Drake Passage," *Science, 156*, 1732–1734 (1967).

Heirtzler, J. R., G. O. Dickson, E. M. Herron, W. C. Pitman III, and X. LePichon, "Marine Magnetic Anomalies, Geomagnetic Field Reversals, and Motions of the Ocean Floor and Continents," *J. Geophys. Res., 73*, 2119–2136 (1968).

Hood, D. W., D. Berkshire, R. Adams, and I. Supernaw, "$CaCO_3$ Saturation Levels of the Ocean." *Texas A&M Project 295 Rep.* Ref. No. 63-30 (1963).

Marshall, B. V., and A. H. Lachenbruch, "Some Recent Heat-Flow Results from the Arctic Ocean" (abstract), *Trans. Amer. Geophys. Union, 49*, 323–324 (1968).

Nansen, F., "The Oceanographic Problems of the Still Unknown Arctic Regions," in *Problems of Polar Research, Spec. Publ. No. 7*, Amer. Geog. Soc., New York, pp. 3–14 (1928).

Opdyke, N. D., N. Glass, J. D. Hays, and J. Foster, "Paleomagnetic Study of Antarctic Deep-Sea Cores," *Science, 154*, 349–357 (1966).

Ostapoff, F., "A Contribution to the Problems of the Drake Passage Circulation," *Deep-Sea Res., 8*, 111–120 (1961).

Sverdrup, H. U., M. W. Johnson, and R. H. Fleming, *The Oceans*, Prentice-Hall, New York (1942).

BIBLIOGRAPHY

Aagaard, K., "The East Greenland Current North of Denmark Strait," unpublished thesis, University of Washington (1966).

Aagaard, K., "Temperature Variations in the Greenland Sea Deep Water," *Deep-Sea Res., 15*, 1–16 (1968).

Arctic Institute of North America, *Proceedings of the Arctic Basin Symposium, October 1962*, AINA, Tidewater Publishing Corp., p. 313 (1963).

Beal, M. A., The Floor of the Arctic Ocean. One sheet, color, 110 cm x 67 cm. U.S. Navy Electronics Laboratory, San Diego (dated August 1966).

Beal, M. A., "Bathymetry and Structure of the Arctic Ocean," PhD thesis, Oregon State University, Corvallis (1968).

Beal, M. A., F. Edvalson, K. Hunkins, A. Molloy, and N. Ostenso, "The Floor of the Arctic Ocean: Geographic Names," *Arctic, 19*, 215–219 (1966).

Beck, A. E., "Heat Flow Studies," Can. Geol. Surv. Paper No. 67-41, pp. 133–146 (1967).

Bloom, G. L., "Water Transport and Temperature Measurements in the Eastern Bering Strait, 1953-1958," *J. Geophys. Res., 69*, 3335–3353 (1964).

Bodvarsson, G., and G. Palmasson, "Exploration of Subsurface Temperature in Iceland," in *Proceedings of the United Nations Conference on New Sources of Energy, Rome, 1961, 2*, United Nations, New York, pp. 91–98 (1964).

Brennecke, W., "Die ozeanographischen Arbeiten der Deutschen Antarktischen Expedition 1911-1912," *Deut. Seewarte, Arch. Hamburg, 39* (1) (1921).

Cabaniss, G. H., K. L. Hunkins, and N. Untersteiner, *US-IGY Drifting Station Alpha Arctic Ocean 1957-1958*. Air Force Cambridge Res. Lab., Spec. Rep. No. 38 (1965).

Faraday, M., "Terrestrial Magneto-Electric Induction," The Bakerian Lecture, Art. 6, Experimental Researches into Electricity, 2nd Series, Section 5, *Phil. Trans. Roy. Soc. London*, 175–176 (1832).

Farmer, H. G., "Long-Period Time-Dependent Motion in a Polar Ocean," in *Proceedings of the Symposium on the Arctic Heat Budget and Atmospheric Circulation*. (J. O. Fletcher, ed.) The RAND Corp., Santa Monica, Calif. (1966).

Fletcher, J. O., *The Heat Budget of the Arctic Basin and Its Relation to Climate*. RAND Corp. Rep. No. R-444-PR (1965).

Fletcher, J. O., ed., *Proceedings of the Symposium on the Arctic Heat Budget and Atmospheric Circulation*, RAND Memorandum No. RM-5233-NSF (1966).

Gordon, A. L., "Potential Temperature, Oxygen, and Circulation of Bottom Water in the Southern Ocean," *Deep-Sea Res., 13*, 1125–1138 (1966).

Hansen, B. L., and C. C. Langway, Jr., "Deep-Core Drilling in Ice and Core Analysis at Camp Century, Greenland, 1961-1966," *Antarctic J.*, 207–208 (Sept.–Oct. 1966).

Hunkins, K. L., "Ekman Drift Currents in the Arctic Ocean," *Deep-Sea Res., 13*, 607–620 (1966).

Hunkins, K. L., "Inertial Oscillations of Fletcher's Ice Island (T-3)," *J. Geophys. Res., 72*, 1165–1174 (1967).

Ibert, E. R., and D. W. Hood, *The Distribution of Carbon Dioxide between the Atmosphere and the Sea*. Texas A&M Rep. No. 63-9-T on Projects 146 and 234 (1963).

Johnson, G. L., and O. B. Eckhoff, "Bathymetry of the North Greenland Sea," *Deep-Sea Res., 13*, 1161–1173 (1966).

Johnson, G. L., and B. C. Heezen, "The Arctic Mid-oceanic Ridge," *Nature, 215*, 724 (1967).

Johnson, G. L., and B. C. Heezen, "Morphology and Evolution of the Norwegian-Greenland Sea," *Deep-Sea Res., 14*, 755–771 (1967).

Keeling, D. C., N. W. Rakestraw, and L. S. Waterman, "Carbon Dioxide in Surface Waters of the Pacific Ocean I, Measurements of Distribution," *J. Geophys. Res., 70*, 6086 (1965).

Lachenbruch, A. H., "Thermal Effects of the Ocean on Permafrost," *Bull. Geol. Soc. Amer., 68*, 1515–1529 (1957).

Lachenbruch, A. H., and M. C. Brewer, "Dissipation of the Temperature Effect of Drilling a Well in Arctic Alaska," *Bull. Geol. Soc. Amer., 1083-C*, 73–109 (1959).

Lachenbruch, A. H., M. C. Brewer, G. W. Greene, and B. V. Marshall, "Temperatures in Permafrost," in *Temperature—Its Measurement and Control in Science and Industry*, Reinhold Publishing Corp., New York, pp. 791–803 (1962).

Lachenbruch, A. H., G. W. Greene, and B. V. Marshall, "Permafrost and the Geothermal Regimes," in *Environment of the Cape Thompson Region, Alaska*. (N. J. Wilimovsky and J. N. Wolfe, eds.) USAEC Division of Technical Information, Oak Ridge, Tenn., pp. 149–163 (1966).

Lachenbruch, A. H., and B. V. Marshall, "Heat Flow Through the Arctic Ocean Floor: The Canada Basin-Alpha Rise Boundary," *J. Geophys. Res., 71*, 1223–1248 (1966).

Lachenbruch, A. H., and B. V. Marshall, "Heat Flow and Water Temperature Fluctuations in the Denmark Strait," *J. Geophys. Res., 73*, 5829–5842 (1968).

Lee A., and D. Ellette, "On the Water Masses of the Northwest Atlantic Ocean," *Deep-Sea Res., 14*, 183–190 (1967).

Lee, W. H. K., and Seiya Uyeda, "Review of Heat Flow Data," in *Terrestrial Heat Flow, Geophys. Monograph 8.* (W. H. K. Lee, ed.) Amer. Geophys. Union, Washington, D.C., pp. 87–190 (1965).

Lee, W. H. K., and C. S. Cox, "Time Variation of Ocean Temperatures and Its Relations to Internal Waves and Oceanic Heat Flow Measurements," *J. Geophys. Res., 71*, 2101–2111 (1966).

LePichon, X., and J. R. Heirtzler, "Magnetic Anomalies in the Indian Ocean and Sea Floor Spreading," *J. Geophys. Res., 73*, 2101–2117 (1968).

Longuet-Higgins, M. S., "The Electrical and Magnetic Effects of Tidal Streams," *Mon. Not. Roy. Astron. Soc., Geophys. Suppl. 5* (8), 285–307 (1949).

Longuet-Higgins, M. S., M. E. Stern, and H. Stommel, "The Electrical Field Induced by Ocean Currents and Waves, with Applications to the Method of Towed Electrodes," *Papers in Physical Oceanography and Meteorology,* Massachusetts Institute of Technology and Woods Hole Oceanographic Institute of Technology and Woods Hole Oceanographic Institution, *13* (1), 1–37 (1954).

Malkus, W. V. R., and M. E. Stern, "Determination of Transports and Velocities by Electromagnetic Effects," *J. Marine Res., 11*, 97–105 (1952).

Metcalf, G., "A Note on the Water Movement in the Greenland-Norwegian Sea," *Deep-Sea Res., 7*, 190–220 (1960).

Misner, A. D., "Heat Flow and Depth of Permafrost at Resolute Bay, Cornwallis Island, N.W.T., Canada," *Trans. Amer. Geophys. Union, 36*, 1055–1069 (1955).

Mosby, H., "The Waters of the Atlantic Ocean, Norwegian Antarctic Expedition, 1927–1928 et SQQ," *Sci. Results, 1*, Norske Vidensk. Akad., Oslo (1934).

Mosby, H., "Water, Salt, and Heat Balance in the North Polar Sea," in *Proc. of the Arctic Basin Symposium,* AINA, Tidewater Publishing Corp. (1963).

Munk, W. H., "Abyssal Recipes," *Deep-Sea Res., 13*, 707–730 (1966).

Nansen, F. "The Oceanography of the North Polar Basin," *Norwegian North Polar Expedition, 1893–1896, 4,* J. Dybwad, Christiania (1902).

Ostenso, N., *Geophysical Investigations of the Arctic Ocean Basin.* Univ. Wisconsin Geophysical and Polar Research Center, Research Rep. No. 4, Madison (1962).

Paterson, W. S. B., and L. K. Law, "Additional Heat Flow Determinations in the Area of Mould Bay, Arctic Canada," *Can. J. Earth Sci., 3*, 237–246 (1966).

Pitman III, W. C., E. M. Herron, and J. R. Heirtzler, "Magnetic Anomalies in the Pacific and Sea Floor Spreading," *J. Geophys. Res., 73*, 2069–2085 (1968).

Postma, H., "The Exchange of Oxygen and Carbon Dioxide between the Ocean and the Atmosphere," *Netherlands J. Sea Res., 2*, 258–283 (1964).

Smith, E. H., F. M. Soule, and O. Mosby, "Marion and General Greene Expeditions to Davis Strait and Labrador Sea under the Direction of U.S. Coast Guard 1928-1931-1933-1934-1935," Washington, D.C. (1937).

Steele, J. H., J. R. Barrett, and L. V. Worthington, "Deep Currents South of Iceland," *Deep-Sea Res., 9*, 465–474 (1962).

Sykes, L. R., "The Seismicity of the Arctic," *Bull. Seismol. Soc. Amer., 55*, 501–518 (1965).

Tait, J. B., *Hydrography of the Faroe-Shetland Channel 1927-1952.* Scottish Home Dept., Marine Res. Rep. No. 2, Edinburgh (1957).

Takahashi, T., "Carbon Dioxide in the Atmosphere and in the Atlantic Ocean Water," *J. Geophys. Res., 66*, 477–479 (1961).

Thorsteinsson, R., and E. T. Tozer, "Structural History of the Canadian Arctic Archipelago since Precambrian Time," in *Geology of the Arctic, 1,* University of Toronto Press (1961).

Timofiev, V. T., "An Approximate Determination of the Heat Balance of Arctic Basins Waters," *Problems of the Arctic,* No. 4 (in Russian), pp. 23–28 (1958).

Tresnikov, A. F., "Nouvelles donnees sur le relief du fond et sur les laux du bassin, Arctique," *Piroda,* pp. 25–32 (February 1960).

Vogt, P., "A Reconnaissance Geophysical Survey of the North: Norwegian, Greenland, Kara, and Barents Seas and the Arctic Ocean," PhD thesis, University of Wisconsin, Madison (1968).

Vogt, P., and N. Ostenso, unpublished manuscript (1968).

Von Arx, W. S., "An Electromagnetic Method for Measuring the Velocities of Ocean Currents from a Ship Underway," *Papers in Physical Oceanography and Meteorology,* Massachusetts Institute of Technology and Woods Hole Oceanographic Institution, *11* (3), 1–61 (1950).

Wertheim, G. K., *Studies of the Electrical Potential between Key West, Florida, and Havana, Cuba.* Woods Hole Oceanographic Institution Rep. 54-68, *No. 2,* also in *Trans. Amer. Geophys. Union, 35*, 872–882 (1954).

Whitman, K., "An Anomaly in Geomagnetic Variations at Mould Bay in the Arctic Archipelago of Canada," *Geophys. J., 8*, 26–43 (1963).

Wilson, J. T., "Some Rules for Continental Drift," in *Continental Drift.* (G. D. Garland, ed.) University of Toronto Press, pp. 3–17 (1966).

Worthington, L. V., "Oceanographic Results of Project Skijump I and Skijump II in the Polar Sea, 1951–1952," *Trans. Amer. Geophys. Union, 34*, 543–551 (1953).

Worthington, L. V., and G. Volkmann, "The Volume Transport of the Norwegian Sea Overflow in the North Atlantic," *Deep-Sea Res., 12*, 667–676 (1965).

Young, F. B., H. Gerrard, and W. Jevons, "On Electrical Disturbances due to Tides and Waves," *Phil. Mag., 40* (235), 149–159 (1920).

4

Polar Glaciology[*]

INTRODUCTION

Within the past half-century, the concept of glaciology has expanded from the classical study of glaciers to encompass the occurrence and evolution—past, present, and perhaps predictable future—of natural ice in all its forms on and within the surface layer of the earth and other celestial bodies and is beginning to embrace glaciological engineering to become a widely interdisciplinary field of science.

The engineering and economic aspects of glaciology are rapidly acquiring importance in the light of the increasing feasibility of doing things that have been considered impossible in the past.

1. Spring and summer snowmelt profoundly affects the flow of water available to cities, farms, and power stations, especially in our western states. The beneficial effects of runoff control (by methods that accelerate or inhibit the rate of snow melting) could be enormous. The impact associated with seasonal snow and ice on the economy of the northern and central United States clearly justifies the modest cost of a comprehensive appraisal of the feasibility of application of new means to control this runoff.

2. The pressure of population density and the necessity of increasing crop and pasture acreage may require development of agriculture in the far northern plains of North America where there are enormous areas in which summer temperatures and sunlight are quite adequate for good plant growth. The impediment lies in the poor soil, in its high ice content, and in the choice of suitable crop or pasture plants.

*A report, "Glaciology in the Arctic," prepared by the Glaciology Panel of the Committee on Polar Research, was published in the *Transactions of the American Geophysical Union,* Volume 48, pp.759–767 (June 1967). Most of that report, with minor editorial changes, is included in this chapter and appendixes.

The scale of northern agriculture can be increased; however, an appraisal of the prospective cost of developing it cannot be made without much more research on the nature of permafrost soils and on their reaction to agricultural practices. Close to one third of the combined land area of the United States and Canada lies above the 55th parallel; it supports a population of only approximately one-half million people. Its development may proceed too slowly if unaided by an explicit policy of concerted effort. It would appear that development of agriculture on a larger scale, initially subsidized but self-sustaining in the long run, is a strong possibility, especially in proportion to the development of large-scale control of total environment (the "astrodome" concept).

3. A major resource of the North American arctic and subarctic lands is fresh water. Only in Alaska and western Canada do abundant, currently unused supplies of fresh water exist. Major schemes have been proposed to transport this water southward. These interregional water-transfer plans pose major challenges to the glaciologist.

PROBLEMS OF GLACIOLOGY

Most of the problems of glaciology concern the relation of snow and ice to the environment in which they form and evolve. This environment is quantified by a set of climatic parameters. On a global scale, the mechanism appears to be predominantly "one-way," that is, climate and the general circulation of the atmosphere essentially determine where snow, ice, and frozen ground can exist. Large-scale feedback mechanisms have been postulated but not substantiated by quantitative argument. On smaller scales, there is no doubt that ice and climate influence each other; on these scales, the possibility of human interference poses a host of challenging problems.

The glaciologist has to deal with the effects of two characteristics of climate: (1) the annual cycle and its irregularities and (2) the secular (longer-time) changes. The "easy" problems of glaciology are concerned with such things as the inventory (size, shape, and location of ice masses) and with physical properties, such as density, temperature, deformation, and metamorphism. The "difficult" problems deal with the effects of weather and the annual climatic cycle; they have to do with the exchange of energy and water substance across a number of interfaces. Of particular practical interest are the effects of the annual cycle and addition, subtraction, and local redistribution of ice and water masses and man's endeavor to modify these effects artificially, in an attempt to control the flow of economically valuable water. The "very difficult" problems have to do with the effects of secular climatic changes on the nature and spatial distribution of ice masses. It is probable that the easily observable and quantitatively recordable changes in the nature and distribution of snow, ice, and frozen ground faithfully reflect secular climatic changes. In some situations, for instance in the distribution of perennial snowfields, the influence of secular change is almost instantaneous. In other cases, such as valley glaciers, there is a time lag of decades to centuries with respect to advance, retreat, and gross mass balance. Larger ice caps and continental ice sheets may react in some ways to climatic change with a time delay of millennia to hundreds of millennia. Hence by studying many different modes of reaction to climatic change, the glaciologist is investigating reactions whose time lag reflects events extending from almost zero time to perhaps a million years into the past. He is mainly concerned with the near end of this time lag. The further he moves down the time scale, the less data he can hope to obtain, but such an approach is valuable because high-frequency effects have decayed (i.e., the signal-to-noise ratio should improve with increase in time from the present).

The *glacial geologist*, by studying evidence of past glaciation, deals with the middle-to-far end of the time span of the climatic-influence function. To him, a thousand years is often compressed into a minor detail.

The *biologist*, especially the botanist, plays an important role in this general endeavor to define quantitatively the relationship between glaciers and climate. Biological phenomena, mainly the plant cover, greatly influence the flow of heat and water onto and through the earth's surface. This flow determines the extent of presently or previously frozen ground, where much of the evidence of past climatic change lies buried and is difficult to decipher.

Synoptic meteorology is a key discipline. It is beginning to provide the first useful numerical models of distribution and evolution of synoptic climatic patterns. These models are representations of large-scale atmospheric circulation patterns, calculated by large computers. The usefulness of the computer output depends on the quality of both the numerical model and the input data. The input data consist partly of energy-balance values covering fairly large areas.

In this approach it becomes advisable for the glaciologist to shift his emphasis in a number of investigations, from *point observations* (for instance, measurement of temperature, wind, and radiation at one or several points on a glacier) to *area observations*. The latter, usually much more difficult, yield the more valuable synoptic data necessary for cause and effect correlation.

Two powerful new tools are becoming available: the geodetic satellites, which permit measurement of deformation of large bodies (air masses, sea-ice covers, and large glaciers), and remote sensing by aircraft and satellites, which permits measurement of average values of such parameters as radiation, temperature, and humidity over small and large areas.

RESEARCH AREAS AND PRIORITIES

Eight major problems in glaciology have been identified, in two groups:

Group A Most timely and urgent to man's understanding of his environment and his ability to use this knowledge for efficient utilization and management of resources, in order of priority:

1. Sea-ice energy balance and dynamics
2. Snow-cover research and control
3. Glacier surges and the sliding of a glacier on its bed

Group B Five additional important problem areas (in no order of priority):

1. Energy-balance studies of glaciers
2. Flow and diffusion through snow and frozen ground
3. Ice formation in running water
4. Physical properties of ice
5. Quaternary glaciology

These eight problem areas, and aspects of international cooperation, are discussed in the sections that follow; the appendixes contain more-detailed reports of arctic and antarctic glaciology and of snow research and control. The present review does not attempt to survey the current status of glaciological research as a whole. Accordingly, it should be understood that there is no intent to de-emphasize those basic, on-going research trends in glaciology whose significance and importance are well established. Rather, attention is directed toward those problems and techniques where new or increased emphasis seems warranted and should lead to the most rapid advances toward solutions of problems of practical and theoretical importance. These problems are characterized by (a) newly developed theories, techniques, and capabilities (observational or computational) and (b) needs and possibilities to study environmental factors on a large scale and on an interdisciplinary basis.

SEA ICE: ENERGY BALANCE AND DYNAMICS

Sea ice accounts (in areal extent) for approximately two thirds of the earth's ice cover. In the Arctic, its thickness is about 3 m; in the Antarctic, about 2 m. Compared with the Greenland and Antarctic Ice Sheets, it is only a thin veneer of ice, but its large areal extent has great importance because of the major influence of sea ice on heat exchange in the oceans and on the exchange between the ocean and atmosphere. The extent of arctic sea-ice cover, averaging about 15×10^{16} cm^2, undergoes fluctuations of 15–20 percent between its annual maximum and minimum, and aperiodic, year-to-year variations of the ice boundary in the north Atlantic amount to several hundred kilometers. In the Antarctic, the extent of sea ice undergoes much larger seasonal variations. In general, sea-ice cover appears to be one of the most variable physical features of the earth's surface.

The important scientific problems of the interaction among oceanic circulation, sea ice, and the atmospheric heat balance and circulation are related to the practical possibility of artificially influencing climate on a large scale. Although the scope of these problems extends well beyond the field of glaciology, the Glaciology Panel believes that ice is a pivotal factor.

ARCTIC SEA-ICE COVER: STABLE OR UNSTABLE?

The inherent instability of the arctic sea-ice cover could result in its removal by natural or human influences. Removal of an unstable sea-ice cover would, in turn, presumably have profound influences on the climate of the northern hemisphere. At least three conflicting views exist on this question:

1. There is an alternation between an ice-free and ice-covered Arctic Ocean as a result of various influences, including change of sea level.
2. The sea-ice cover is unstable: if it were destroyed, the arctic heat balance would be altered toward conditions that would prevent reforming of the sea-ice cover.
3. The sea-ice cover is stable, that is, equilibrium conditions favor a sea-ice cover. If the cover were removed, it would re-establish itself within a few years.

These hypotheses cannot be conclusively proved or disproved without consideration of the entire ocean–atmosphere circulation with all its ramifications. For instance, it seems possible that increased heat advection into the Arctic, instead of causing more ice to melt, might lead to a greater

production of ice: increased circulation (higher wind velocities) causes more ice deformation, divergence, and a greater number of open leads. During most of the year, the heat loss from open water is two orders of magnitude greater than from thick ice. If the increase of the area of open water is substantial, even an excessive anomaly of heat advection cannot compensate for the local loss, and the result will be an increased ice production.

Important evidence concerning stability of sea-ice cover may be found in the sedimentary record on the floors of the oceans. It has recently been shown that there is strong evidence for the uninterrupted existence of sea ice on the Arctic Ocean during the last 70,000 years. Some uranium isotope analyses indicate that the present, slow rate of sedimentation of about 0.2 cm/1000 years may have prevailed for the last 150,000 years. This evidence, *per se*, does not provide proof either for or against the theory of instability of the sea-ice cover. However, it strongly contradicts ice-age theories requiring rapid variability.

The further pursuit of this highly promising research will require longer cores than have been taken so far: cores reaching back into the Tertiary, covering a span of time during which major climatic changes are known to have occurred, and also cores taken at specific locations, particularly near the present edge of the sea ice, in order to investigate possible variations of its extent in the past.

NUMERICAL MODELS OF ATMOSPHERE AND OCEAN

The instability hypotheses may soon be tested by high-speed digital computers that allow the numerical evaluation of model atmospheres and oceans. Because of present computer limitations, these models cannot now make full use of the input information available (boundary conditions, distribution of heat sources). However, new computers are forthcoming whose enormous capacity and speed will allow more complete solutions. The accuracy of these solutions will be limited only by the accuracy and adequacy of the input data rather than by oversimplifications of the model. The input data for such models are clearly deficient for the arctic regions: *an observational program to fill these gaps is needed.*

An analysis of all available data on the heat balance indicates no major inconsistencies with observed ice conditions. For the ice-free ocean, the surprising conclusion is that, in summer, the atmosphere would receive less energy and would be cooler than at present. The result would be an increased meridional temperature gradient and more vigorous zonal circulation in the atmosphere as a whole, contrary to what one might expect with a smaller meridional temperature gradient along the surface. Also, the annual surface heat balance with or without ice would be close to zero; thus, the question of "instability" remains open.

SEA ICE: VOLUME, CONDITION, AND DYNAMICS

Another series of unanswered questions concerns the present amount and condition of the sea ice and its dynamics. Aircraft and submarine observations lead to some apparently irreconcilable conclusions. According to one set of data, the most frequent ice thickness in the Arctic is 2 m. This would mean that most ice is less than 2 years old and that the rate of ice production is several times greater than previously believed. If this ice production were to go into ridging, the mean thickness would have to be greater than indicated by submarine observations. If it goes into ice export (Greenland Sea) the previous export estimates are too low.

Infrared imagery from aircraft shows an area of open water in the Arctic Ocean of roughly 10 percent throughout the year. This figure seems to be in keeping with the relatively large quantity of young ice but contradicts much of the supposedly well-established knowledge of the heat budget. Experiments indicate that the annual heat loss of open water is about 17.5 kJ m^{-2}, two orders of magnitude greater than that of old ice. If the aircraft observations are correct, the heat budget of the entire ocean would be essentially determined by the open leads; the heat exchange over old ice would be of minor influence.

The purported size of the area of open water emphasizes the need for an understanding of the large-scale dynamics. In a theoretical model, it was necessary to treat the ice as a fluid of very high viscosity, which leads, for the mean annual ice flux, to an unrealistically great convergence in the region of the Pacific gyral. In reality, the strength of large sheets of natural sea ice must be highly anisotropic, with a high resistance to compression and shear and almost no resistance to extension. Such anisotropies could be incorporated into a theoretical model if the respective numbers were known.

RECOMMENDATIONS

Theoretical Work

The following recommendations are listed in descending order of importance; full use should be made of modern computers in implementing them:

1. Models should be developed of existing air, ice, and ocean circulation patterns, sea-ice conditions, and energy fluxes to predict atmospheric circulation and precipitation patterns for conditions different from the present ones, e.g., for an open Arctic Ocean, for glacierized continents, or for both or for a deglacierized Greenland or Antarctica.

2. Calculations of sea-ice deformation and movement by wind, including ice and water stresses, should be refined and continued, particularly for nonsteady conditions. This will require presently unavailable information on large-scale deformation in sea ice.

Experimental Work

An order of priority cannot be assigned to these diverse recommendations:

1. Year-round observations should be made of all radiative processes in the arctic atmosphere, including (a) total emission from the top of the atmosphere (by satellite), (b) shortwave and long-wave flux divergences (by aircraft and radiometer sonde), and (c) long-wave emissivities of typical arctic clouds.

2. Measurements should be made of surface albedo, areal averages, and changes with season, by regularly scheduled aircraft, and of the relation to the onset of snowmelt circulation patterns and heat advection.

3. The relationship between heat balance and ice thickness should be studied. This relationship can, except for very thick ice, be estimated from surface temperature as measured by airborne infrared radiometers.

4. The amount of open water should be investigated as a function of location and season (including extent of meltwater puddles), and the possible role of the Arctic Ocean as a source of precipitation for the surrounding land areas.

5. The distribution of ice thickness values, including frequency and size of pressure ridges, should be measured. It is of particular importance to know whether there are changes from year to year and, if so, how great they are. Standard profiles, at least one per year (at the same time of year) should be taken by submarine.

6. Ocean currents, particularly the flow of water in and out of the Arctic Ocean and ice export into the Greenland Sea (magnitude and variability), should be studied.

7. The relationship of year-to-year changes of the sea-ice boundary in the North Atlantic to oceanic circulation patterns should be determined.

8. The dynamics of ice movement in the interior of the Arctic Ocean, in particular, the deformation of the pack ice (correlation of air stress divergence with ice flux divergence), should be determined. This will require a network of stations with accurate positioning and observations of the air and water stresses.

9. Ocean-bottom cores of at least 10-m length should be acquired from predetermined locations on rises and ridges in the central Arctic Ocean and along a profile from the present edge of the pack ice into the Barents Sea. In addition to the lithologic and paleontologic analyses of the cores, ^{18}O/^{16}O ratios should be determined in order to establish paleotemperatures.

10. Physical properties of sea ice should be studied in greater detail. Special attention should be given to: (a) the

radiative and dielectric properties, particularly in connection with modern methods of remote sensing, (b) all processes pertaining to the partition of liquid and solid phase (e.g., oriented crystal growth and solute entrapment), (c) brine migration and desalination under both natural and artificial conditions.

11. Observational techniques and theoretical considerations developed in the study of arctic sea ice should be applied to the more "logistically difficult" problem of the antarctic pack ice.

ANTARCTIC PACK ICE

Seasonal variations in the area covered by pack ice are much larger in the Antarctic than in the Arctic. Under present climatic conditions the maximum area of antarctic pack ice is about 20×10^{16} cm^2 (8 percent of the southern hemisphere) and the minimum is approximately 3×10^{16} cm^2, whereas in the Arctic, the maximum and minimum are roughly 16×10^{16} cm^2 and 14×10^{16} cm^2, respectively. Thus the pack-ice area is greater in the Antarctic than in the Arctic and also undergoes much larger seasonal variations. Longer-term variations and their influence on global climate are probably also much larger in the Antarctic. The meager data available on past variations of ice extent are consistent with this premise but are very incomplete. The investigation of relationships between antarctic pack-ice extent and global climate is the central theme which should give coherence and purpose to future programs in antarctic seas. Two principal aspects of such programs deserve elaboration: (a) investigation of contemporary interaction between ice extent and global climate, with emphasis on discovering cause and effect relationships; (b) determination of past extent of antarctic pack ice, especially during periods of global climatic extremes.

Contemporary Interaction between Antarctic Ice Extent and Global Climate

To gain an understanding of the physical processes involved, it is of fundamental importance to observe systematically the limits of the pack ice and the amount of open water within the pack, in both time and space. To interpret large-scale time and space variations of pack ice in terms of heat exchange between ocean and atmosphere, detailed studies will be necessary, in certain regions, of the physical processes by which heat is exchanged, of the resulting growth and dissipation of ice, and of the related physical effects on ocean and atmosphere. The surface cooling and salinification lead to the formation of most of the bottom water for the world ocean. The questions of where this heat exchange takes place and how the dense surface waters sink to the

bottom and drain into the deep ocean are central questions of physical oceanography. Upward from the surface, the warming and modification of the atmosphere by oceanic heat and moisture influences atmospheric circulation in important ways. The detailed formulation of field programs to study these processes calls for much ingenuity and effort and will probably require coordinated observations at the surface and by instrumented aircraft through all seasons of the year.

Extent of Antarctic Pack Ice during Periods of Paleoclimatic Extremes

Although secular variations of antarctic ice extent seem to be among the more important factors influencing global climate, it is very difficult to determine from field evidence just how great these variations have been in the past or, indeed, even the direction of such variations. For example, it would be of great value to know the extent of antarctic sea ice during the mid-eighteenth-century cooling, the warm epoch of 900–1200 A.D., and the Hypsithermal from *ca.* 7000 to 600 B.C. Eventually we hope to simulate the global climate of these periods, using mathematical models of atmospheric and oceanic circulation, but the formulation of conditions to be simulated should be based on observational evidence. Certain indirect approaches to this problem show promise. For example, rates of snow deposition at the South Pole seem to bear a definite relation to pack-ice extent observed in the Weddell Sea since 1903. Since deposition records can be determined for a much longer time series, it may be possible to draw inferences about former pack-ice extent. More direct evidence may become available from study of bottom sediments and the regime of the pack ice.

SNOW RESEARCH AND CONTROL*

The winter snow cover is widely utilized for water supply, as a hydroelectric reservoir, for recreation, and as an aid to transportation. Man's purposeful interference with the natural character of winter snow has been relatively minor. Most applied snow research has been strongly oriented toward such missions as forecasting runoff, improving water yield, or controlling snow avalanches. A strong flavor of empiricism permeates many aspects of snow science. The results of empirical methods are not in keeping with the pace of modern science and technology or with human needs. The scientific research needed to provide the basis for technical advances in snow utilization and control has been highly uneven and in many cases is lacking. Part of this lack is due to the complexities of dealing with such a transient and

*See Appendix C for fuller discussion of this topic.

variable three-phase system as the winter snow cover, and part is due to the absence of substantial commitments of funding and support to such research. Scientific research on the winter snow cover deserves attention from the glaciological and general scientific community because, of all geophysical phenomena, the snow cover is one of the most accessible and amenable to artificial controls. Research on the snow cover also provides an important connection between meteorology, hydrology, and glaciology: for instance, only in the form of a deposited snow pack can the distribution of precipitation be directly measured.

LARGE-SCALE PHENOMENA

For many purposes, only the bulk properties of snow are significant. An extensive and persistent snow cover interacts with large-scale weather phenomena. Snow modification on a continental scale—at present, a very remote prospect—might profoundly alter climate. In the large-scale view, the economic effects of snow are dominated by its function as a water reservoir.

A New Approach to Snow Hydrology

Measuring water storage in winter snow and forecasting its runoff is the province of snow hydrology. Improvement in snow hydrology requires a fundamental reassessment of methods. Required accuracies can be achieved only by considering the ice-mass and energy balances of hydrologic basins. A firm theoretical basis is needed to describe snow accumulation and ablation over large areas. Especially critical are the large-scale processes of energy exchange between snow and the atmosphere, for these determine the character of snowmelt and occurrence of floods. Meteorological satellites that can scan atmospheric water-vapor profiles over large areas offer the intriguing prospect that accurate flux divergence measurements combined with energy-balance measurements and routine hydrological observations can be used to calculate snow-cover storage in lieu of estimates based on widely scattered ground samples. Spacecraft could also be designed to report the amount of snow-covered area over large regions on a daily basis, and these data could be related to large-scale meteorological analyses. However, the vapor flux divergence and the snow-covered area measurements will require development of new data-handling procedures; a prodigious amount of new information will be produced.

Artificial Regulation of Snow Storage

Management of snow as a water resource depends on alteration of the winter snow cover over large areas and will be related to modifications in the local climate. Such artificial

control seems to be possible, but no fully effective techniques have yet been developed. Forest management has been tested: it has the advantage of maximum aesthetic appeal; a disadvantage is the slow rate of growth of vegetation at high altitudes and latitudes. For this reason, experiments need to be performed simultaneously with a wide variety of plants in as many different climates and soils as possible.

SMALL-SCALE PHENOMENA

Most snow management and engineering research today is being done in the domain of small-scale phenomena, i.e., phenomena related to the internal structure of the snow cover.

While knowledge is reasonably well developed for some snow properties (the mechanics of high-density snow is probably the best example) there are some notable gaps, including the character of liquid and gas diffusion in snow and the role of crystallographic structure in determining such physical properties as strength and thermal conductivity.

Improved instrumentation is needed for reliably recording and telemetering snow depth, for the *in situ* measurement of snow crystal types and mechanical properties, for measurement of wind transport of snow, and for the rapid and accurate determination of free-water content.

AREAL STUDIES

The duration, distribution, temperature, and water content of winter snow are mostly known today from scattered observations at points on the ground. The assessment of snow conditions on an area-wide basis would open up a new dimension in snow hydrology and meteorology for scientific study as well as management. The rapid technological development of both passive and active sensors for aircraft and satellites points to the realization of such techniques in the near future. Satisfactory snow survey sensors depend on accurate knowledge of the dielectric and reflective properties at infrared and microwave wavelengths and the way these properties are affected by surface roughness, snow density, crystal structure, and free-water content. The *in situ* measurement of factors affecting the microwave dielectric properties is especially required, because laboratory tests cannot provide the necessary ground truth for operational tests of sensors.

The environmental effects on snow—the relation of snow-cover structure to climatology—is also a neglected field for which very few quantitative data are available, although these effects are important to such diverse interests as avalanche forecasting and satellite surveys of snow distribution. The climatic differences in snow structure are large. The systematic, long-term acquisition of snow data in different climates requires minimal instrumentation. Trained observers, undisturbed and accessible observation sites, and a standardized program of data collection and reporting are essential.

There is a serious deficit of information about the variations of snow conditions in mountainous terrain. Orographic effects on winter precipitation cause large differences in snowfall over short distances. These same effects strongly determine the patterns of wind, temperature, moisture, and radiation which control snowmelt. Local variations in water storage in mountainous terrain are thus ultimately determined by local weather patterns over distances of a few kilometers. The distribution of avalanche paths and their relative activity are also controlled by the interaction of local storm winds and terrain.

RECOMMENDATIONS

Many of the recommendations can best be implemented by establishing basic snow research stations in a few carefully selected but widely different climates. These stations should be specifically oriented toward comprehensive studies (at all scales) of winter snow within the broad framework of modern glaciology.

1. A sound theoretical framework should be developed describing the accumulation and ablation of winter snow in large river basins.

2. Emphasis should be placed on forest management as the primary practical means of manipulating winter snow to the advantage of man.

3. Basic research studies are needed on the diffusion of fluids through snow.

4. Investigations should be made into the metamorphism and mechanical properties (especially rheology) of snow.

5. Basic instruments required for snow research should be developed.

6. A comprehensive investigation of mesoscale snow and weather phenomena in mountainous terrain should be initiated.

7. Research should be accelerated on the remote sensing of the snow cover.

8. A systematic data-acquisition network should be established to determine the relations of snow-cover structure to climate on a synoptic and long-term basis.

9. A series of informal working conferences should be held among scientists and engineers familiar with the various scales of snow phenomena. An interchange of ideas and exploration of a common terminology would be fruitful.

10. Careful consideration should be given to the possibility that many of the recommendations relating to snow research and control can best be implemented by basic snow research stations in a few carefully selected but widely divergent climates.

GLACIER SURGES AND SLIDING OF A GLACIER ON ITS BED

The cause and dynamics of surges and the exact mechanism of the sliding of a glacier on its bed are the two outstanding problems remaining to be solved in the field of glacier mechanics. It appears very likely that these problems are closely connected. Until these problems are solved, it will not be possible to relate glacier variations quantitatively to changes in climate or to other causes.

The majority of glaciers flow at rather slow and constant rates (a few centimeters to 1 m per day) and advance and retreat slowly in accordance with changes in the climate. Surging glaciers, on the other hand, periodically discharge an ice reservoir in a short interval (a few months to a few years) with sudden increases in ice flow rates to very high values (which may exceed 1 m or more per hour). Ice displacements during surges are often measured in kilometers and frequently exceed 10 percent of the glacier's length. After a surge, the glacier enters a period of "quiescence" lasting from 10 to over 100 years, during which time its speed of flow is as slow as, or slower than, that of normal glaciers. This cycle tends to be repeated at more or less regular intervals. Surging glaciers can be recognized even during quiescent periods by their unique surface features. In western North America, more than 200 glaciers displaying such features have been identified, but these represent less than 1 percent of the glaciers of the region. All evidence so far suggests that the period and timing of the surges is determined by some unique condition in the individual glacier; no relation to short-term external causes (such as changes in climate or shaking by earthquakes) has been demonstrated.

Have the great ice sheets ever surged? One ice-age theory already has been constructed on the assumption that the Antarctic Ice Sheet periodically surges and that its next surge will be the start of the next ice age. Should a large segment of the Antarctic or the Greenland Ice Sheets ever surge, the world's sea level would rise quickly by a significant and possibly disastrous amount. In studies of the fluctuations of the ice sheets that existed in the last ice age, it is usually assumed that these fluctuations are directly caused by changes of climate; glacier variations have been used to refine climatic histories. However, if these ice sheets or the existing Antarctic Ice Sheet surged, the argument would be reversed: a surging ice sheet would have an effect on the albedo of the earth, land, and ocean areas and would certainly cause, not be caused by, a pervasive change in climate.

RECOMMENDATIONS

1. Instrumentation should be developed for measuring sliding of a glacier on its bed. How surging (as well as nonsurging) glaciers slide over their beds appears to be the cen-

tral problem, which is far from solution because we have no instruments for measuring sliding and there are no direct measurements of sliding in the deeper parts of surging or nonsurging glaciers. Slippage measurements should be made on nonsurging glaciers and on surging glaciers before and after they have surged. The condition of the basal ice in contact with the bed should be given additional study in the hope that it may reveal sliding mechanisms. Tunneling along the bed is presently the only method for getting the necessary information, but some observations can be made on the exposed basal ice of small surging glaciers which have long been quiescent.

2. Studies should be initiated on soon-to-surge glaciers. Recent work has made it possible to predict which of the many glaciers in Alaska, British Columbia, and the Yukon are likely to surge in the near future. A few of these glaciers that may soon surge should be selected and extensively studied in their presurge condition. They should be studied continuously until they surge, while they surge, and after they have surged. Studies have begun on one small glacier which is expected to surge soon. Although it is reasonably certain that this glacier alternates between inactivity and sudden, brief advances, the flow velocities to be expected are completely unknown and may not be of the same order of magnitude as the large surging glaciers which have been observed. To ensure a better chance of obtaining more complete information, at least one soon-to-surge glacier study should be made on a larger glacier in a different climatic environment. Because water lubrication is a suspected cause of surges, the runoff of water at the terminus of a soon-to-surge glacier (and that from several neighboring nonsurging glaciers for control) should be monitored continuously. Water pressure might be monitored in bore holes drilled to the bed of a glacier.

3. The nonrandom distribution of surging glaciers should be explained. Can geologic studies (rock type, nature of the bed material, structure, permeability, groundwater pressure), comparing areas of surging glaciers with areas of nonsurging glaciers, reveal distinctive differences?

4. Heat flow under glaciers should be measured. Since a large glacier is a relatively constant-temperature "lid" on the crust of the earth, it may be possible, by drilling through the center of a large glacier in an area of fairly simple topography, to obtain a measure of the geothermal heat flow. Several such drilling experiments might settle the question of the importance of abnormal heat flow on the cause of surges. Also, this drilling program could include instrumentation to measure subglacial pore-water pressure, glacier-ice temperature, englacial water pressure, and other parameters which might affect bedslip and the development of surges. If feasible, these experiments should be performed in both surging and nonsurging glaciers in order to contrast conditions. Feasibility calculations should be made on this experiment.

5. The characteristics and types of surging glaciers need detailed study. Are there two distinctive, exclusive classes of glaciers (surging and nonsurging), or do all the gradations of behavior occur? Some glaciers appear to be borderline cases, but quantitative field studies are necessary to determine whether this is so. Is the instability which leads to spectacular surges possible (at a reduced scale) in all glaciers? Are there several classes or types of surging glaciers? Most of what we know about surges is derived from aerial reconnaissance studies. It is likely that some increase in this activity coupled with much more effort on the ground would produce useful new information.

6. Wave-motion and ice-velocity patterns observed in surges should be duplicated with numerical models of three-dimensional, time-dependent glacier flow. These models should include a bedslip relation derived from modern theory and a realistic flow law, in an attempt to duplicate surge behavior and thus to gain insight into how the decoupling from the bed occurs. Also, a search should be made in numerical modeling and theoretical studies for the possibility that certain parameters, such as those of bedrock and mass balance, might make a stable longitudinal profile impossible.

7. Pleistocene ice-sheet surges should be investigated. A search should be made for evidence that any of the great continental ice sheets has surged. Sudden increases in sea level resulting from such an ice sheet spreading out to sea might be considered the most direct and accessible evidence, but other evidences should be sought. Theoretical studies of the possibility and consequences of a major ice-sheet surge should be vigorously pursued.

8. A glaciological contingency fund should be established. Many glacier surges run their complete course in about a year, which is about the usual time necessary to organize, propose, fund, and begin a research project. Consequently, only the waning stages and the aftereffects of surges have been studied in any detail. An emergency or contingency fund should be established to permit a small group of glaciologists to go into the field within days, or at the most within a few weeks, upon notice of any sudden and important glaciological event. One task of this group could be to set up hydrologic, photogrammetric, and geophysical programs when a major surge develops. Careful selection of the group *and* the event is, of course, necessary, but once the decision is made, sufficient money should be made available promptly so that the important preliminary stages can be properly documented.

ENERGY-BALANCE STUDIES OF GLACIERS

The existence of any form of ice or snow is largely dependent on its surface energy (heat) balance. This balance is subject to great variations at all time and space scales, and it has proved most elusive to scientific inquiry.

For many years, attempts have been made to measure simultaneously the energy and mass balance of a glacier to derive a cause and effect understanding of the interplay between climatic changes and glacier variations. Mass balances are relatively easy to measure, whereas energy balances are difficult even with the best available instruments. Therefore, the literature now contains an undesirable bias. Hydrologists have attempted combined measurements of energy balance, mass balance, and runoff from mountain snowpacks, but the energy-balance measurements have not been sufficiently rigorous, comprehensive, or sustained to provide the understanding necessary for a useful step forward in snowmelt forecasting. Similar problems have been encountered in the study of sea and lake ice and frozen ground.

Some terms in the energy balance, such as turbulent heat transfer, are difficult to measure directly and have been measured only for short periods during optimum conditions. Work is now under way to develop automatic weather stations, but none of them is being operated along with an intensive, manned energy-balance program. This is the only way automatic stations can be truly tested and evaluated.

Another aspect of this difficult problem in methodology is the extension of results obtained at single points to provide values averaged over larger areas. Good micrometeorological instrumentation is expensive, and placing sufficiently large numbers of these installations over a test area is a completely impractical way to derive valid areal results.

RECOMMENDATIONS

1. Continuous heat-balance studies should be made at selected sites. Rather than perform fragmented and unsophisticated energy-balance measurements in many areas, we should now undertake rigorous, accurate, long-term, continuous heat-balance studies at selected glaciers, snowpack experimental areas, and other important glaciological sites. Automatic stations should be tested in conjunction with these programs. Only in this way will it be possible to discover "simple" and useful correlations between easily measured energy parameters, such as shortwave radiation, and mass and water balances of glaciers and snowpacks.

2. Since the ultimate need is to determine energy balances of areas and not of points, efforts should be made to exploit the development of remote-sensing instrumentation, especially in the infrared and microwave parts of the spectrum. This could include ground-based and/or airborne radiometers. Such measurements can be properly evaluated only if they are done in the vicinity of a comprehensive energy-balance measurement site, and if essential ground-truth information (such as moisture content and snow temperatures) is collected at many different locations in the terrain.

FLOW AND DIFFUSION THROUGH SNOW AND FROZEN GROUND

The movement of liquid water and other substances through snow is a complex process because the flow proceeds in an irregular and unstable way depending on slight variations in permeability and thermal conductivity, and the mass flow is accompanied by large heat flows as phase changes take place. It is impossible to predict water flow from a warming snowpack, because we cannot define quantitatively the rate-controlling processes. This is of great practical importance in an understanding of snowmelt runoff, glacier runoff in winter and spring, and rain-on-snow floods. Also, these heat and water-substance flow and diffusion processes control the metamorphism of the snow, and since we cannot predict the flow and diffusion rates, we cannot accurately predict the structural changes in a snowpack. These structural changes largely determine snow avalanche hazard and the pressure due to snow creep on structures.

Another manifestation of the same process is the movement of water and solutes through porous ground at temperatures below 0°C. In this case the situation is even more complex, with heat and mass flow rates being dependent on subtle and poorly understood interactions between thermodynamic and hydraulic processes. It is impossible to utilize groundwater supplies properly or to dispose of sewage and other contaminants in the ground in areas of perennial or seasonal frozen ground if we do not understand the basic mechanisms involved. In fact, the whole state of knowledge of surface–groundwater interactions, so vital to modern hydrologic utilization and management, breaks down when the ground begins to freeze and the movement of groundwater interacts with the temperature field. This is of obvious and immediate impact in those areas where permafrost occurs; it is perhaps of more subtle but greater total importance in the larger, more populous areas where there is deep seasonal freezing but no permafrost.

RECOMMENDATIONS

1. Theories of the thermodynamic–hydraulic processes of flow and diffusion in snow and frozen ground should be developed. Unsolved problems include how the rate of water flow is controlled by refreezing, how the hydraulic properties of a participating medium (e.g., ice particles) are modified by the mass and heat fluxes, how these processes work in a medium that is partly inert (e.g., soil particles), and how complications such as capillary tension and water pumping to a freezing interface affect the processes.

2. New instrumentation needs to be developed for field and laboratory measurement of flow and diffusion. For instance, no device presently exists that will measure the flow

of liquid water at a point inside a snowpack without causing an artificial disturbance of the flow regime. Although heat flows may be large, the actual temperature changes in a snowpack may be subtle, and these cannot be properly measured in some situations. Vapor transport in snow or frozen ground, and water and solute transport in freezing or thawing ground, also cannot be directly measured in the field without improved instrumentation.

3. Quantitative field-measurement programs should be implemented to define properly the influence of permafrost and seasonal frost on surface-water and groundwater regimes. This includes the movement of water, temperature changes, the movement of solutes, and the interactions of these processes with changes in vegetation and infiltration conditions at the surface. Ion diffusion and zone-melting phenomena near the boundaries of a frozen layer also need further study, both in the field and in carefully controlled laboratory experiments.

ICE FORMATION IN RUNNING WATER

Understanding of the process of ice formation and behavior in turbulent water is meager. One can compute from meteorological parameters, to a very rough approximation, the ice thickness on a very slowly moving stream or reservoir if the ice forms by surface freezing only; and under certain ideal conditions and with no frazil ice present, one can quantify the flow of water under an ice cover if sufficient data from slope-discharge stations are available. Beyond this, we have little quantitative information about the effect of ice on rivers. Frazil-ice formation can neither be predicted nor can it, in its early stages, even be readily detected and measured. Formation of ice jams cannot be predicted or alleviated by simple techniques, and the rate of dissipation of an ice cover cannot be related to simple hydrologic or meteorologic parameters. The mechanics of formation of anchor ice is still not completely understood, even in qualitative terms.

The lack of quantitative understanding of ice in rivers makes measurement of their flow almost impossible; this has important economic consequences for such things as shipping, shore installations, and flooding. Furthermore, incomplete understanding prevents proper management or alleviation of the direct problems caused by ice. Frazil ice clogs water intakes for power plants and cooling-water applications; it helps to form and cement ice jams that can cause disastrous floods before or at the time of breakup. Reservoir regulation might be used to alleviate ice problems downstream; however, adequate knowledge is not now available. It is important to have a basic understanding of the mechanics of formation and dissipation of this ice and the ability to predict its occurrence from knowledge of weather records, stream temperature, and stream discharge.

RECOMMENDATIONS

1. Theories need to be developed on the mechanics of ice formation in turbulent supercooled water and on the energy-balance–heat-flow characteristics of a river reach.

2. Instrumentation should be developed for continuous monitoring of water supercooling and/or frazil-ice formation, total ice mass (solid and slush) in a stream, and either the under-ice roughness or the vertical velocity profile in the water.

3. Coordinated measurements should be made of energy balance, streamflow, and ice formation–ablation in typical river reaches using modern instrumentation and sufficient measurements to define all parameters involved.

4. Ice-jam structure and dynamics should be studied with the view to developing management techniques.

PHYSICAL PROPERTIES OF ICE

Research in ice physics forms the foundation of modern glaciology. Without it much of glaciology would reduce to the collection of empirical data and the development of purely speculative theories. Moreover, in ice physics we see a most profitable interaction between glaciology and other scientific disciplines. For example, studies of the crystallographic and physical properties of ice are attracting the interest of many solid-state physicists; the physics of ice and water play a central role in clouds and precipitation processes; molecular chemists are keenly interested in ice as the example *par excellence* of a hydrogen-bonded material; and the recently discovered catalytic action of ice in accelerating a large class of biochemical reactions has aroused great interest among molecular biologists.

Interest is not lacking in any of these fields; vigorous growth seems the rule. Some fields of ice physics have intrinsic importance to new, fast-developing fields of glaciology. These include: dielectric and other properties of snow and ice which are of importance to new remote-sensing techniques and rheology of large ice masses because of the difficulty in extrapolating laboratory and theoretical results to newer experiments on glaciers, sea ice, and snowpacks.

RECOMMENDATIONS

1. Dielectric and radiative properties of snow, ice, and frozen ground need further study. The technology of remote sensing can provide the glaciologist with a vast amount of new information, both synoptic and sequential, which could lead to breakthroughs in many of the important problem areas mentioned in this report, such as large-area energy balances, snow hydrology, and sea-ice dynamics. However, data now available cannot be used profitably because of a

lack in the understanding of the factors that determine the dielectric properties of snow, ice, and frozen ground. A systematic approach calls for a two-pronged attack.

(a) Measurements should be undertaken of dielectric properties of snow, ice, and frozen ground at those frequency ranges used for remote sensing (especially 1–100 GHz). These should include measurements of bulk properties as well as of the influence of surface properties on emissivity and reflectivity.

(b) Significant "ground-truth" data should be collected in order to interpret remote-sensing results. The problem here is mainly conceptual: Which measurements are important? Which scales of, for example, surface roughness, are significant? There are two requirements: continued theoretical study at various scales of interaction of those properties that influence the return from remote-sensing tests and coordinated remote-sensing experiments with simultaneous measurements on the ground of those properties (such as temperature, density, moisture content, transmissivity, and reflectivity of the surface layers) thought to have an important effect on remote sensing. Only in this way can the potential of remote-sensing techniques be properly evaluated, and the large mass of existing remote-sensing data (taken with little or no proper ground-truth support) be utilized.

2. The rheology of large ice masses needs further study. The flow law of ice has been studied from the point of view of dislocation theory with considerable success, and much detailed work has been done in the laboratory on the viscoelastic properties of ice, snow, and frozen ground. Theoretical and numerical studies of large ice and snow masses have advanced to the point where sophisticated large-scale flow-law criteria are required. Unfortunately, extrapolation of theoretical and laboratory results to the flow of large masses of solid ice, such as glaciers, sometimes leads to conflicting or inaccurate results. This is apparently due to slight temperature differences and unknown structures of anisotropies in the ice mass. For more complicated ice masses, such as a snow cover or ice in frozen ground, the situation is even more difficult. It is patently impossible to extrapolate from laboratory results to the behavior of large, heterogeneous, and anisotropic media, such as a sea-ice cover comprised of many individual floes, or a rapidly flowing snow avalanche. Large-scale experiments on stress, strain, and strain-rate relations are needed in order to define large-scale flow laws properly. This work needs to be done on creeping and avalanching snow, mountain glaciers, major ice caps, and sea ice. These experiments will be costly, for they require expensive instrumentation and logistics and the use of new techniques such as satellite geodesy.

QUATERNARY GLACIOLOGY

The study of past spatial and temporal variation of snow and ice over the globe—the task of historical glaciology—is strongly interdisciplinary. It involves biological as well as many physical sciences and is a highly significant aspect of paleoclimatology and Quaternary research. The relationship between climatic changes and those of snow and ice is not yet established in quantitative terms on any of three time scales: short range (years to decades), medium range (decades to millennia), and long range (millennia and longer).

It is believed that there will soon be reasonably realistic numerical techniques for analysis of the earth–atmosphere system that will model past and future large-scale changes in climate. These predictions must be checked against quantitative evidence provided by climates of the past, and such evidence will help to establish priorities among the numerous factors causing climatic change. Furthermore, historic data give insight into the reaction of living organisms—in particular, man—to changes of the environment; the data are also of hydrologic interest (groundwater in glacial deposits, for example) and of engineering importance (foundation problems, for example). Reliable chronology based on modern absolute-dating techniques form the backbone of paleoclimatic investigations.

Geochemical investigations are highly important to the study of present and past polar environments and should be extended through additional field and laboratory studies. The cosmic-ray-produced isotopes ^{14}C, ^{3}H, ^{32}Si, ^{26}Al, and ^{10}Be have been utilized for the dating of ice. More extensive use of explosion-produced ^{14}C and ^{3}H is recommended for the investigation of recent events. One of the most useful temperature and time indicators, $^{18}O/^{16}O$ ratios of precipitation, is being used at present and should play an increasingly important role in the future. Additional chemical analyses of glacier ice and present-day snow cover and of lake sediments and water will provide the necessary data and base levels for paleointerpretations, and further investigations of present-day and formerly frozen ground will identify modes of low-temperature chemical deposition and weathering.

RECOMMENDATIONS

Interdisciplinary paleoenvironmental studies involve many highly interdependent fields. The following recommendations carry no order of priority except that the first item is clearly the most important at this time.

1. A major effort should be made to analyze further the deep-drill ice cores now available from Greenland and the Antarctic. These cores represent the first continuous samples through large ice sheets. Core studies permit the direct determination of the internal structure and physical and chemical properties of the ice. Such information should assist in interpreting the internal reflections and prebottom echoes that have been observed by seismic and electromagnetic methods. Moreover, these cores offer the only avail-

able continuous record of several climatic parameters extending from the present into the Pleistocene and will allow reconstruction of variations in the composition of the atmosphere, the influx of soluble and insoluble cosmic particles, the levels of airborne radioactivity and atmospheric pollution, and the wide distribution of volcanic dust. The results should be of considerable interest to geophysics in general. In addition, the cores can yield, for a given location, a time record showing rates of snow accumulation (with isotopic composition), of terrestrial dust fallout, and, perhaps, of local air temperature. The present policy of making these cores widely available to qualified investigators and of utilizing a wide range of techniques in core analysis should be continued. The level of core-processing activity should be augmented to avoid an appreciable lag between core recovery and analysis.

2. The next antarctic drill hole should be located in an area of low accumulation and flow rates in order to obtain a record with a very long time span.

3. Very sensitive in-hole strain gauges should be developed for vertical strain rate and for horizontal shear strain rate to further refine plastic-deformation theory (flow law). (The instrument design criteria are so stringent that success cannot be guaranteed.)

4. The interpretation of ice-sheet temperature profiles should be refined. Drill holes yield very accurate measurements of temperature as a function of depth, but the theory of interpreting temperature profiles should be advanced.

5. Long, ocean-bottom cores should be obtained and analyzed. They provide one of the best sources of information for determining the sequence and character of Quaternary glacial and nonglacial climates.

6. Detailed studies of Neoglacial moraines by means of techniques of geomorphology, stratigraphy, dendrochronology, lichenometry, and radiometric dating should be made to provide data for evaluating the response of different groups of glaciers in various environmental situations to worldwide changes of climate. Neoglaciation is the climatic episode of glacier expansion subsequent to maximum shrinkage during the postglacial warm interval (Hypsithermal). The relationship of past glacier fluctuations to climate and climatic changes can be especially well investigated through study of late Neoglacial moraine sequences, because the events are recent enough to be fresh but old enough to screen out minor factors. Although Neoglacial advances during the last several millennia probably provide the most easily decipherable record at medium time scales of climatic influences, precise data on distribution, date, and extent of glacier variations during this period are fragmentary.

7. The stratigraphy of ice-free polar areas and of lakes and bogs should be investigated in detail. Many presently ice-free areas of Antarctica, particularly the dry valleys of Victoria Land, have had glaciers entering them from opposite ends, as shown by arrangement of moraines. Present

antarctic glacial chronologies are based largely on moraines; no subsurface studies have been attempted. To check or amplify the chronology of events recorded by the moraines and in nearby marine cores, a core-drilling program needs to be started in the dry-valley region. One drill rig capable of being transported by helicopter, yet able to core to depths of a hundred meters in frozen drift would suffice. The resulting holes should be instrumented for heat-flow studies. Similar studies in other ice-free polar areas, such as northern Greenland and Alaska, are desirable.

The combined effects of changes in climatic parameters (radiation, precipitation, evaporation, temperature) are sensitively reflected in lakes and bogs by both the bottom sediments and their organic inclusions. Limnologic studies and bottom-sediment analysis of a number of selected lakes within and near formerly glaciated areas could throw light on long periods of climatic history, particularly if the lake basins have little inflow or outflow.

8. Terrestrial heat flow should be measured in permafrost areas. Permafrost (perennially frozen ground) is defined on the basis of temperature as ground that remains continuously below $0°C$ for more than two years. Changes in surface conditions, such as vegetation, thaw depth, and water bodies, alter the thermal regime of permafrost and are commonly related to climate. These changes can be detected by measurement and interpretation of geothermal gradients which are sensitive to events within the last several thousand years. To permit reliable climatic interpretations, more information is needed on geothermal gradients in various permafrost environments. Investigations should include the study of recent ground changes and their possible correlation with easily determinable climatic and ecological parameters. Similar investigations will assist in predicting formation and thawing of permafrost.

9. Further study of present and past periglacial phenomena, and of their relation to other climatic indicators, is needed to provide definitive and quantitative information. The polar regions contain a variety of patterned ground and other features related to frost action. "Fossil" forms occur in thick sections of unconsolidated material. In temperate zones, fossil forms may be related to former frost climates, and some forms have long been used as indicators of cold climates. Their study can thus yield information of paleoclimatic significance. However, of the fossil periglacial phenomena only ice-wedge casts, primary sand or soil wedges, and fossil pingos are presently known to provide quantitative information regarding former temperature and moisture conditions. Many phenomena are still of questionable value, and dating is mostly relative.

10. Paleoecological studies should be given greater emphasis. The aim of paleoecology is to provide a reconstruction of ancient ecosystems, which are natural systems wherein abiotic (geological, climatic, soil) and biotic (floral and faunal) factors combine to form the natural environ-

ment. The study of fluctuations in spatial distribution of species during the Quaternary Period, in response to glacial advances and retreats, mountain making, and sea-level and climatic changes, involves many disciplines and is of great importance in the evolution of past and present ecosystems. Although a number of investigators are concerned with these problems, there has been but little attempt to obtain a co-ordinated approach. International meetings held under the auspices of the International Union for Quaternary Research (INQUA) are providing one means, but increased effort at the national level would also help to bridge the gap between biologists and physical scientists concerned with Quaternary environments.

11. A better understanding of subglacial processes and of the role of meltwater in the origin of subglacial features is essential for improving concepts of former glacial conditions and requires continued emphasis on both field and labora-tory investigations and on the problem of bridging the scale gap between them. Numerous subglacial features apparently result directly from the erosion, deposition, and deforma-tion of underlying material by glacier ice; indirectly they are affected by subglacial meltwater under pressure. How-ever, very few of the features have been observed in the process of formation, hence their origins are mostly inferen-tial. Study of basal ice conditions associated with the origin of large folds in sedimentary bedrock (like those of the Mud Buttes of Alberta, Canada) and with the origin of large drumlin fields and thick lodgement till should be made to check our concepts of ice flow and our estimates of former ice thickness, temperature, and other related parameters. How blocks, many meters on a side, are plucked from horizontal or concave bedrock surfaces, and why soils and unconsolidated sediments are eroded in one spot and left undisturbed in another also present unsolved problems.

INTERNATIONAL COOPERATION

Polar research is almost synonymous with international scientific cooperation. Such international scientific coopera-tion has roots going back to the first and second Interna-tional Polar Years, 1882–1883 and 1932–1933, in which several nations focused attention primarily on the Arctic. The International Geophysical Year—originally conceived as the third International Polar Year—represents the greatest cooperative international scientific undertaking that the world has known. Some twenty-seven nations took part in the glaciology program which covered most of the world's ice-covered areas. The IGY program included the combined and cooperative efforts of twelve nations with 48 stations on the margins and in the interior of Antarctica and a large num-ber of stations in the Arctic. The antarctic cooperative pro-gram has continued without interruption under the auspices of the Scientific Committee for Antarctic Research (SCAR).

Glaciology encompasses the study of ice in all its forms, especially ice that occurs naturally on the earth. The two great concentrations of ice on earth are polar: (a) the Ant-arctic Ice Sheet and the sea ice surrounding Antarctica; and (b) the Greenland Ice Sheet, lesser ice sheets of the arctic region, and the perennial sea-ice cover of the Arctic Ocean. Another form of ice occurs in permafrost and is a circum-polar phenomenon. Although representing less than 1 per-cent of the total ice volume of the earth, ground ice is of great practical importance in polar regions and is the com-mon denominator in international permafrost research.

International cooperation in polar studies is practically a matter of necessity for two main reasons. The first relates to logistics and remote locations: scientists engaged in polar research are dependent on very limited resources in trans-portation and supplies; therefore, it is essential that these scientists make optimum use of combined facilities. This has been done extensively in Antarctica. The situation is some-what different in the Arctic, where the problems of distances are not so great and where the research is, in large measure, being conducted on national territory. The second principal reason for international scientific cooperation in glaciology in polar regions or lower latitudes concerns the limited num-ber of experts trained in glaciology. No one country boasts a large amount of talent in this highly specialized field. Con-sequently, without the formulation of policy on this matter, it has been implicitly recognized that the small number of specialists in this area must to one extent or another join forces in order to achieve progress in this complex scientific field.

COOPERATION IN THE ANTARCTIC

The scientific cooperation that began in Antarctica during the IGY has led to a continuing scientific research program involving high degrees of cooperation among the scientists of many countries and stations in Antarctica. Every year, a variety of exchanges takes place among scientists at various stations. There are completely free and casual visits of scien-tists of one station to scientists of another station, which, from the point of view of protocol, are no more complicated than visits from one university to another within the United States; the freedom of this interchange is limited only by the severe logistics and transportation problems of Antarc-tica. The international cooperation in Antarctica includes not only scientific cooperation but also logistic aid from one country to another: transport, rescue, search, and as-sistance by ships, icebreakers, and airplanes of the various countries to personnel of other countries. In addition, the scientific cooperation in Antarctica led to one of the most remarkable developments in modern history: The Antarctic Treaty. Under this treaty, the entire continent of Antarctica is set aside from political claims and made available exclu-sively for scientific research and the benefit of mankind.

COOPERATION IN THE ARCTIC

Arctic research has been characterized by a different kind of scientific cooperation than in Antarctica. The entire arctic land is national territory of seven countries: Canada, Denmark, Finland, Norway, the Soviet Union, Sweden, and the United States. Until the 1930's when the Soviet Union began establishing research stations on the ice of the Arctic Ocean, virtually all research in the Arctic was performed on land. Logistics problems in the Arctic are serious burdens but are far less severe than the corresponding problems in Antarctica. Thanks to the generous encouragement and assistance of the Government of Denmark, a substantial amount of research has been conducted in Greenland on an international basis. Most of the international scientific cooperation in other parts of the Arctic has been characterized mostly by bilateral cooperative arrangements; programs have been broad in scope and in the number of people involved.

Now that scientists of many countries are beginning to look at the Arctic as a system rather than as a series of isolated problems, and now that aircraft and submarine capabilities permit free access to virtually any part of the Arctic Ocean Basin, it becomes imperative that the countries concerned with research in the Arctic look toward ways of more effective international collaboration in research on the main problems related to the Arctic Ocean Basin and the adjacent perennially frozen land masses.

INTERNATIONAL HYDROLOGICAL DECADE

The International Hydrological Decade (IHD) is now the major new international program which includes glaciology. Glaciology is involved because about three fourths of all the fresh water in the world is stored in the form of ice. In the western United States, the water stored in snowfields and glaciers is released to provide a large proportion of the streamflow during spring and during the hot, dry seasons. Also, the study of glaciers provides an efficient means for understanding the relationships between the snow and ice at high altitudes to the water regimes of downstream areas. The International Hydrological Decade, 1965–1974, was conceived in recognition of the fact that certain significant hydrologic (including glaciologic) problems can be studied effectively only on regional, international, continental, or global scales. The purpose of this program is to improve scientific knowledge in hydrology, to increase the number and effectiveness of scientific hydrologists, and to stimulate communication among scientists. Major concerns of the IHD include the world water balance and special programs involving basic data collection and analysis, inventories, water balances, research topics of international flavor, education, and training.

Three major programs of the IHD involve snow and ice. These are: worldwide inventory of perennial and seasonal snow and ice masses; measurement of glacier variations on a worldwide basis; and combined heat, ice, and water balances at selected glacier basins.

In the process of providing a better understanding of the relationships between water, snow, and ice—a principal purpose of the IHD—these programs should result in significant advances in basic knowledge of glaciology. The inventory program will tell us for the first time how much glacier ice and frozen ground there is and where it occurs and will give us a synoptic, global view of the seasonal snowpack which is an important element in any analysis of world climate and energy balance. The glacier variations project will give us the first statistically valid data on the fluctuations of glaciers in different parts of the world. The combined balances program attempts to answer one of the most fundamental problems in glaciology: How can changes in a glacier's mass be directly related, through scales of ever-increasing size, to its meteorological environment? This program involves three great chains of stations: a north–south chain from Alaska to the Antarctic; a west–east chain at latitudes 40–50° N from the West Coast of North America to Central Asia; and a west–east chain at the Arctic Circle from Alaska east to the polar Urals.

Active participation by American glaciologists in these three projects is essential to the success of the international program. The numerous glaciers in Alaska have never been inventoried, and we have almost no synoptic information on the distribution of the snow cover of the United States. Although many glacier variation measurements have been made in the United States, these need to be coordinated so that the resulting data are available for large-scale analyses. The combined balances programs in the United States are especially important because only in U.S. territory do all three great chains of stations come together.

RECOMMENDATIONS

1. Ways should be explored to promote and increase collaboration and cooperation among the countries concerned with research in the Antarctic and in the Arctic.

2. United States participation in the International Hydrological Decade should be increased to a level proportional to the importance of the hydrological problems of the IHD to the future needs of the country.

Glaciology in the Arctic

GLACIERS

The current behavior of arctic glaciers may hold important clues to an understanding of modern climatic trends and to the development of ice ages. Perhaps the greatest problem remaining to be solved in the field of glacier dynamics is the mechanics of the sliding of the glacier on its bed and, in particular, the cause of glacier surges. Most of the glaciers that are known to surge are valley glaciers, but the greatest known surge or advance occurred in the ice cap on Nordaustlandet (North East Land), Svalbard (Glen, 1941). It has been postulated that our great ice sheets also can surge, and, when they do, an ice age starts. In a basic study of the stability of arctic ice masses on land, the following three questions should be answered:

1. What is the relation of glaciers to the climatic environment of the Arctic now, i.e., what are the major climatic and orographic factors responsible for their maintenance?

2. Can glacier changes be caused by processes that are not directly attributable to their net mass balance, e.g., by changes of the meltwater distribution or bedrock temperature?

3. How can data derived from arctic glaciers be used in determining the climate of the past?

In a comparison of polar climates, we find a strong contrast between the Arctic, which is dominated by maritime conditions, and the Antarctic, which is heavily influenced by the Antarctic Ice Sheet with elevations ranging from 2000 to 4000 m. However, the Greenland Ice Sheet is second only to the Arctic Ocean Basin as a special feature of the north polar region. It is comparable with the Antarctic Ice Sheet, even though its area is only one seventh as large and its center is nearly 20° from the pole. General and specific comparisons between the Greenland and Antarctic Ice Sheets have been made (Benson, 1967), and the potential for using Greenland as a laboratory for polar ice-sheet research is good. It provides an opportunity to conduct specific experiments on boundaries of an ice sheet with ocean and with land and, thus, to complement the research in Antarctica. By selective use of the ice sheets in both polar regions, we can effectively increase our over-all potential to study critical environmental problems. Concurrent comparative studies would be especially effective: for example, comparative studies of stations (on the two ice sheets) that have identical mean annual temperatures and rates of accumulation. Comparisons could also be made of the dry valleys of the McMurdo Sound area (77-78° S) in Antarctica with their nearly identical counterparts in Peary Land (82-84° N) of northeast Greenland. These areas have approximately equal temperatures and rates of precipitation, and both are noted for vertical cliffs on the snouts of their valley glaciers which terminate on deserts.

Many of the problems specific to the Greenland Ice Cap are part of the extensive and continuing program of the Expédition Glaciologique Internationale au Groenland (EGIG), an international research effort maintained by Denmark, France, Switzerland, the Federal Republic of Germany, and Austria.

RECOMMENDATIONS

1. Determinations should be made of the thermal regimes and the mass, heat, and water balances of representative glaciers. Observations should be carried on for a number of years sufficient to establish reliable averages, and they should include total accumulation and ablation as well as net mass balance. Particular attention should be paid to the uniformity of observational techniques, especially in heat-balance

studies. Such observations will provide the basic data for relating the behavior of glaciers to climate and for understanding the feedback effects between glacier and climate fluctuations in different scales of time and size.

2. Search for paleoclimatic evidence should be undertaken within the glaciers and in their vicinity. Such studies should include analyses of deep cores from Greenland and other glaciers, including stratigraphy, distribution of particulate matter, discontinuities revealed by radar soundings, radioisotope dating of biological remnants, oxygen isotope analyses of ice and entrapped air, and morainal features.

3. A study should be made of the conditions existing at the bottom of glaciers and ice caps and their suspected relation to glacier surges, for example, by means of a series of instrumented boreholes in a glacier that may be expected to surge within the next five or ten years.

4. Additional laboratory and field studies should be made of the flow law of ice, recrystallization and reorientation of ice crystals, and further development of the theories pertaining to the dynamics of ice caps and glaciers.

SEASONAL SNOW COVER

Onset and disappearance of seasonal snow cover mark a drastic change of the physical characteristics of the earth–atmosphere interface and of the way in which the two media interact. A layer of snow lies on sea ice, glaciers, and frozen ground much of the year. An understanding of mass and energy balances for any of these ice features is dependent on knowledge of the timing and the thermal and radiative properties of the snow layer. Such knowledge is of general importance in studies of atmospheric circulation and the world water balance and is of specific importance to utilization of the Arctic by man.

Areas of prolonged coverage are potential sources of glaciation. To understand fully the genesis of a glacier or ice cap by accumulation, investigations will have to proceed from interpretations of past and present behavior of seasonal snow to quantitative analyses of the relationships of snow cover, atmospheric circulation, and climate, on a local, regional, and global scale.

RECOMMENDATIONS

1. Full use should be made of pertinent satellite data in studying snow cover, with special reference to timing and albedo in different areas. Special attention should be directed to development of multifrequency passive microwave radiometers because of their potential value in sensing many different snow-cover properties through a cloud cover.

2. Areas of maximum snow accumulation and prolonged coverage by seasonal snow should be studied along with perennial snow cover in connection with prevailing circulation patterns. Average cyclone tracks, as presented for the entire northern hemisphere (Klein, 1957) and for the Arctic in winter (Keegan, 1958) and summer (Kunkel, 1959), should be related to specific case histories of snowstorms and the resulting snow cover in the Arctic for several consecutive years. In particular, the self-enhancing effects caused by reduced albedo from unusually heavy snowfall in a given year or sequence of years should be investigated.

The specific case histories should include $^{18}O/^{16}O$ ratios of all precipitation, both snow and rain. These ratios are the most useful labels available for interpreting both seasonal and perennial snow strata, and they provide a means of distinguishing between precipitation derived from Atlantic, Pacific, and arctic sources.

3. The vegetation cover around perennial snow patches should be studied, as it may reflect long-term variation of their extent.

FROZEN GROUND

Over 25 percent of the earth's surface is characterized by perennially frozen ground (permafrost), and much more is subject to seasonal freezing and thawing. Yet chemical, physical, and geologic processes in the ground at subzero temperature (°C), and processes resulting from freezing and thawing of soil or rock, are far from completely understood (Building Research Advisory Board, 1966). With respect to climatic implications, frozen ground, like glaciers, reacts dynamically to climate and can provide a record of climatic changes, particularly over time intervals long enough to mask minor changes.

RECOMMENDATIONS

1. Field and laboratory investigations of processes related to freezing and thawing of soil or rock need to be continued. Cores should be taken from both continuous and discontinuous (marginal) permafrost and analyzed for chemical composition, date of deposition, water content, and, where possible, paleotemperature. High-accuracy temperature sensors should be emplaced throughout the perennially frozen layer in appropriate locations to determine the thermal diffusivity and water transfer. The migration of water-soluble substances near the upper and lower margins of the permafrost and through the permafrost should be studied.

2. Mapping of contemporary permafrost, including distribution, depth, and temperature data where feasible, thickness of active layer, and nature of materials and natural cover, should be continued.

3. Special attention should be given in areas of marginal permafrost to detailed investigations (including depth and temperature profiles and correlative meteorologic and climatologic observations) that will provide datum planes for studying short- and longer-term variations in permafrost conditions.

4. The hydrologic cycle of rivers and small streams should be investigated in connection with the over-all study of permafrost areas. The freezing of these waterways for more than half of the year causes them to behave quite differently from the same size streams in regions where freezing is unimportant. The mechanism involved in causing streams with relatively small discharge rates to overflow and flood widespread areas needs more investigation for scientific as well as practical reasons.

5. Mapping and dating of fossil periglacial features such as ice-wedge casts and other evidences of former permafrost should be furthered to establish the distribution of past permafrost and to assist the study of climatic changes. Compared with Europe, very little work has been done in North America. In general the dating and compilation of such features to determine paleoclimates over broad areas would benefit from increased stress on critical evaluation of the evidence.

QUATERNARY CHRONOLOGY

Interdisciplinary studies relating to Quaternary chronology in the Arctic involve such diverse fields as glacial geology, geomorphology, geophysics, oceanography, botany, zoology, and anthropology. All contribute to an understanding of past climate and the nature and effects of climatic change, and all are of concern to glaciology to the extent that ice is, or was, a significant environmental factor. Some of the more pressing types of investigations relating to ice in this manner are listed below.

RECOMMENDATIONS

1. Glacial stratigraphic sequence in the Arctic is still largely unknown, because most glaciers ended where there is now sea and because arctic glaciers can advance and recede without greatly modifying the terrain. Careful studies of lithologic, fabric, and mechanical composition of deposits are needed, where glacierization is a historic event, for better understanding of the significance and origin of such features as ground moraine layers, drumlins, and eskers.

2. Detailed studies of critical areas of multiple drift need to be continued and coupled with marine shelf sediment studies and Arctic Basin core studies to establish the size and sequence of past glaciers. Modern laboratory techniques will

greatly aid this work (isotopic dating, fabric analysis, lithologic studies, chemistry of paleosols, mechanical and micro-surface studies of particle origin).

3. Arctic lake-bottom cores and soils should be examined for paleoclimatic evidence reflected in the distributions of fossil pollen, insects, mollusks, and other features.

4. Isolines of emergence should be checked where known and established where not known, so that the location and thickness of former ice sheets can be reconstructed with greater accuracy. This will require the identification, leveling, and dating of former strandlines, as well as much more detailed gravity surveys (isostatic anomalies) than are now available.

LOGISTICS AND SUPPORT

Logistics in the Arctic, as in other relatively inaccessible regions, is an integral element of research programs. In some ways, logistics rather than the scientific disciplines is the identifying and unifying aspect of a research project. Both the sampling of ocean-bottom sediment and the measuring of solar radiation at the North Pole, though hardly related, depend on a working platform, transportation, and a logistical and administrative backup which are largely the same and which, at present, no individual research group (academic or otherwise) can afford.

The U.S. Antarctic Research Program has a general research policy, central funding, and a unified logistical setup, which have helped to maintain a coherent and continuing research effort with adequate communication among the various projects and a considerable degree of international coordination and long-range planning.

Since the end of IGY, a large portion of the arctic research discussed in this report has been funded by ONR, Geography Branch, which, since the establishment of station Arlis I, 1960, has also provided most of the logistical support through the Arctic Research Laboratory (under contract with the University of Alaska). It is the opinion of the Panel that the level of funding by ONR of research projects has been generally adequate and that there have been few instances where a significant and pertinent scientific project, for which sufficient interest and manpower were available in the academic community, had to be abandoned for lack of support. On the other hand, logistical support of drifting stations in the Arctic Ocean (aircraft support, radio communications, power), has been austere and has doubtless contributed to the failure to attract new talent to the field.

The implementation of a set of recommendations pertaining to sea ice would require the concerted effort of a number of investigators greater than in any group presently engaged in this type of research. It would also require an assurance of multiyear funding and greatly expanded logistics. The following facilities and support would be needed:

1. The continuous availability of one four-engine, long-range aircraft (C-130) for both scientific and cargo flights.

2. One semipermanent floating research facility ("barge" or ice island), at least 500 km away from the nearest land, between longitudes 40° W and 140° E, which would require, in addition to the customary installations:

(a) 2 helicopters (range about 200 km) with maintenance facilities and crew.

(b) 2 light single-engine aircraft with maintenance facilities and crew, or 1 small, twin-engine turboprop plane (or vertical takeoff airplane when they become available).

(c) Sufficient heavy equipment (grader, bulldozers) and crew for runway maintenance and preservation. At present, no aircraft can land from the time when the snow-pack becomes soft (usually June 1–10) until some time after freezeup (late September). This long intermission is very detrimental and may not be necessary with an adequate capability for moving snow and leveling ice.

(d) Radio communications which allow the investigator in the field to contact his home base at all times. A powerful hf transmitter, a ham radio, and at least two professional radio operators on duty would be required.

(e) At least two temporary satellite stations about 100 km from the main station, manned by a crew of at least three. These stations, located on sea ice, would have to be within helicopter range of the main station. They should operate for limited periods of one to three months.

(f) Shipboard-type equipment for deep coring and taking of large samples of the ocean floor.

(g) At least one under-ice observation chamber (as used by USARP in McMurdo Sound).

(h) The main station would require about 100–200 kW power, compared with 10–20 kW now available at Fletcher's Ice Island (T-3).

SUMMARY

Several years have passed since the Committee on Polar Research (CPR) issued the report, *Science in the Arctic Ocean Basin.* The CPR Glaciology Panel, believing it timely to reassess the development and problems of arctic glaciology, has endeavored to identify the lines of research that are most likely to lead to important results in the near future and has attempted to call attention to important factors related to arctic research, including logistics problems and international cooperation.

It is the consensus of the Glaciology Panel that greater emphasis should be placed on the development of arctic glaciology and that the present limited and fluctuating research efforts and level of support are not compatible with the magnitude and significance of the scientific problems of the Arctic. A number of areas of research have been identi-fied and listed in this report. Investigations are currently under way in some of these areas, but considerably more research will be required. A theme common to all these problems is that of the heat–mass balance. This is the overriding consideration, whether the research concerns sea ice, glaciers, seasonal snow cover, or frozen ground. However, the Glaciology Panel believes there is one large segment of arctic glaciology that deserves special and specific mention: the Arctic Ocean Basin.

The Arctic Ocean Basin and the arctic atmosphere interact on a large scale with the atmosphere and oceans in the lower latitudes. Recently available numerical models for computer programs for worldwide weather and climate studies have pointed out the deficiency of input information for computing circulations at high latitudes. Recent hypotheses on the effect of the ice cover in the basin (or lack of it) on the climate of the world again have indicated the need for more data. There are indications that the sea-ice cover may be unstable and could possibly be removed. The effect of this removal on the climates of the world and the technological implications of an ice-free Arctic Ocean are both factors of great import.

An important factor in the timeliness of a broad arctic program is the International Hydrological Decade. Its major objective, an assessment of the global water balance, lends emphasis to the need for increased observations and computations of the vapor transport across the boundaries of the Arctic, the water balance of the tundras, and the energy exchange of the perennial and seasonal snow cover.

As in any remote, inaccessible area, the problem of logistics is a unifying element, shared and depended upon by all investigators. This is another reason for considering the geographical region of the Arctic as identifying a broad program of research. Details of the scientific aspects of this program have been presented in a sequence that reflects, in the Panel's opinion, an order of priorities: (1) Arctic Ocean Basin, (2) Glaciers, (3) Seasonal Snow Cover, (4) Frozen Ground, (5) Quaternary Chronology. The background in topic 1, especially problems related to sea ice, is more thoroughly discussed than is the background for other topics, whose subjects have been adequately treated in recent glaciological literature.

This report deals with but a fraction of the problems of the Arctic. It may be expected that, in the coming decades, climate control, food shortage, and population pressure will bring new and unexpected challenges and the need for increased understanding and mastery of the arctic environment. A first step toward preparing for these challenges would be an assessment of the critical unsolved problems in all branches of science and the preparation of recommendations for future research, with the aim of developing a comprehensive research program. The Panel has endeavored to make this assessment in relation to arctic glaciology.

ACKNOWLEDGMENTS

The report represents efforts by many Panel members, but special thanks of the Panel go to Norbert Untersteiner, who prepared several drafts of the report based on recommendations evolved in several meetings and in many personal communications. The Panel itself held three meetings devoted to the subject: the second of these was held at the conference center of McGill University at Mont St. Hilaire, Quebec. The Panel invited a number of distinguished U.S. and Canadian scientists to join in the discussions on arctic glaciology. The report greatly benefited from the contributions of these guests; the responsibility for the report remains with the Panel.

REFERENCES

Badgley, F. I., "Heat Budget at the Surface of the Arctic Ocean," in *Proceedings of the Symposium on the Arctic Heat Budget and Atmospheric Circulation.* (J. O. Fletcher, ed.), pp. 267–277, The RAND Corp. (RM-5233-NSF) (1966).

Benson, C. S., "Polar Regions Snow Cover," in *Proceedings of the International Conference on Physics of Snow and Ice*, Hokkaido University, Sapporo, Japan (1967).

Building Research Advisory Board, *Proceedings, International Conference on Permafrost*, NAS-NRC Publ. 1287, Nat. Acad. Sci.–Nat. Res. Council, Washington, D.C. (1966).

Campbell, W. J., "The Wind-Driven Circulation of Ice and Water in a Polar Ocean," *J. Geophys. Res., 70*, 3279–3301 (1965).

Donn, W. L., and M. Ewing, "The Theory of Ice Ages, 3," *Science, 152*, 1706–1712 (1966).

Fletcher, J. O., *The Heat Budget of the Arctic Basin and Its Relation to the Climate*, The RAND Corp. (R-444-PR) (1965).

Glen, A. R., "The Latest Map of North East Land," *Geog. J., 98*, 206 (1941).

Hunkins, K., and H. Kutschale, "Quaternary Sedimentation in the Arctic Ocean," in Proc. 7th INQUA Congr. (1965).

Keegan, T. J., "Arctic Synoptic Activity in Winter," *J. Meteorol., 15*, 513–521 (1958).

Klein, W. H., "Principal Tracks and Mean Frequencies of Cyclones and Anticyclones in the Northern Hemisphere," U.S. Weather Bur. Res. Paper 40 (1957).

Ku, T. L., and W. S. Broecker, "Rates of Sedimentation in the Arctic Ocean," in Proc. 7th INQUA Congr. (1965).

Kunkel, B. A., *A Synoptic-Climatological Study of the Arctic Circulation in Summer*, Sci. Rept. 7 [AF Contract 19 (604)-3063], Department of Meteorology and Climatology, U. of Washington (1959).

Lyon, W., "Ocean and Sea Ice Research in the Arctic Ocean via Submarine," *Trans. N.Y. Acad. Sci., Ser. 2*, 23 (1961).

Untersteiner, N., "Calculating Thermal Regime and Mass Budget of Sea Ice," in *Proceedings of the Symposium on the Arctic Heat Budget and Atmospheric Circulation.* (J. O. Fletcher, ed.), pp. 203–213, The RAND Corp. (RM-5233-NSF) (1966).

Wittman, W., and J. Schule, "Comments on the Mass Budget of Arctic Pack Ice," in *Proceedings of the Symposium on the Arctic Heat Budget and Atmospheric Circulation.* (J. O. Fletcher, ed.), pp. 215–246, The RAND Corp. (RM-5233-NSF) (1966).

APPENDIX B

Antarctic Glaciology

The Antarctic Ice Sheet stands as a unique feature of the surface of the earth. It covers an area of some 13½ million sq km, about 98 percent of the antarctic continent, with a mean thickness of almost 2 km. Comprising 90 percent of the ice on earth, it not only dominates the landscape and climate of the south polar regions but exerts its influence on oceans and lands far to the north. For these reasons the study of the ice sheet presents the most outstanding problem of antarctic glaciology.

The interest of the glaciologist, however, centers not primarily on the effects of the ice in cooling the atmosphere and oceans but on the nature and history of the ice sheet itself. The chief objectives of this study fall into two main categories: (a) an improved knowledge of the physical and chemical properties and dynamic behavior of the Antarctic Ice Sheet, and consequently of the ice itself as a material, and (b) a better understanding of former, especially Pleistocene, ice sheets everywhere: their causes, their action on the underlying and surrounding land, and the consequences of their growth and decay. Within these categories we can recognize several major problems which we will outline, together with some recommendations of the Glaciology Panel for effecting their solution.

GEOGRAPHIC DESCRIPTION

During the ten years of antarctic research starting with the International Geophysical Year, one of the major emphases in antarctic glaciology has been simply to provide basic knowledge of Antarctica and its ice sheet, including the determination of surface elevations and topography, the location of individual features of the ice sheet and ice shelves, the thickness of the ice, the topography of the subglacial floor, and the location and description of ice-free areas. On a reconnaissance basis these goals have been largely completed. It can be stated with some certainty that no major geographic feature of the Antarctic Ice Sheet remains to be discovered, and even the subglacial topography can be outlined on a regional scale for all the continent except the American Highland and the interior of Wilkes Land.

This does not mean, however, that work on the geographical description of the ice sheet should cease, but rather that larger-scale mapping should now be undertaken. It would be of immense value to the glaciologist to have at his disposal reliable, uniform, regional contour maps of the surface and ice thickness for the whole continent. Such maps are essential prerequisites to a meaningful analysis of the behavior and history of the ice as a whole and also provide the basis on which to select critical areas for investigation of specific problems.

In this regard, the development of the full potential of the airborne electromagnetic sounder is of extreme importance. A system which will provide continuous profiles of surface topography and ice thickness from an aircraft is rapidly approaching operational capability on a routine basis. When this is achieved, it will be possible to accomplish profile coverage of the entire Antarctic, with a 100-km flight line spacing, in something on the order of 1000 flight hours.

RECOMMENDATION

1. The technique of airborne electromagnetic sounding should be developed to the point where it can be used routinely from aircraft. The aim should be to produce maps of glacial and subglacial topography and ice thickness, on a scale of perhaps 1:5,000,000 for the entire ice-covered Antarctic. It is important that survey aircraft be equipped with modern instruments for as accurate determination as possible of position and absolute elevation. To enhance the value of the surveys, aircraft should also be equipped with airborne magnetometers and, if the velocity of the aircraft can be determined with sufficient accuracy, with airborne gravimeters.

MASS BALANCE OF THE ICE SHEET

Determination of the mass balance of the ice sheet is important to both the dynamical and historical aspects of glaciology. Is the flow of the continental ice a long-term steady-state process, or do surges occur? Is the total amount of ice in the Antarctic increasing or decreasing? How do regimens vary between different ice-drainage systems, in particular, between those systems which are primarily inland and those primarily coastal?

Short-term balance or imbalance may not be representative of the behavior of the ice over a period comparable with the dynamic response time of the ice sheet, which probably exceeds 10,000 years. The problem is not only to determine the mass balance for, say, a particular year, but to find long-term averages and variations. A secular change in accumulation rate has been reported for the South Pole, but there has as yet been no corroborative evidence.

For the three systems that drain most of the ice from the deep interior of the Antarctic, and that debouch through the Ross, Amery, and Filchner Ice Shelves, there appears to be a statistically significant positive mass balance. Since a corresponding sea-level lowering is not observed, it may be that the other regions, primarily coastal, are losing a corresponding amount of ice. This intriguing possibility clearly needs further investigations.

Problems arise in the measurement of both mass input and mass output terms in the antarctic balance equation. Stratigraphic studies in snow pits have provided much valuable information on accumulation rates, but, because of difficulties in interpretation, considerable misinformation as well. Recent improvement in geochemical techniques has largely eliminated the errors in accumulation measurements. The problem of horizontal variability, such as results from sastrugi and surface "waves," still remains, however, and must be solved in order to allow the interpretation of local variations of accumulation with depth, measured in deep cores, in terms of variations in average accumulation rates.

All accumulation measurements to date have been confined to the upper layers of the ice. With the inception of deep drilling, including cores through the entire ice sheet, age measurements to large depths will be required, and the methods employed for near-surface analyses will not be applicable. Preliminary success obtained in Greenland with radiocarbon dating points to a possible solution to this problem.

Mass output rates are more poorly known along most of the antarctic coast than are the input rates, although the output along the front of the Ross Ice Shelf has been measured quite accurately. Rates of ablation and discharge along other sections of the coast are badly needed.

A major source of error in mass output calculations is uncertainty about the extent of melting or freezing on the undersides of the major ice shelves. A few estimates have been made on the basis of strain and accumulation rates on the Ross Ice Shelf, but there is considerable disagreement about the extrapolation of the observations to the major part of the ice shelf, and still more uncertainty about extrapolation to other ice shelves.

RECOMMENDATIONS

1. Core drilling should be undertaken as promptly and extensively as possible to provide reliable mean rates and temporal variations of accumulation. Some holes, both deep and shallow, should be closely spaced to investigate the significance of special features observed in one core.

2. Techniques for age determinations in ice should be emphasized, particularly those, such as radiocarbon dating, which may extend the effective time range beyond a few hundreds of years.

3. The mass balance of the Antarctic Ice Sheet should be studied on a basis of individual drainage systems, not just for the continent as a whole. For this purpose, it would be useful to study the ablation and discharge rates corresponding to particular types of ice termini, as an aid to interpolation where direct measurements of mass output are not available.

4. Each ice-sheet station, temporary or permanent, should serve as a base for intensive study of an extended area, such as a square, 100 km on a side. The variability of accumulation and the continuity of snow strata within the area should be examined, with emphasis on stratigraphic and other studies in pits and drill holes, detailed observations on sastrugi, micrometeorology, and continuing measurements on surface undulations to determine their effect on accumulation rates and whether they are stationary or are moving relative to the body of the ice. Also, a shaft should be dug to a depth of about 20 m at each station to allow a glaciologist to study the entire stratigraphic cross section starting with the uppermost snow cover. Two or more holes, drilled with hand augers, should be drilled at the bottom of shafts to extend the time period of the accumulation observations.

5. The mass and heat exchange of the underside of ice shelves should be determined. These efforts should utilize new and existing oceanographic data at the ice front, surface strain measurements (especially short-term strain at the land junction), observations of temperature near the base of the ice, sonic reflection times from transducers emplaced deep within the ice, theoretical analyses, and, if possible, direct measurements under the ice.

6. The problem of refreezing of runoff and accretion by nucleation of supercooled water in the boundary zone between land ice and sea ice should be investigated.

7. Photography from satellites should be used to study calving of glaciers and ice shelves. Attempts should be made to correlate calving observations with meteorological, oceanographic, and dynamic measurements.

8. Studies should be made on the effect of the vast belt of sea ice surrounding the antarctic continent on the nourishment of the continental ice sheet. Seasonal, irregular, and secular changes in the sea ice should be investigated, making maximum use of satellite sensing and other experience gained in the study of arctic sea ice.

DYNAMICS OF THE ICE SHEET

Because of the vast size of the Antarctic Ice Sheet, it has been difficult to make significant headway toward an understanding of its over-all dynamics. Ideally, it would be possible, knowing the accumulation rates and surface subglacial topography of the intervening region, to trace the path of a snow particle falling on the surface in the interior to its discharge at the coast. This would involve as an intermediate step the calculation of temperatures within the ice.

Our knowledge falls far short of this ideal. In fact, analysis of the dynamics of a major, cold ice sheet has only just begun. Some lines have been established for strain measurements, but these are scarce and have not yet produced many results, except on the fast-moving ice shelves. Extensive improvements in field observations of velocities and strain rates, and especially the variation of these quantities with depth in the ice and with distance along flow lines, are urgently needed. Advantage should be taken of satellite positioning for movement studies. Techniques, such as deep core-drilling and microwave distance-measuring, are now available for obtaining the requisite field data.

A knowledge of conditions at the bed of the ice is crucial in determining the mode of ice flow. The presence or absence of meltwater is probably the primary factor in controlling the amount of sliding of the ice on its bed; furthermore, the flow properties of ice are strongly temperature-dependent, and they may undergo rapid change close to the melting point. Since significant shear strain rates occur near the base of the ice, the basal temperature becomes doubly important.

Measurements in deep drill holes will, of course, reveal the temperature at the base of the ice. The hole recently completed at Byrd Station not only penetrated ice at its melting point at the base of the ice sheet but was flooded by water to a height of several tens of meters above the base. Drill holes are expensive and time-consuming, however, and therefore there will never be a great many of them. Robot probes should decrease the cost of obtaining deep temperature data, but other, indirect, means of determining temperature are needed. There is some hope that the means may be provided by the careful analysis of seismic and electromagnetic reflection properties. A seismic echo, for example, would theoretically undergo a phase change depending primarily on whether the material beneath the ice was wet or frozen; an electromagnetic signal would experience energy absorption strongly dependent on temperature.

Another approach which has been used in the study of ice dynamics is the intensive study of a region selected as a naturally occurring scale model of the main ice sheet. This has been the approach to the examination of the Roosevelt Island ice cap and Wilkes ice dome, but the information has yet to be completed in the vertical dimension.

Further theoretical work on the dynamics of the Antarctic Ice Sheet would be useful, but the acquisition of data to test the validity of existing theories is a more critical need at the present time.

RECOMMENDATIONS

1. Flow-line studies* with proper relation to stations where deep drilling has been, or will be, carried out should be conducted. Relatively shallow holes, perhaps to 500 m, should be drilled elsewhere along the flow line.

2. The joint proposal by France, the Soviet Union, and the United States for the establishment of a strain network between Vostok and Dumont d'Urville, with deep drilling at Vostok and at another point along the flow line should be implemented.

3. Deformation studies should be conducted in all deep bore holes to determine the vertical variation of strain rates.

4. Marker horizons for reference in future investigations should be established; the suitability of radar reflecting layers for this purpose should be examined.

5. "Model" ice-cap studies on Roosevelt Island should be completed through a program of intermediate-depth drilling.

6. Study of glacier surges in Alaska should be continued as an aid in establishing whether very high velocities can occur in the Antarctic Ice Sheet and, if so, how they would affect the extent of the ice shelves.

7. Indirect techniques should be developed for determining the temperature structure in the ice, particularly at the base of the ice sheet. Heat-flow measurements should be made below the ice sheet where drill holes have been extended into the rock beneath.

*As recommended by the SCAR Working Group on Glaciology (*SCAR Bulletin No. 14*, p. 621, 1963).

8. Further theoretical studies of ice movement to interpret field observations in a logical fashion and to guide the direction of future research should be conducted. Particular emphasis should be placed on the problems of the over-all stability of the ice sheet and the possibility of surges of limited segments within its boundaries.

PHYSICAL AND CHEMICAL PROPERTIES OF THE ICE

In gross, the ice sheet appears to be isotropic and homogeneous, with the exception of density changes in the upper few hundred meters. In more detail, however, it exhibits a considerable number of physical and chemical variations; we will mention a few of the more striking ones. A strong crystal fabric was found at depth in the Ross Ice Shelf and is probably characteristic of ice shelves. Far more surprising was the recent discovery of highly oriented ice through a zone extending from about 300 m to 1000 m above the base of the ice at Byrd Station, the ice below comprising very large, randomly oriented crystals. Corroboration of the existence of highly anisotropic ice at depth has been obtained from seismic measurements in West Antarctica. A seismic reflector a few hundred meters above the base of the ice, which is widely present in West Antarctica, may be related to the upper boundary of a basal isotropic layer such as that at Byrd Station or with a layer or layers of debris-laden ice.

Structural anisotropy is strongly developed near the surface of the ice, resulting from wind and radiation crusts; combined with the rapid variation of wave velocity with depth, this produces a unique acoustic medium—one which is both highly anisotropic and highly inhomogeneous, yet contains no discontinuities of acoustic significance.

Electromagnetic sounding, on the other hand, has revealed, within the upper kilometer of the ice, a large number of discontinuities capable of reflecting an observable amount of energy. These may be related to ice lenses which, if due to unusual climatic or other large-scale conditions, might be used as marker horizons. Electromagnetic-wave velocity measurements, simply made from reflection studies, might give a rapid determination of density–depth variations to a depth of several hundred meters.

The content of chemical impurities in the ice decreases markedly with distance from the coast. At a given point in the interior it may also vary seasonally as the sea ice pack waxes and wanes. It is possible that the content of salts in any portion of the ice may reveal the distance from the coast at which that ice was deposited on the surface.

Oxygen-isotope ratios show large variations, both regular and irregular, with depth in the ice sheet. Although these ratios have not proven very successful as a tool for absolute age determinations, the variations may yield information about the redistribution of precipitation on the surface and about paleoclimates.

RECOMMENDATIONS

1. Physical and chemical measurements of as many types as possible should be made on the ice cores from drill holes and also, for correlative purposes, in the ice *in situ* near the holes.

2. Special areas should be selected, for study by a wide variety of techniques, especially electromagnetic sounding, seismic sounding, and drilling. Because of the established interest of the area, the many studies already made, and the disagreement between seismic and electromagnetic soundings, Roosevelt Island is suggested as the first of these areas.

3. Evidence should be sought for the causes of observed electromagnetic and seismic reflections from within the ice sheet.

4. Further study of the variations of chemical impurity content and isotopic composition of the ice, their causes, and their possible value in tracing glaciological processes should be carried out.

HISTORY OF THE ANTARCTIC ICE SHEET

There is ample evidence that the Antarctic Ice Sheet was once thicker and more extensive than it is at present. Moraines and glacially carved (but presently ice-free) valleys are common in the coastal areas; striated rock surfaces and erratic boulders occur up to several hundred meters above the present ice surface on mountains and nunataks in the interior. Studies aimed at dating the succession of glacial retreat and advance, however, have been limited to a very few localities along the coast—and even there have led to disputed results.

The suggestion has been made that during glacial maxima the grounded ice sheet may have extended everywhere to the edge of the continental shelf. The present mean negative free-air gravity anomaly on the Ross Ice Shelf could be a reflection of the retreat of the grounded ice 10,000 to 30,000 years ago. But the primary evidence relating to the former extent of the ground ice in the Ross Sea lies in the ocean bottom sediments, both under the Ross Ice Shelf and in the open sea.

How long Antarctica has been covered with ice is not known, but evidence is growing that it has been for at least several million years. Indications of glacial action 2.7 million years ago, and perhaps more than 10 million years ago, have been reported for different regions near the coast; glacial debris in deep-sea cores implies that widespread glaciation in East Antarctica began at least 4 million years ago.

RECOMMENDATIONS

1. Further studies of glacial history in ice-free areas should be carried out. The dry valleys of Victoria Land are particularly convenient in this regard, but it is important to extend studies to widely differing areas in order to distinguish between local events and those involving the ice sheet as a whole.

2. There should be increased emphasis on examining bottom sediments of oceans surrounding Antarctica. Studies of the effects of sea ice and shelf ice on the present assemblages of microfauna are needed to aid in the interpretation of cores marginal to the continent. It is thus important that core drilling be carried out under present ice shelves and in areas of permanent and periodic sea-ice cover.

3. Studies of long-term changes in sea level relative to the antarctic coast should be initiated. In combination with improving knowledge of absolute sea-level changes, these should indicate whether there are current isostatic movements of the continent.

4. Gravity measurements should be extended, particularly at the fringes of the continent, in an attempt to observe any anomalies that might throw light on variations in ice thickness and the positions of the ice margins.

5. Evidence relating to the possibility of different glacial histories in East and West Antarctica should be sought.

6. An adequate network of bench marks should be established in Antarctica as an aid to the determination of absolute elevations of the ice surface and changes in the relative heights of both the ice surface and the sea.

TECHNIQUES

Major advances in glaciological knowledge have often been the consequence of improvements in equipment and techniques. Several such improvements can be visualized for the near future.

RECOMMENDATIONS

Emphasis should be placed on the development of the following:

1. Portable core-drilling equipment for penetration to intermediate depths: Although the deep-drilling equipment is now operational, the bulk of the equipment and the time required to drill throughout the ice preclude the completion of a large number of holes. Supplementary portable equipment capable of penetrating ice shelves and small ice caps up to 1000 m thick would permit additional valuable drilling. The CRREL* thermal drill partly satisfies this need but has a depth limit of about 500 m.

2. Robot probes for transporting measuring instrument equipment deep into the ice without the necessity for drill-

---

*U.S. Army Cold Regions Research and Engineering Laboratory, now the Terrestrial Sciences Center.

ing a hole: Such a probe, which melts its way down through the ice using power supplied from the surface, is in the advanced stages of engineering development. Less advanced at present is the consideration of the instrumentation desirable in the probe for various research objectives.

3. Electromagnetic sounding equipment, for operation both from surface vehicles and from aircraft: Although this equipment is already providing many valuable data, there are significant improvements which are still needed in its sensitivity, resolution, clarity and accuracy of recording, and adaptability to automatic reduction of routine data.

4. Techniques for dating ice at all levels in the ice sheet: Geochemical techniques in particular have proven very fruitful, and continued refinement should be encouraged. The distribution of microparticles in the ice may prove useful for dating and correlation.

5. Satellite instrumentation and techniques: Especially important are the improvement of photographic definition to permit the study of features as small as sastrugi, the development of radar and multispectral sensors, provision of navigational equipment of sufficient accuracy for ice motion studies, the measurement of calving rates of glaciers and ice shelves, and the study of sea-ice distribution. It is important for analysis of satellite data that comparison be made in selected areas with observations made concurrently at lower levels.

6. Instruments for accurate measurement of blowing snow flux: Considerable progress has been made on this problem and work should be continued.

7. Vehicles for conducting measurements on the underside shelf ice: Possibilities include robots, small, manned submersibles, and naval submarines. These vehicles would be valuable in determining the mass and heat exchange between shelf ice and ocean.

OPERATIONS AND FACILITIES

It is essentially impossible for an investigator to proceed independently to any locality in the Antarctic to carry out his research. Large problems of logistic support are involved, and the scientist is limited in his work to programs for which support can be provided. It is important, therefore, to consider facilities and operations which would best promote the execution of the desired research objectives. The following recommendations are made from the standpoint of the antarctic field glaciologist.

RECOMMENDATIONS

1. Traverses of short mileage and heavy concentration on specific research programs should supplant the extended traverses, because the broad exploration phase of traverse programs has ended. Short traverses take advantage of the capability of aircraft to transport equipment and personnel to selected areas.

2. Drilling, both shallow and deep, should be made a major tool of glaciological research. Such drilling should be pursued as promptly and extensively as possible. The importance of drilling has already been mentioned in connection with several research recommendations, the major objectives being: study of the core, study of hole deformation, temperature measurements, density measurements, and correlation of these direct observations with results of indirect techniques such as seismic and electromagnetic sounding and nuclear scattering. Such studies would be particularly aided by cooperative international programs. A new hole should be located in an area of low accumulation and flow rates in order to obtain a record with a very long time span.

3. Temporary stations, meant for a few winters' use, should become a major adjunct of future antarctic research. There should be a continuous series of such stations in future years with sites carefully selected to take into account major research objectives, especially flow-line and dry valley studies.

4. The dry valleys should be subjected to systematic studies, some of which will require the establishment of winter stations. Of particular importance to glaciologists are comprehensive measurements on "ideal," or "model," glaciers and possible correlations with the flow of the ice sheet from the plateau, long-range studies of the relationships between glaciers and climate, and investigations of Pleistocene history. Dry valley stations would also be valuable for research on permafrost, patterned ground, wind erosion, mass-wasting on slopes, and weathering.

5. Increased emphasis should be placed on cooperative international programs as a means of extending logistic capabilities and of obtaining maximum scientific advantage from them.

APPENDIX C

Snow Research and Control

INTRODUCTION

Snow forms a transient, sedimentary veneer on much of the earth's land surfaces. The diverse economic effects of this snow layer are incalculable. It is a major and renewable hydrologic reservoir; in many areas of North America more than half of the utilized water is derived from melted winter snow. Flood damage from spring snowmelt is a recurring hazard in many river basins. The obstacles and hazards to ground transportation alone are formidable (there were more than 250 avalanche fatalities around Rogers Pass in the 75 years following construction of a transcontinental rail line through the Selkirk Mountains). In high latitudes the winter snow often is not a hindrance but provides a reliable roadbed for transportation.

Winter recreation is still a relatively small part of snow economics, but the growth rate is spectacular. The number of motor toboggans produced in this country has tripled in two years and was near 250,000 in 1969. General population growth, especially that in the arctic and subarctic regions, can only increase the impact of the annual winter snow cover on man's activities.

Very few snow investigators have concerned themselves exclusively with basic research in the properties of snow. Most applied snow research has been strongly oriented toward such tasks as forecasting runoff, improving water yield, controlling snow avalanches, or transporting supplies and erecting structures on polar ice sheets; many techniques have been developed by trial-and-error methods.

Snow research has been hampered by the complexity of a three-phase system and by the extreme variability of snow properties found in nature. These problems are a challenge to the pure scientist and are of great practical importance to the engineer. Solution of these problems will assist in mak-

ing winter snow cover an actively managed part of man's environment.

The winter snow cover is widely utilized today for water supply; snow-related natural phenomena, such as meltwater discharge and avalanching, are forecast with varying degrees of success. The purposeful interference by man with the natural character of winter snow—either by modifying its deposition or by altering its postdepositional character, e.g., by such activities as snow-drift control with fences, erection of structures to inhibit avalanches, or selective forest cutting to improve snow storage—is still relatively minor. The concept of snow as an actively managed natural resource is in its infancy, although the deposited winter snow cover is more accessible and amenable to artificial influence than most other geophysical phenomena. The rising economic pressures of water use, transportation, and winter recreation require serious consideration of the winter snow as a managed resource in the near future.

We lack the necessary fundamental understanding of physical processes of snow on which a rational program of management must be based. Snow management on a scale which would gain significant economic benefits through controlled water yield will be costly and will cause long-term alteration of the environment. Mistakes will be expensive, and the ecologic effects sometimes irreversible. If such snow management is to be systematically applied, then the fundamental laws governing the ice balance of drainage basins must first be clearly understood.

Snow influences a broad area of geophysical phenomena simply by its presence or absence. On a large scale the winter snow cover stores water, modifies surface albedo, insulates the ground, and modifies plant and animal habitats. For many purposes, only the bulk properties of snow are significant when it covers large regions of the earth's surface and persists for long periods of time in the high latitudes. To a first approximation, the details of internal snow-cover structure are of little interest to this broad area. Scientific interest in large-scale snow phenomena is strongly oriented toward mass and energy exchanges across the interfaces (earth–snow and snow–air).

On a smaller scale (thousands of cubic meters or less), structural and physical properties of snow become much more important. These properties largely determine the role of snow in such human activities as transportation, recreation, construction, and communication. Rapid internal changes often dominate the patterns of snow behavior. Because of the more evident relation to human activity, more theoretical work has been done on the smaller scale than on the larger scale.

THE LARGE-SCALE RELATIONS OF SNOW TO ITS ENVIRONMENT

A large-scale snow cover interacts with large-scale weather phenomena. The sharp increase in surface reflectivity (albedo) which accompanies snow deposition completely alters the radiation regime at the earth's surface. A change in surface albedo and emissivity over widespread areas of the continents modifies both local and large-scale weather patterns, but the exact nature of this modification is not yet established. The interaction of snow cover and world weather patterns has yet to be incorporated into numerical weather-prediction schemes because the uncertainties presently inherent in these schemes, particularly for snowfall prediction, do not warrant addition of still another variable.

The prospects of inducing major environmental changes by alteration of the winter snow are limited but must be taken into account. As an example, sustained and successful winter cloud-seeding over wide areas might increase the extent and duration of snow cover. What effects this would have in turn on local or general climate are not presently known. The possibility of a triggering action leading to weather changes far greater than those originally sought cannot be overlooked. An understanding of the basic relationship between winter snow and prevailing weather is essential to avoid the danger of accidentally inducing unwanted changes.

The economic effects of snow are dominated by its function as a water reservoir. A major economic activity is the assessment of water storage in the winter snow and the forecasting of its discharge as meltwater runoff. The critical need to apportion a limited water supply to a rapidly growing population, especially in the western United States, generates a rising demand for accurate measurements and forecasts. This need also requires a careful scrutiny of possible methods of increasing water storage in the mountain snow covers and manipulating the character of its discharge.

A NEW APPROACH TO SNOW HYDROLOGY

Measuring water storage in winter snow and forecasting its runoff is the province of snow hydrology. Because the factors affecting ice and water balances of hydrologic basins are many and complex, and available data about these factors are scanty or difficult to collect, snow hydrology has resorted to a statistical procedure known as the index method of measuring and forecasting. The primary index is the snow-course measurement, usually in a sheltered forest glade, where snow depth and water content are sampled at 10 to 20 points. Each snow course provides on the average an index for about 2500 sq km. Information on such other factors as precipitation, temperature, and soil moisture are also introduced as indices. Forecasts of runoff depend on deviations from long-term means obtained by multiple regression analysis.

The index method has serious limitations: (a) It requires snow-course and river-discharge records for many years before reliable correlations can be established. The method cannot be introduced quickly in new areas. (b) Modification of either the snow-course environment or the watershed alters their relationship and destroys the correlation. (c) The index method relies strongly on averages. It fails to accommodate the abnormal snow or weather patterns which often are the crucial ones economically. (d) The inherent limits of accuracy cannot be surmounted by simply adding more snow courses or increasing the number of indices.

Problems of the index method are illustrated by the Columbia River Basin, where current techniques in snow hydrology are well developed. In the Columbia Basin, 150 to 200 forecasts a year are prepared for stream runoff between April 1 and September 30. These forecasts are based on April 1 snow surveys and other data. Average forecast error ranges from 8 to 14 percent, with occasional errors up to 40 or 50 percent. By comparison, the usual deviation of one year's streamflow from a long-term average is no greater than 12 to 20 percent. Forecasts based on the index method thus improve the average accuracy only by a factor of about two. Greater forecasting precision is needed. Errors of even a few percent in assessing storage in the winter snow or determining its projected melt rate can cost millions of dollars to major hydroelectric systems, irrigation plans, or flood-control measures. Current efforts in snow hydrology include extensive real-time data telemetering from river basins and computerized correlation analyses. Such measures will surely improve snow measurements and runoff forecasts, but they do not remove the inherent limitations of index methods.

Ultimate improvement in snow hydrology requires a fundamental reassessment of methods. This is the overriding problem in snow research today. Accuracies required now and especially in the future can only be achieved by considering the ice-mass and energy balances of hydrologic basins. It is necessary to work with physical quantities instead of index numbers. A firm theoretical basis is needed to describe snow accumulation and ablation over large areas. Especially critical are the large-scale processes of energy exchange between snow and the atmosphere, for these determine the character of snowmelt and occurrence of floods. Development and test of theories will not be easy, for precisely the same reasons that forced snow hydrology to adopt index methods in the first place, but modern technology offers prospects which were not available 50 years ago. The following example illustrates one of these prospects:

The possibility exists in theory of deducing the absolute water storage in a river basin as the difference between measured input and output. Output consists of surface and subsurface discharge, while input (precipitation) is equal to the depletion (flux divergence) of atmospheric water vapor over a given area. This divergence can in principle be calculated from rawinsonde data at stations surrounding the given area. Over parts of the United States today, the station density is almost sufficient to give water-vapor flux-divergence data usable for some hydrologic purposes. With the advent of meteorological satellites that can scan atmospheric water-vapor profiles over large areas, the intriguing possibility exists that accurate flux-divergence measurements combined with energy-balance measurements and routine hydrological observations can be used to calculate snow-cover storage in lieu of estimates based on widely scattered ground samples.

ARTIFICIAL REGULATION OF SNOW STORAGE

Management of snow as a water resource, and possibly as a means of climate control, depends on alteration of the winter snow cover over large areas. Such artificial control seems to be possible, but no effective techniques have yet been suggested. Innovative ideas are needed. Until they are forthcoming, controlling or increasing water yield from snow will depend on the long-recognized possibilities of appropriate forest management. Research has already demonstrated that water yield can be improved, but this research has dealt mostly with patterned removal of trees from timbered basins. The complementary practice of selective afforestation has yet to be explored. A clear theoretical basis for predicting the best arrangement and best type of vegetation to ensure optimum snow storage needs to be developed.

The use of vegetation to achieve snow-management goals has the advantage of maximum aesthetic appeal in contrast to the use, even locally, of artificial structures or manipulation. The principal disadvantage of vegetation is the slow rate of growth, especially at high altitudes and latitudes. Therefore, to obtain useful results at an early date, experiments with types and patterns of plant growth need to be made simultaneously with a wide variety of plants in as many different climates and soils as possible, with the full

expectation that many of the experiments will fail.

The large-scale snow phenomena discussed in this section have the following in common:

(a) The phenomena are complex, development of basic equations is difficult, and testing theories in the field is apt to be time-consuming and expensive. There is a lack of basic theory to describe the large-scale interchange of mass and energy between snow and its environment.

(b) The quantities of snow involved in economically significant or scientifically important effects are large. Water-equivalent volume is measured in cubic kilometers.

(c) Artificial manipulation of snow in these areas will be slow to realize but offers the ultimate prospect of large economic gains through controlled or improved water yield.

(d) Large-scale snow modification, if it ever becomes technically and economically feasible, raises the possibility of irreversible climate changes whose character may or may not be predictable.

RECOMMENDATIONS

1. A sound theoretical framework should be developed, describing the accumulation and ablation of winter snow in large river basins. The framework should include treatment of surface energy balance, meltwater discharge, distribution of precipitation, and effects of terrain. This is especially important to snow hydrology, which deserves to be elevated from the realm of engineering applications to a proper earth science. Recruitment of qualified physical scientists is essential.

2. Emphasis should be placed on forest management as the immediate practical means of manipulating winter snow to the advantage of man. A careful review of first principles is required. Because experiments are necessarily lengthy, especially in alpine climates, it is essential that field testing accompany rather than follow theoretical developments.

THE SMALL-SCALE RELATION OF SNOW TO ITS ENVIRONMENT

Most existing snow-management and engineering research today is being done in the small-scale domain; prospects are most promising for immediate and practical expansion of such management. In many cases, techniques have already been established, field experiments are economically feasible, and practical improvements can be expected from applied research. While knowledge is reasonably well developed for some snow properties—the mechanics of high-density snow is probably the best example—there are some notable gaps.

One gap concerns the character of fluid diffusion, both liquid and gas, in snow. There is conflicting evidence about the existence and magnitude of air and water-vapor convection in snow. The percolation of meltwater and its effects on snow properties, particularly during the early stages of metamorphism, play a crucial role in avalanche formation and apparently are important in meltwater discharge. Hypotheses about the details of meltwater discharge are largely speculative.

Another gap is related to the role of crystallographic structure in determining such physical properties as strength and thermal conductivity. The importance of crystal types and sintering to snow behavior has long been recognized, but there is surprisingly little quantitative information available.

The transport of snow by the wind cannot yet be quantitatively predicted, especially in mountainous terrain where it governs avalanche formation, water storage, and runoff timing. In addition to the transport of snow particles by wind, there are also problems raised by the presence or absence of supercooled cloud droplets.

The effects of certain organic chemical traces on snow recrystallization have demonstrated that a powerful lever exists for profoundly modifying the mechanical properties of snow. The physical processes involved need to be understood before practical applications can be developed.

Snow is a remarkably unstable substance. Low-density new snow is especially unstable. Large differences in crystallographic, thermal, and mechanical properties are introduced by weather differences at the time of deposition. The subsequent changes in the snow—metamorphism, sintering, densification, settlement—also differ widely. All snow problems that must take into account its internal structure and physical properties relate to measuring and understanding the process variously called snow "maturation," "ripening," or "evolution." The diversity of paths this process can take is an obstacle to development of a unified conceptual framework to describe it.

The time sequence of structural changes in snow is significant to transportation (both snow removal and load-bearing capacity) and to avalanche formation. It governs the development of snow pressures (creep and glide on slopes and settlement on level ground), which are a major engineering problem. It appears from recent biological studies that they also influence the winter habits of animal life in areas of persistent snow cover.

Several unsolved problems in instrumentation are obstacles to a better understanding of snow structure and behavior. A simple, reliable device to telemeter or record snow depths with 1-cm accuracy has yet to be developed. Numerous schemes have been proposed, but none has stood the test of operation under all types of adverse weather. A reliable snow depth-meter would find immediate and widespread use in every branch of snow science. Devices such as the radioactive snow gauge and the snow pillow are now available to record or telemeter total water content of the snow cover, but none is yet available that will do the same

for a single layer of new snow to an accuracy of < 2 mm of water. The *in situ* measurement of snow crystal types, strength properties, and liquid-water percolation without disturbing snow structure has not yet been achieved. Such measurements are essential to research on low-density new snow and on the rapid changes accompanying intrusion of liquid water. They cannot be conducted in the laboratory, because removal or disturbance of snow specimens immediately alters their character. There is no simple, quick, and accurate method to determine the liquid-water content of a snow sample, either *in situ* or separated from the snow cover. Because liquid-water content varies rapidly in space and in time, a speedy method is essential to the study of melting snow.

Although there are many likely areas for practical improvement of management techniques in small-scale snow phenomena, the following promise the most valuable improvements and at the same time offer prospects of scientific advances.

RECOMMENDATIONS

1. Basic research is needed on the diffusion of fluids through snow, with special attention to the percolation and retention of liquid water in the snow cover (important to runoff forecasting) and to the effects of this percolation on snow structure (important to avalanche formation). The question of gas flow through snow by convection or wind diffusion should also be examined in the laboratory and field.

2. Investigations should be made into metamorphism and mechanical properties (especially rheology) of snow. The effects of crystal structure, conditions governing depth hoar formation, and properties of low-density snow all deserve special attention.

3. Basic instruments required for snow research should be developed.

AREAL STUDIES

Snow science has suffered to a certain degree from a polarization of interests around the two extremes of scale discussed above. Work on the details of snow structure sometimes has failed to take into account the larger climatological variables, while large-scale snow studies have tended to overlook the significance of structure. There has been remarkably little exchange of ideas, for instance, between snow hydrology and avalanche forecasting, although each can benefit from techniques and methods of the other. The evolution of glaciology is rapidly destroying this polarization by offering a comprehensive scientific viewpoint about the geophysics of ice. Glaciologists in the older, more restricted, sense have in fact led the way toward integrating divergent viewpoints about snow; for instance, the techniques of assessing annual water storage on the polar ice sheets have been borrowed nearly entirely from avalanche technology, not from hydrology. The most productive areas of snow research in the near future appear to be those concerned with large- and small-scale interactions. The following areas can specifically be identified as promising.

REMOTE SENSING OF THE SNOW COVER

The duration, distribution, temperature, and water content of winter snow are mostly known today from scattered observations at points on the ground. Aerial reconnaissance is just beginning to provide information on duration and distribution. The prospects of using satellites for this purpose are still largely unrealized. The assessment of snow conditions on an area-wide basis would open up a new dimension in snow hydrology and meteorology for scientific study as well as management. The largest immediate advantage would accrue to snow storage and runoff forecasting, where the availability of large-scale data acquisition systems would for the first time permit accurate, real-time determination of daily input and output of the snow reservoir in large river basins. Such knowledge is an essential prerequisite for realistic planning of large-scale snow management and for the development and testing of basic ice-mass and energy-balance equations for large river basins.

The rapid technological development of both passive and active sensors for aircraft and satellites points to the realization of such techniques in the near future. Satisfactory snow survey sensors depend on accurate knowledge of the physical properties of snow. The most important are the dielectric and reflective properties at infrared and microwave wavelengths. The ways in which these properties are affected by surface roughness, snow density, crystal structure, free-water content, and the distribution of ice layers need to be determined. The *in situ* measurement of factors affecting the microwave dielectric properties is especially required, because laboratory tests cannot provide the necessary ground truth for operational tests of sensors.

Remote sensing, particularly from satellites, will not become an active part of snow management overnight. Numerous operational and technical problems will have to be surmounted. For instance, it will be difficult to separate the radiation properties of snow from those of rocks and trees in the terrain typical of many large river basins. Several sensors operating simultaneously in different parts of the radiation spectrum or with different polarizations will be needed to measure a snow layer which exists on the ground among a dense stand of conifers. But the prospective benefits of organized area-wide observation of snow, from both scientific and practical viewpoints, warrant continued devel-

opment in this field. An improved knowledge of snow structure will in this case eventually lead to improved understanding of its large-scale behavior.

ENVIRONMENTAL EFFECTS ON SNOW

A single theme relates to snow research in widely divergent areas: the relation of the physical properties of snow to climate. Although the broad effects of different climates on winter snow-cover evolution are understood in qualitative terms, there is a remarkable lack of specific information from different parts of the world. The observations that provide this information are the simultaneous collection of standard climatological data and observation of snow properties such as density, temperature, crystal types, stratigraphy, and strength. Such observations have been systematically collected and published for long periods only from several sites in Switzerland and at two stations in North America. To the knowledge of the compilers of this report, they are not available elsewhere.

The climatic differences in snow structure are large. Mechanical strength is the most variable; tensile and shear strengths may differ by one or more orders of magnitude from one climate to another in snow of similar density, age, and origin. The types of snow crystals, either deposited or metamorphosed, which are common in one climate may be absent in another where entirely different structural changes are the rule.

The systematic, long-term acquisition of snow data in different climates requires minimal instrumentation. Undisturbed and accessible observation sites are essential, but these are already available in many cases in the form of hydrological snow courses. Standard daily climatological records from adjacent sites are required; hence, the daily presence of an observer is essential.

Data on snow climatology available today are provided almost entirely by avalanche warning network stations in Europe and by a much more limited network in the United States. The importance of enlarging such observations to yield a wide sampling of climate and snow conditions will become apparent when remote-sensing satellites generate large amounts of snow data. The variations of snow with climate are essential ground-truth data for remote sensing.

MESOSCALE PHENOMENA

Orographic effects on winter precipitation cause large differences in snowfall over short distances. These same effects strongly determine the patterns of wind, temperature, moisture, and radiation that control snowmelt. Local variations in water storage in mountainous terrain are thus ultimately determined by local weather patterns over distances of a few kilometers. The distribution of avalanche paths and their relative activity are also controlled by the interaction of local storm winds and terrain.

Small-scale and large-scale relations between snow and environment have been discussed above, but there is remarkably little to report about the mesoscale. This is due to the difficulties of collecting reliable field data at this scale. Small-scale studies, such as determining snow pressures on a hillside structure, are relatively easy to execute. Large-scale ones are extremely difficult, but such economic necessities as forecasting snow runoff have led to alternatives like the index method. The mesoscale has not been developed.

Glaciologists have come to recognize that weather variations over a few kilometers are often critical to the mass balance of alpine glaciers. Attempts to modify snow drift patterns to control runoff from small alpine basins have encountered the unpredictable patterns of wind flow and snow transport over mountain ridges. Improved knowledge in these and related areas ultimately rests on a better understanding of the mass and energy exchanges between an alpine snow cover and its environment. The importance of developing a sound theoretical basis for these exchanges has already been cited in respect to large-scale snow phenomena. The same applies to the mesoscale. In the latter case, data collection in the field on an area-observation basis is the critical problem, because variations of snow and weather are on a scale too small for such techniques as satellite observation but too large for point observation. The key to mesoscale studies lies in telemetry from reliable snow sensors and in a staff of competent observers who can travel freely in winter snow and steep terrain. Both are in short supply.

RECOMMENDATIONS

1. A comprehensive investigation of mesoscale snow and weather phenomena in mountainous terrain should be initiated. The lack of information about mesoscale variations in mass and energy balance is comparable in importance to the deficit of theory for snow hydrology.

2. Research should be accelerated on the remote sensing of snow-cover properties and distribution, with special attention to the establishment of adequate ground-truth stations and to the *in situ* determination of physical snow properties critical to sensor operation.

3. A systematic data-acquisition network should be established to determine on a synoptic and long-term basis the relations of snow-cover structure to climate. Some elements of such a network already exist or are being developed. Interagency cooperation among federal agencies in the United States would be fruitful and would permit maximum utilization of current facilities at minimum cost.

GENERAL RECOMMENDATIONS

1. A series of informal working conferences should be held among scientists and engineers familiar with the various scales of snow phenomena. An interchange of ideas and exploration of a common terminology would be fruitful.

2. Careful consideration should be given to the possibility that many of the recommendations relating to snow research and control can best be implemented by basic snow research stations in a few carefully selected but widely divergent climates. These stations should be specifically oriented toward comprehensive, all-scale studies of winter snow within the broad framework of modern glaciology. Such stations need be very few in number. In some cases they may simply constitute the expansion of existing facilities or programs. To be effective, they must be dedicated to an intensive, long-term program of snow research and must be staffed by highly competent physical scientists. Modest but adequate funding on a continuing basis would in the long run be much more productive than even large support on the limited project basis which often characterizes mission-oriented snow research.

5

Polar Geodesy and Cartography

In preparing this study, the Panel on Geodesy and Cartography was faced with the problem of what constituted the polar areas of the world. As cartographers and geodesists, the most obvious answer was the areas north of the Arctic Circle and south of the Antarctic Circle; both are along parallels of latitude 23°30′ from their respective geographic poles. However, most mapping programs and priorities are established to meet the needs of map users, not map makers. Accordingly, it seemed logical to explore the needs for maps and geodetic data of the disciplines represented by other panels of the Committee on Polar Research (CPR).

The answers by other scientific disciplines involved in polar research to the question, "In what areas are you interested?" indicated that they vary widely. Glaciologists are interested in glaciers anywhere they occur as evidence of a polar condition in that particular area. Political scientists are interested in the 60° S parallel as the delineating boundary of the Antarctic Treaty, although no similar geopolitical line exists for the Arctic. Life scientists find the tree line in the Arctic and the Antarctic Convergence in the south to be significant ecologically. Other disciplines, such as geology, geophysics, and meteorology, are especially concerned with the interrelationships between the subpolar and polar areas. The Panel chose the areas within the Arctic and Antarctic Circles as the primary areas to be considered in this study, but it has also attempted to treat the adjacent subarctic and subantarctic areas.

For this study, it was assumed that oceanographic charting of ocean-bottom topography is within the discipline of cartography. The Panel has coordinated this report with the Panel on Oceanography and will work closely with it in the future to resolve any problems of mutual interest.

The Panel on Geodesy and Cartography has duly considered in this report the mapping needs of the other scientific disciplines and has attempted to evaluate the degree to which existing or planned coverage meets these individual requirements. Many CPR panels, however, were unable to designate specific scales or map content or both as being uniformly needed by their disciplines, preferring instead to state these requirements in a general way. Accordingly, the Panel on Geodesy and Cartography has proceeded in many instances to state requirements for mapping and geodesy in the absence of specific guidance. Current status and future plans are outlined in this study for polar areas of interest, and on the user rather than on the Panel rests the ultimate decision of whether this coverage is adequate for the scientific use intended.

The unclassified aspect of the CPR long-range study perhaps affects the content of this Panel's contribution more than any other single panel. For the Arctic, maps, charts, aerial photography, geodetic data, and some of the systems by which they are acquired and produced are classified material. There has been no attempt to determine or otherwise assess the extent of classified information and related activities for the arctic areas. This is not a problem in the Antarctic, as nations are governed by the peaceful provisions of the Antarctic Treaty. There may be information in some parts of the Arctic that is not listed in the study or on the status charts that accompany it. The coverage indicated on the following pages is that which generally is available to U.S. and foreign polar scientists.

There are three distinct areas of interest for cartography in the polar regions: *military, economic*, and *scientific*. Existing charts do not satisfy any of these interests. Military interest in the Arctic Ocean is much greater than in the Antarctic Ocean and is primarily aimed at under-ice navigational safety. Economic interest is also greater in the Arctic, where under-ice maritime commerce between Europe or the American east coast and the Far East has been postulated. The only maritime nation that has regularly penetrated into the arctic seas is the Soviet Union, and its efforts have been confined to the margin of the Eurasian continent. Economic charting in antarctic waters will not receive this impetus until commercial deposits in Antarctica can be developed. Scientific interest in the polar oceans, other than in the strict topographic character of the sea floor, is directed toward the interpretation of observed physical data and the resolution of extant hypotheses. The nature of polar circulation must be known to understand the global circulation of the oceans. Knowledge of the crustal structure of the earth beneath the polar oceans is inadequate, and the relief and structures must be known to integrate them into the global tectonic pattern. Sea-floor spreading and continental drift need testing, and anomalous geophysical patterns must be correlated with bathymetric data for interpretation.

Emphasis should be directed toward acquisition of data and production of bathymetric charts commensurate with the needs of safe navigation. Surveys for acquisition of these data with slight modification to cover anomalous features and specific areas of interest should satisfy the immediate needs of all engaged in polar research. Bathymetric surveys in the polar regions have lagged behind photogrammetric mapping programs because of the inaccessibility of the ice-covered waters, the difficulty of providing navigational aids, and the logistic requirements of the platforms used for conducting the surveys. In the Antarctic, most of the surface ships capable of penetrating the ice cover provide logistic support for all other aspects of polar research.

Proliferation of names of bathymetric features in the polar regions has seriously concerned chart publishers. They have often felt compelled to use the names presented by the authors of texts that accompanied the charts, when they knew that the names and terms were not in accord with those used by the U.S. Board on Geographic Names (BGN). The BGN established the Advisory Committee on Undersea Features (ACUF), and this committee is the authority for standardization of nomenclature of bathymetric features for all U.S. Government agencies. ACUF has standardized the terms to be used and has defined these terms so that they can be readily applied to newly discovered features. In view of the need for standardization of nomenclature, all newly proposed names in the polar oceans should be submitted to this committee for approval. This problem is no longer serious for land features, though it once was, especially in the Antarctic. Through the efforts of the BGN Advisory Committee on Antarctic Names (ACAN), antarctic scientists and others are encouraged to submit proposed names for early decisions before the names are printed in reports or on maps. Cooperation with similar groups of other nations has also been effected, eliminating a problem that verged on causing extensive confusion. The cooperation and methods now working so well in the Antarctic show what can be done and could be a pattern for similar regulation in treatment of names in polar oceans.

ARCTIC ALASKA

PAST CARTOGRAPHIC ACCOMPLISHMENTS

Because of the remoteness of arctic Alaska and its unusually difficult working conditions, little mapping was undertaken during the early years following the purchase of Alaska in 1867. The Navy Department, the U.S. Coast Guard, and the U.S. Coast and Geodetic Survey conducted several exploratory survey and charting operations along the arctic coast, but it was not until after 1900 that exploratory surveys were undertaken in the interior of arctic Alaska. Initially these surveys were conducted in conjunction with mineral resource investigations, and the maps were published as inclusions to U.S. Geological Survey *Bulletins*. Systematic operations for uniform map publication began after 1920.

The greatest strides in mapping of arctic Alaska were made from 1945 to 1960. By the end of World War II, most of arctic Alaska had been mapped, but the mapping consisted of crude exploratory surveys. During the period 1945–1952, all available source material was used to compile 1:250,000-scale maps covering Alaska, but those covering arctic Alaska were considered poor by modern standards and have been replaced.

In 1945, the U.S. Coast and Geodetic Survey (USC&GS) undertook the charting of the coast of arctic Alaska from Point Hope to Demarcation Point. The hydrographic and topographic surveys for the charts were accomplished from 1945 to 1953. The 30 charts at 1:50,000 scale covering the coastline were published between 1955 and 1958 as classified documents. They have recently been declassified and made available for public use.

Accurate topographic mapping of the northern Alaska coast was completed by the U.S. Army's 30th Engineer Topographic Battalion in 1955, but the maps were published only in military editions.

In 1955, the U.S. Geological Survey (USGS) undertook the Brooks Range Project to complete accurate 1:250,000-scale mapping of an area of about 120,000 square miles in arctic Alaska using modern photogrammetric methods. The project area extended 500 miles westward from the Alaska-Canada boundary, south to the Arctic Circle, and north to existing mapping along the arctic coast. Using new mapping techniques for this extensive project, the field operations were completed in about two months during the summer of 1956.

CURRENT CARTOGRAPHIC PROGRAMS

U.S. Geological Survey

The USGS distributes 1:1,000,000-scale mapping of arctic Alaska completed by the Army Map Service, now known as the U.S. Army Topographic Command (TOPOCOM). This mapping conforms to the International Map of the World 1:1,000,000-scale series standards except for certain cartographic specifications. The USGS also has complete 1:250,000-scale coverage of the area. The TOPOCOM has compiled a considerable amount of 1:50,000-scale mapping along the arctic coast. The USGS is presently preparing 1:63,360-scale civil editions of these compilations with 50- and 100-ft contour intervals. The extent of the coverage is shown on Figure 6.

The Brooks Range project was published at the scale of 1:250,000, which was considered adequate at the time. However, interest in more detailed mapping has recently developed due to significant oil discoveries along the north slope. To accomodate proposed development of the area, plans are being made to complete the 1:63,360-scale mapping by the mid-1970's, with initial emphasis on the central part of the area.

The USGS recently made a notable contribution to the geography and history of Alaska in the publication of Professional Paper 567, *Dictionary of Alaska Place Names*. This 1084-page volume contains nearly 44,000 entries of geographic names that are presently applicable and have been affixed to places and features of the Alaskan landscape.

U.S. Coast and Geodetic Survey

The USC&GS produces coastal charts of the United States. Its present charting program in Alaska involves preparing the recently declassified arctic coast charts for public issue.

The USC&GS also publishes a status report of horizontal and geodetic control that has been accomplished in the area. The extent and location are shown in Figure 7. It also updates and publishes various categories of aeronautical charts of the area.

Aerial Photography

All Alaska has been photographed for mapping. The acceptable mapping photography was taken during the period 1948–1957 through the combined efforts of the U.S. Navy, the U.S. Air Force, and the USGS. Most of this work employed single-lens photography at 1:40,000 scale, utilizing 6-in. focal length cartographic cameras. The Brooks Range was photographed by the USGS with transverse twin low-oblique photography at 1:60,000 scale. The area known as Naval Petroleum Reserve No. 4 (extending west from the Colville River to 162° W longitude and north of the Brooks Range to the Arctic Ocean) was photographed by the U.S. Navy at 1:20,000 scale. Indexes showing the location of this photography have been prepared by the U.S. Army Corps of Engineers. In some areas, later and larger-scale special-purpose or mapping photography has been taken by various U.S. Government agencies. For information about aerial photography in Alaska, contact the Map Information Office, U.S. Geological Survey, Washington, D.C. 20242.

RECOMMENDATIONS

1. The USGS should expedite current plans to complete 1:63,360-scale map coverage of arctic Alaska.
2. The program of completing 1:63,360-scale civil editions of TOPOCOM coverage of the arctic coast should be continued by the USGS.
3. The USGS should recognize and implement the requirement for mapping at a larger scale than 1:63,360.

ARCTIC CANADA

HISTORY OF CARTOGRAPHIC AND GEODETIC PROGRAMS

The first detailed mapping of the Canadian Arctic was undertaken during World War II when this area became an air supply route leading both to Asian Russia and to northern Europe. A crash program to provide aeronautical charts for these routes was set up, and in spite of the many obstacles, adequate charts were provided for use on these vital lines of communication. The scale of 8 miles to 1 inch was chosen, and with the National Topographic System format of 2 deg in latitude by (depending on the latitude) 4, 8, or 16 deg in longitude, the whole of Canada was covered with 221 sheets. All available geographic information was used in the plotting. In the Arctic, shorelines from hydrographic charts were generally accepted as drawn, but to confirm this information and to locate inland landmarks a series of astrofixes were taken. In 1943, about 50 of these points were read, and an additional 72 were taken in 1944. The plotting of map detail was greatly facilitated by the use of trimetrogon photography which was being taken over Canada by the U.S. Air Force (USAF) in 1943 and 1944. Of the 221 sheets of the series all but 20 were published by March 1944. The series was completed by March 1945, but it must be understood that many of the sheets of this series were labeled "preliminary" and contained areas marked "unexplored."

During the same period some arctic hydrography was carried out, mainly in support of the Arctic Air Lift by providing charts for routes for the sea supply of such arctic airports as Frobisher Bay and Coral Harbor.

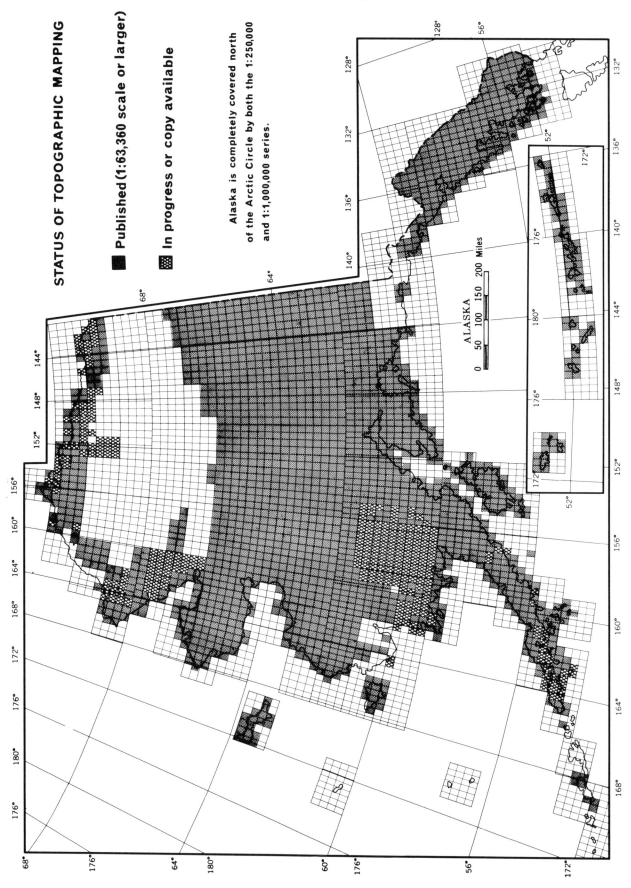

STATUS OF TOPOGRAPHIC MAPPING

■ Published(1:63,360 scale or larger)

▨ In progress or copy available

Alaska is completely covered north of the Arctic Circle by both the 1:250,000 and 1:1,000,000 series.

ALASKA

0 50 100 150 200 Miles

FIGURE 6   Status of topographic mapping, Alaska.

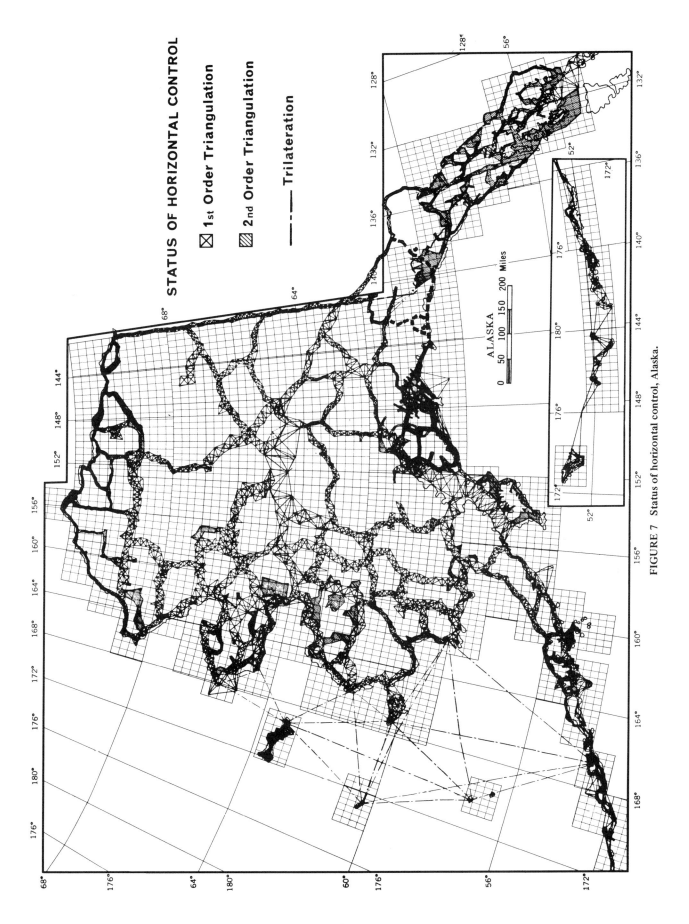

STATUS OF HORIZONTAL CONTROL

⊠ 1st Order Triangulation

▨ 2nd Order Triangulation

—·— Trilateration

ALASKA

Miles

0 50 100 150 200

FIGURE 7 Status of horizontal control, Alaska.

Post-World War II Programs

Wartime activities in the Canadian Arctic had focused the attention of all Canadians on this part of their country. Following World War II, Canadian and American military authorities considered that this region might well be of future strategic importance. At the same time, Canadian industry was expressing interest in the Arctic, and many commercial concerns joined the military in pointing out to the Canadian Government the need for a comprehensive arctic mapping program.

Geodetic control was the first requirement. Any plan to cover the Canadian Arctic quickly by conventional geodesy was out of the question. The techniques developed during the war for pinpoint bombing were examined. Of these the Shoran Control System was considered most efficient for precise distance measuring. In 1947, this system was incorporated into a trilateration project which in 10 years would provide a complete net of triangles with sides about 200 miles long, covering the whole of northern Canada. The extent of this net is illustrated in Figure 8. It is interesting to note that in 1957, at the peak of operations of this survey, it was, and still is, the largest concentration of survey effort that has ever been mobilized in the Canadian Arctic. There were 4 Lancaster photo aircraft, 6 DC-3 support aircraft, 12 Shoran ground stations and crews, and support personnel totaling 200 men.

The second basic requirement for arctic mapping was air photo cover. In 1947, a very extensive program was launched which over the following 20 years would lead to the complete vertical coverage of Canada. The Canadian Arctic was covered during the period 1958–1962.

In 1947, plans were made for the complete topographic map coverage of the Dominion at the scale of 1:250,000. This scale was chosen because it was the largest that could be completed within the time limit of 20 years set by the military, with the mapping resources available. Work at larger scales had to continue also at an accelerated rate, and although the 1:250,000 program was important, it was by no means the only priority work.

Two government agencies were involved in surveying and plotting these maps: the Surveys and Mapping Branch of the then Department of Mines and Technical Surveys and the Army Survey Establishment of the Department of National Defense. The Arctic was divided into two regions with the Army Survey Establishment responsible for the western sheets and the Surveys and Mapping Branch responsible for those of the east. The specifications for all sheets were identical, and the user can determine which agency produced a map only by consulting the credit note. This program was virtually completed on time. Twenty years and a few months after a basic decision was made, 895 of the 918 sheets of this series were published (Figure 9), and the rest are available in a preliminary monochrome form. All the maps of this series for areas falling to the north of the Arctic Circle have been published.

Large-Scale Mapping

Early in the execution of the 1:250,000 program, it became apparent that certain areas of the Canadian Arctic needed maps at larger scales. The Department of National Defense required tactical maps in general along the mainland coast from the U.S. border to the King William Peninsula. Some of the Distant Early Warning Line (DEW Line) sites were constructed in this area, and part of the requirement was in support of this project. Also, the local defense of other arctic installations, such as Frobisher Bay, required large-scale maps. In addition to the military requirement, large-scale maps were needed in support of both scientific activity and the exploratory work of the petroleum and mining industry. Examples of scientific mapping include the Thompson Glacier map, the Meighen Island maps, and the Ellef Ringnes Island coverage, all at 1:50,000 scale. Present coverage at this scale is shown in Figure 10.

Hydrographic and Aeronautical Charting

Postwar interest in the Arctic, in particular the construction of the DEW Line, created the urgent need for better charts of these waters. The work of the Hydrographic Service was made considerably easier by the mapping activity on shore. Nevertheless, the problems faced and overcome by the hydrographers were considerable.

Since World War II, these reconnaissance charts at 8 miles to the inch have been revised, and most of them have now been converted to a 1:500,000 scale. In recent years, topography on the newer sheets has been revised from the 1:250,000-scale maps. The sixty-eight 1:1,000,000-scale air charts, drawn to International Civil Aviation Organization standards, which cover Canada, have been derived from the 8-mile-to-the-inch series.

Post-Shoran Geodesy

The second-order Shoran geodetic net covering the Arctic was completed in 1957. Attention was then focused on methods of increasing the accuracy of this net. The first action was to push northward a loop of conventional triangulation from the first-order networks of southern Canada. This work reached Cambridge Bay, where a tie was made with the Shoran station at that site.

The Geodetic Survey was continually seeking new systems for long-range geodetic measurement. Two novel methods have been employed recently in the Arctic. The first observations on satellites were used by the USC&GS in their worldwide program to provide geodetic positions. Canadian civilian and military agencies cooperated with their Ameri-

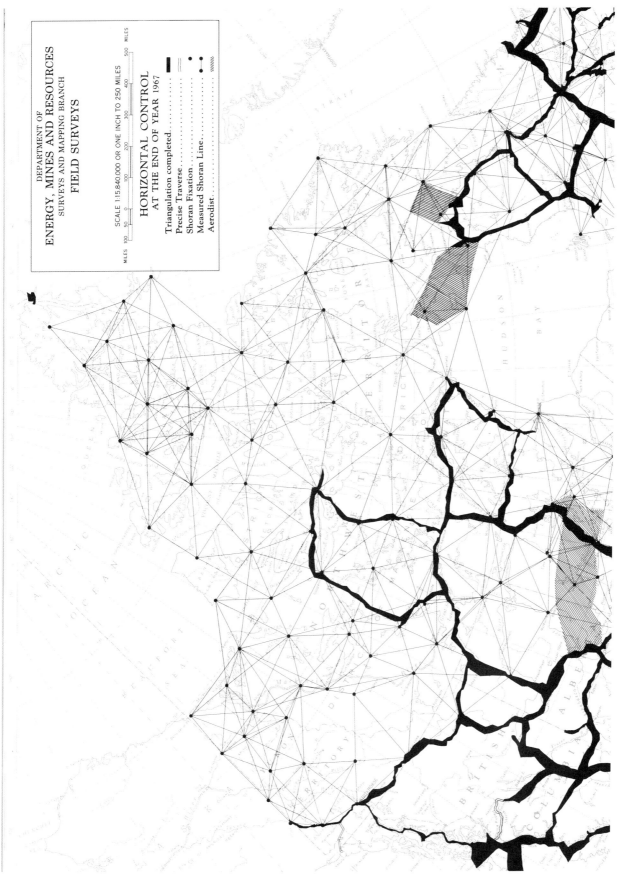

FIGURE 8   Horizontal control, trilateration net, northern Canada.

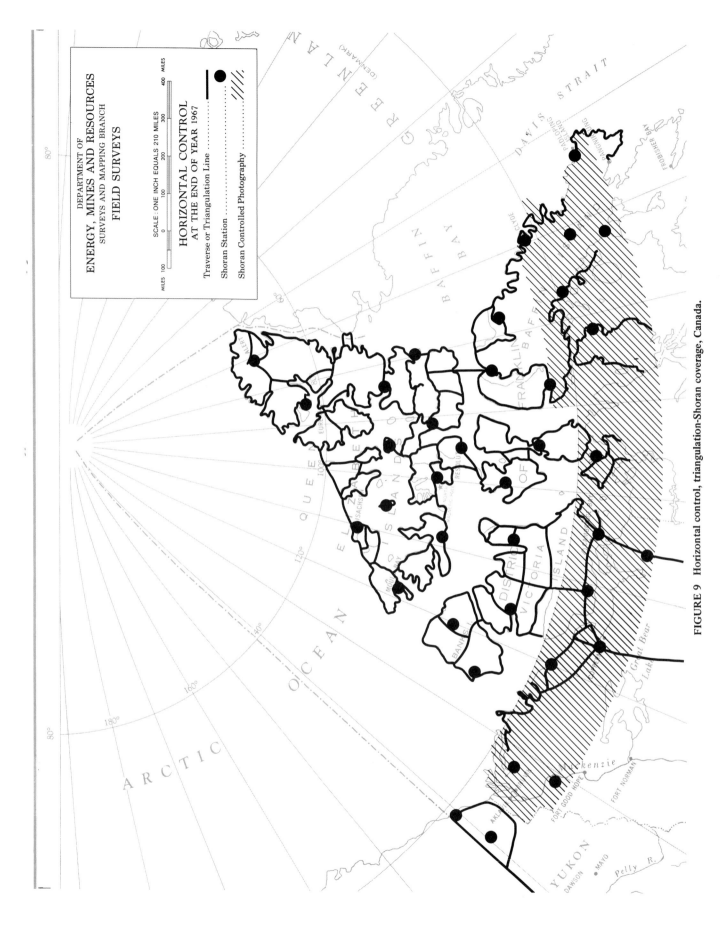

FIGURE 9 Horizontal control, triangulation-Shoran coverage, Canada.

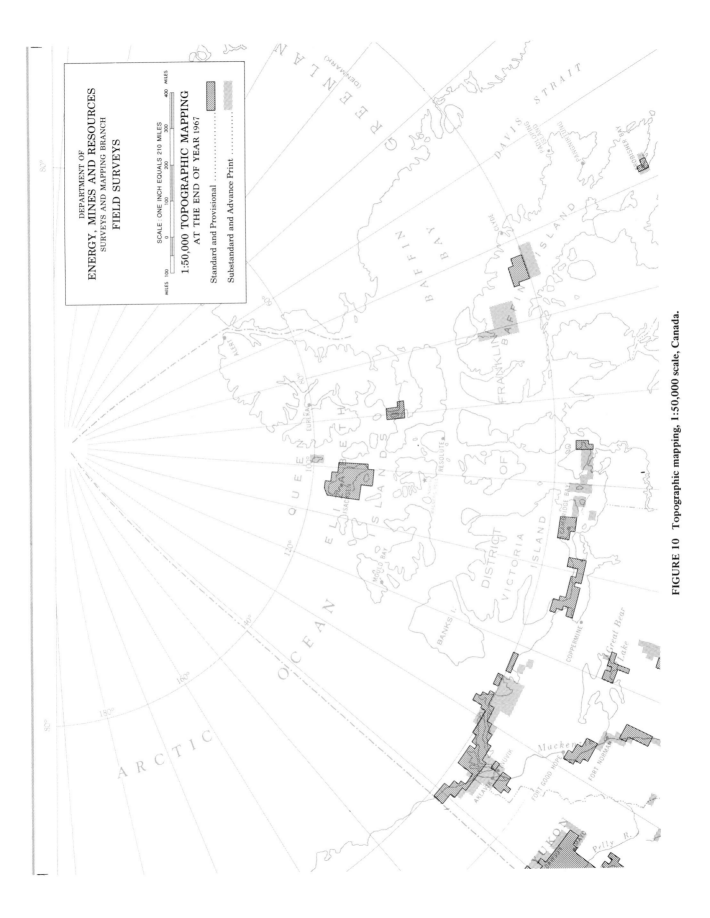

FIGURE 10 Topographic mapping, 1:50,000 scale, Canada.

can colleagues on this work, which will provide additional strength to the arctic Shoran net by giving independent values for positions at Cambridge Bay and Frobisher Bay. The Frobisher station has not yet been tied to the Shoran net, but at Cambridge Bay, that crossroads of Canadian arctic geodesy, the benefit of satellite triangulation was evidenced, causing positional shifts of about 15 meters in the conventional triangulation and Shoran.

The other nontraditional method of measurement employed by Canadian geodesists was the use of the aerodist. This is an airborne version of the tellurometer and has been used in the Canadian Arctic to make measurements across Hudson Strait. The procedures being used at present are designed to produce first-order accuracy.

The present status of geodesy in the Canadian Arctic is shown in Figures 8 and 9. Figure 8 indicates the locations of the geodetic first-order net in the Arctic, satellite observation stations, Aerodist trilateration, and the Shoran trilateration net. Figure 9 shows the tellurometer traverses which are estimated to be second-order control. No precise leveling has been carried out in the Arctic.

Cartography

Small-scale maps of 1:1,000,000 and 1:500,000 (8 miles to the inch) completely cover the Canadian Arctic. The latter are older sheets and are being converted to the metric scale as they are revised. Medium-scale maps, the 1:250,000 series, cover the entire Arctic and are all contoured and up to date. Some large-scale maps, 1:50,000 and larger, are available for the Canadian Arctic. Figure 10 shows the location of 1:50,000 mapping. Site plans of all arctic settlements have been drawn at 1:10,000 and larger scales.

CURRENT PROGRAMS IN GEODESY AND CARTOGRAPHY

The most promising area of the Canadian Arctic, from the point of view of immediate petroleum exploitation, appears to be the valley and delta of the Mackenzie River. It is therefore proposed to augment the geodetic control in this area and follow with a program of topographic mapping at 1:50,000 scale. The geodetic control will be extended, by Aerodist techniques, west to the Alaskan boundary and then progressively eastward across the Barren Lands. The topography will follow, probably by photomapping at a 1:50,000 scale.

Staking of mineral claims in the Coppermine area has been quite active during the past year and has led to plans for additional mapping in the area. Here too, photomaps will probably be produced initially.

Further utilization of Hudson Bay as a shipping route has led to considerable cartographic activity. The improved hydrographic charts have assisted in reducing insurance rates for ships active in this region, and the Hydrographic Service intends to continue this work. Topographic mapping at a 1:50,000 scale, planned for the northwest shore to a depth of one or two sheets, will facilitate the location of anchorages and the detailed exploration of the interior.

On Baffin Island, the iron ore deposits in the Mary River district are being developed, which will probably lead to an extension of existing topographic mapping.

RECOMMENDATIONS

One of the most pressing needs in the Canadian Arctic is the requirement for a more accurate determination of sea level and the establishment of certain inland elevations. Furthermore, there is a need for greater cartographic coverage of the Canadian Arctic at scales larger than 1:250,000. While the present horizontal control is considered suitable for medium-scale mapping, the ultimate objective, leading to the production of maps at larger scales, is first-order stations at 50- to 100-mile intervals with a systematic breakdown of lower-order positions as required. Directing our attention toward these goals, we make the following recommendations:

1. Several tidal stations should be installed at select locations along the Canadian arctic coastline, and subsequently, selected precise level lines should be established.
2. A cartographic program should be initiated to map select areas of Canada north of the Arctic Circle at scales of 1:125,000 and 1:50,000.
3. The proposed North American densification satellite station on Prince Patrick Island should be established.

GREENLAND AND SURROUNDING WATERS

STATUS OF CARTOGRAPHIC COVERAGE

While almost all the area of Greenland is covered by maps of various scales, the quality of the cartographic products is not uniform. The mapping of Greenland was organized at an early date by the Geodetic Institute of Denmark, which provides most of the large- and small-scale topographic maps of the inhabited areas. This institute provides complete coverage of the island at a 1:250,000 scale, excepting the extreme northern coastal areas.

CURRENT MAPPING AND CHARTING PROGRAMS

The U.S. Naval Oceanographic Office (NAVOCEANO) has a continuing program for production and revision of hydrographic charts in the Arctic Basin area, including Greenland. These charts at various scales show bathymetric data, navigational data, and variations in the ice conditions. NAVOCEANO published and distributes the Air Navigation Charts (Code V30). These charts, at scales of 1:2,187,400 and 1:2,188,800 (Mercator projection), are used for long-range air navigation and plotting. They show contours and gradient tints at minimum intervals of 1000 ft.

The TOPOCOM present program consists only of keeping stocks of U.S. and foreign maps of Greenland up to date. There are no plans for TOPOCOM mapping in this area. The USAF program maintains all navigational charts to reflect recent changes in cartographic and navigational data.

Current index maps showing availability of U.S. and Danish maps of Greenland are listed in Appendix A.

RECOMMENDATIONS

The scientific explorations of Greenland and its surrounding waters can be accomplished in a more effective manner by the completion of high-quality maps of the island and charts showing variations in the oceanographic and ice conditions and bathymetric data, especially of the continental shelf.

Charts published by NAVOCEANO for Greenland's coastal areas are largely reproductions of Danish charts, or modifications thereof, with data added from U.S. Navy (USN) surveys. It seems quite apparent that the major effort needed to improve charts of Greenland would be cartographic compilation from existing charts, photography, and data holdings, as opposed to data acquisition. While survey requirements are small by comparison to the total area of Greenland's coastal waters, there is a need to survey some 2700 square miles of water area.

We also make the following specific recommendations:

1. A systematic hydrographic development program should be initiated to survey the harbors and approaches to Thule and Unamak, Egedesminde, Godthaab, Jakobshavn, and Kusanartok.

2. Consideration should be given to the development of methods for making precise measurements between Greenland, Iceland, Svalbard, and Norway for the purpose of detecting present-day movement of the north Atlantic Ocean rift zone.

3. Side-looking radar imagery should be employed to provide, for the first time, a synoptic view of the entire Greenland Ice Sheet and its outlet glaciers. Such cartographic coverage would allow completion of the Greenland coastal areas map, would reveal geologic and glacial features not discernible by other means, and would provide a method for rapid horizontal positioning of oceanographic data.

4. A program should be undertaken to produce high-altitude photography of the main outlet glaciers of Greenland. Orthophotomaps and photoplans made from high-altitude photographs will provide a convenient method for measuring the changes in movement of glaciers and their rates of recession.

5. The triangulation net of Greenland should be expanded, particularly in the northern coastal areas and in geographic areas where other high-priority scientific work is scheduled.

6. A system of rapid position determination, similar to the Electronic Position Indicator, should be employed to improve navigation and to aid in locating the movement of ice islands and other features of scientific interest along the Greenland shoreline and the continental shelf.

ARCTIC OCEAN BASIN

RECENT AND CURRENT CARTOGRAPHIC PROGRAMS

Much of the unclassified charting effort in the Arctic Ocean has been limited to those areas accessible to surface navigation. With the exception of the relatively small amount of data acquired from the ice islands and early ships frozen into the ice, almost all the data have been collected around the fringes of the ice pack. Three small-scale charts (1:4,205,000), recently published by NAVOCEANO, provide continuous coverage between 50° N and 80° N. A new Canadian bathymetric chart of the western Arctic Ocean has been published in support of the General Bathymetric Chart of the Oceans (GEBCO). Figure 11 shows the status of the charting.

The present U.S. effort in charting the Arctic Ocean regions is in support of the resupply missions to various military installations. Data are still being acquired from the ice islands, but unfortunately little of it is being added to charts because of the low military priorities in the area.

The ACUF to the U.S. Board on Geographic Names recently concluded a study of bathymetric nomenclature for arctic waters. This study was initiated at the request of a group of scientists engaged in arctic research (Beal *et al.*, 1966) and resulted in the approval of 54 bathymetric names for use by all arctic investigators in the future.

GEODETIC CONTROL NETWORKS

Amerasia Basin

If bathymetric surveys made in the Arctic Ocean along the northern coast of Alaska are to be positioned by short-range electronic equipment, a network of triangulation with a station spacing of 10 to 15 km is available for the shore-based stations. The Shoran network in northern Canada, plus the tellurometer traverses around the islands in the Canadian Arctic, would provide excellent control for any

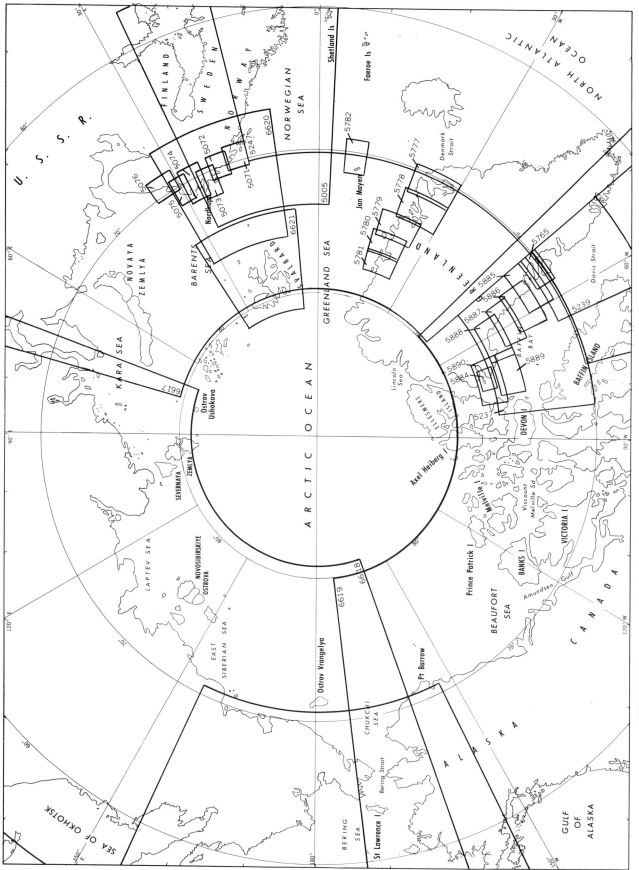

FIGURE 11 Oceanographic charting of the arctic regions. H.O. 2560 at radial scale of 1° = 1 cm covers the entire Arctic.

short-range network in that region. The north coast of Greenland also has a limited amount of control which could be used for this special purpose. If the hydrographic and oceanographic surveys extend beyond the limits of short-range systems, Loran A and Loran C coverage is available. Figures 12 and 13 indicate the coverage and the location of the control stations for these long-range hyperbolic systems. Omega, one of the newest electronic positioning systems and sometimes referred to as the "ultimate," is also available in the arctic regions. However, with the present configuration of only four of the eventual eight master stations in operation, its use is not recommended. Omega also functions as a hyperbolic system, but the stations are not identified as "master" or "slave." Any two stations used as a pair define a hyperbolic line of position. Positioning errors may be as great as 1 or 2 km because of diurnal effects due to the height of the ionosphere. Tables for Omega are available from NAVOCEANO if no other system is available. The USN Navigational Satellite System is available for the entire area and with care will provide position control within an accuracy of 200 or 300 m. Stations in the worldwide geometric satellite network, plus those of the North American densification network, serve to strengthen and improve these various systems by providing accurate scale and orientation. Additional information on all these systems is published in the *Proceedings of First Marine Geodesy Symposium* (1966).

Eurasia Basin

A limited amount of geodetic control exists along the northern coastline of Norway and the Soviet Union. In northern Siberia, arcs of triangulation have been extended along the rivers northward to the Arctic Ocean. Bathymetric surveys employing short-range systems for control could be adequately positioned in the western part of the region, but in the eastern area the shore-based control is very widely spaced. Figures 12 and 13 indicate the coverage available from Loran A and Loran C systems.

RECOMMENDATIONS

Bathymetry of the Arctic Ocean Basin

To assist in understanding the tectonic and geophysical relationships of the known structures in the Arctic Ocean Basin, we make the following recommendations:

1. A general bathymetric chart of the basin, showing the major relief features and physiographic provinces, should be prepared.
2. As soon as possible, an active data acquisition program should be instituted, commencing with under-ice reconnaissance surveys by nuclear submarine.

3. Continued soundings of the sea floor from present ice island stations should be supplemented by temporary stations more advantageously located and by light aircraft making additional observations a few hundred miles from drifting stations.

Geodesy in the Arctic Ocean Basin

Eventually the worldwide geodetic satellite network will geometrically connect all continents and will strengthen the existing Loran systems. While the Panel endorses this worldwide system, we further recommend:

1. A classical triangulation connection should be made across the Bering Strait, tying together the surveys in Alaska and eastern Siberia.
2. The discussions on the feasibility of the connection recommended in 1, initiated more than 30 years ago by representatives of the United States and the Soviet Union, should be reopened.

GENERAL RECOMMENDATIONS FOR THE ARCTIC

To furnish a base for future scientific investigations and to provide a means for better organization of results of these efforts to date, it is recommended that the following maps be prepared. These recommendations are substantially in agreement with the recommendations made earlier by the Committee on Polar Research (1961, 1963):

1. A general map of the Arctic at a scale of 1:3,000,000 should be prepared, based on a polar stereographic projection and similar to the two-color American Geological Society map presently available for the Antarctic.
2. A general-purpose map of the Arctic Basin should be prepared, including all Greenland extending south to approximately 60° N latitude at a scale of 1:5,000,000, similar to the American Geographical Society map of the Antarctic. This map, published in a multicolor edition, should provide a synoptic view of all resources of the Arctic. It should also include up-to-date bathymetric data of the Arctic and recent knowledge of the great continental shelf of this area.
3. The preparation of an Arctic Map Folio Series for the Arctic, patterned after the American Geographical Society *Antarctic Map Folio Series*, would ultimately have great scientific value, particularly for organizing the scientific data of the International Oceanographic Years, 1970-1980. The atlas should include those portions of the arctic oceanography now covered in the *Serial Atlas of Marine Environment* (1962 continuing), compiled by the American Geographical Society, and the *Oceanographic Atlas of the Polar Seas, Part II* (1958).

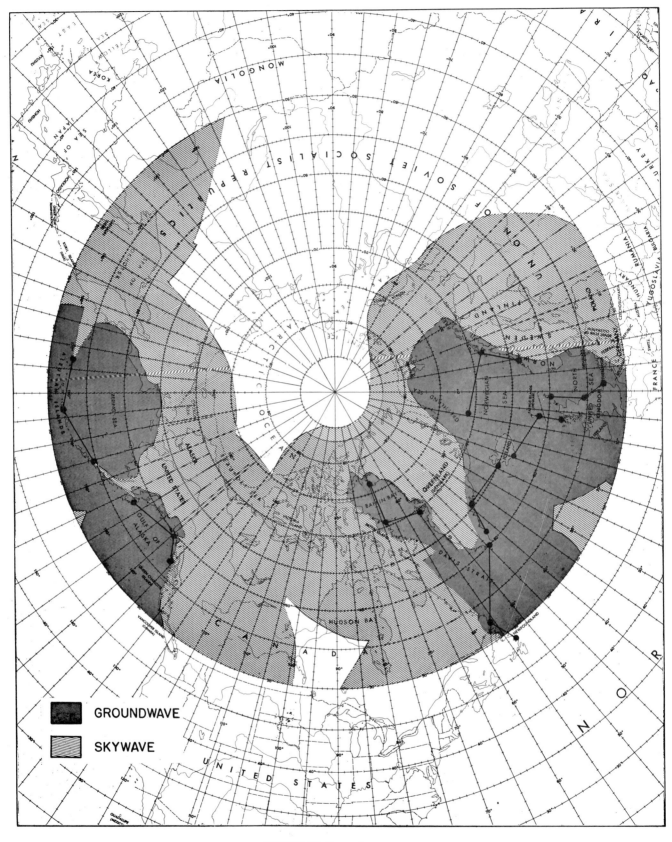

FIGURE 12   Loran A coverage.

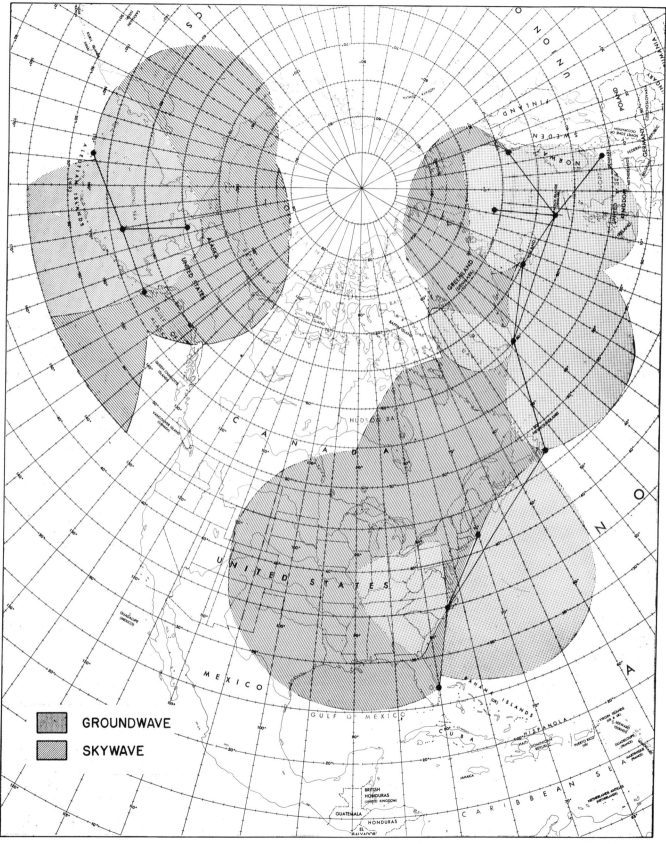

FIGURE 13 Loran C coverage.

ANTARCTICA

The unique spirit of international cooperation in the Antarctic extends to mapping and charting and has eased the task of keeping abreast of the latest progress in cartographic coverage by all the nations active in Antarctica. During the second meeting of the Scientific Committee on Antarctic Research (SCAR) in Moscow in 1958, a temporary Working Group on Cartography was authorized. At a later SCAR meeting it was converted to a permanent Working Group on Geodesy and Cartography. As a result of the activities of the working group, SCAR has made a series of formal recommendations to member governments pertaining to standards, technical specifications, and symbols for antarctic surveys and maps. Maps of Antarctica produced by the USGS conform to these recommendations.

Another SCAR recommendation called for the exchange between member nations of all cartographic data of areas within the interest of SCAR. The Working Group maintains and regularly distributes a current list of topographic maps and aeronautical and hydrographic charts of Antarctica. The focal point within the United States for the international exchange of these data is the USGS in its function as the U.S. Antarctic Mapping Center. It also maintains the Antarctic Map and Aerial Photography Library in Silver Spring, Maryland, in which are stored some 1200 foreign and U.S. maps and charts of Antarctica and nearly 250,000 aerial photographs, including most of those taken by the USN during Operation Highjump and the Ronne Antarctic Research Expedition and all those taken by the USN since the International Geophysical Year as a part of the U.S. Antarctic Research Program.

EAST ANTARCTICA

Past Mapping Achievements

The first maps of East Antarctica to be compiled from aerial photographs were those of the Wohlthat Massiv, published in 1939. These maps were produced in Germany from photographs obtained during the German Antarctic Expedition (1938-1939) led by Captain Alfred Ritscher. In 1946, maps of the coastal region between 15° E and 90° E appeared; these maps resulted from aerial photographs taken during the Norwegian expedition of 1936-1937, led by Lars Christensen. Both these expeditions, however, were ship-based operations; the accuracy of the resulting maps was diminished by the lack of ground control for the photographs.

In 1946-1947, staff members of the USN Operation Highjump photographed the eastern coast of Antarctica from 164° E to 15° E, as well as regions in West Antarctica. During the following austral summer, limited ground control for these photographs was established when personnel of the USN Operation Windmill occupied a number of geodetic stations along the antarctic coast between 163° E and 90° E. Reconnaissance maps at a scale of 1:500,000 were compiled from the Operation Highjump photographs and were published between 1956 and 1960 by the USGS.

Shortly after completion of Operation Highjump and Operation Windmill, the Norwegian–British–Swedish Antarctic Expedition (1949-1952) obtained aerial photographs, and in 1958-1959 the coverage was extended by the Norwegian Antarctic Expedition. During both periods, triangulation and other ground control were obtained. As a result, between 1961 and 1964, the Norsk Polarinstitutt was able to publish 12 map sheets at a scale of 1:250,000 which cover much of the mountain ranges of western Queen Maud Land.

Norwegian parties were not alone in producing maps in the late 1950's and early 1960's. All the nations active in East Antarctica during the International Geophysical Year (1957) compiled maps at various scales, some from aerial photographs and others from ground surveys. The countries that participated are Australia, Belgium, France, Japan, Norway, Republic of South Africa, the Soviet Union, and the United States. Much of this mapping utilized aerial photographs with varying amounts and types of ground control.

Folio 3 of the *Antarctic Map Folio Series* (1964 continuing), published by the American Geographical Society in cooperation with the USGS, is a ready reference. Plates in this folio show coverage of photography, maps, and geodetic control for the period up to and including the austral summer of 1963-1964. The coverage of the aerial photography obtained for mapmaking is shown in Plate 9 of Folio 3; geodetic ground control is shown in Plate 11. Plates 5, 6, and 7 are indexes of maps at scales greater than 1:1,000,000 which were produced in the period between 1954 and 1964.

Summary of Current Mapping Activities

Most of the nations that are still conducting research in East Antarctica are continuing mapping activities.

Australian workers are filling in areas needing aerial photography and ground control and are gradually revising their black-and-white unpublished maps at scales of 1:100,000 and 1:1,000,000. Maps printed in color at scales of 1:250,000 continue to appear. In the 1964-1965 austral summer, a 550-km tellurometer traverse was carried out in the Mawson area, astronomical observations were used to locate two positions near 113° E, and elevations were determined by barometer in the Wilkes area. During the 1966-1967 summer, a 152-km tellurometer traverse was run from Depot Peak (65°02′ S, 64°36′ E) to Mount Wishard (70°19′ S, 65°15′ E).

The first Belgian–Dutch expedition (1964-1965) obtained aerial photographs of the eastern Sør Rondane Mountains and then obtained ground surveys the following season (1965-1966) for the same region. In January 1968, a joint Belgian–South African party took vertical photographs along the coast and in the Sverdrup and Gjelsvik Mountains for mapping purposes.

Aerial photographs taken by the Japanese Antarctic Research Expedition in 1962 have resulted in the following maps: West Ongul Island, 1:5000, December 1964; Padda Island, 1:25,000, February 1966; Teoya Island,[*] 1:5000, February 1966; and Ongulkalven Island, 1:5000, February 1966. A map compilation of the Langhovda area at a scale of 1:50,000 has recently been completed. Plans for the 1968-1969 summer include a survey along the Soya Coast.[*]

The Expeditions Polaires Francaises planned topographic work from Dumont d'Urville during the 1966-1967 season.

In 1966, the Norsk Polarinstitutt produced two map sheets at a 1:250,000 scale to expand the coverage of the series published between 1961 and 1964 (*Antarctic Map Folio Series*, Folio 3, Plate 6).

WEST ANTARCTICA

Cartographic Programs Since 1957

Fewer than half of the nations participating in the International Geophysical Year (IGY) program in Antarctica conducted topographic mapping activities during 1957 and 1958. Not until it became apparent that antarctic investigations were going to continue long after IGY was the mapping of Antarctica begun in earnest as part of a long-range program of scientific research.

The U.S. Antarctic Research Program (USARP) is one of the largest national efforts in the Antarctic, and the mapping program conducted by the USGS to support USARP is one of the largest among the SCAR nations. Perhaps more than any other single discipline in the Antarctic, mapping requires the close support of the U.S. Naval Support Force, Antarctica (Task Force 43), especially Naval Air Development Squadron Six (VX-6), which is responsible for all air logistics and procuring aerial photography. Mapping priorities result from consultations with the National Science Foundation (NSF), which funds mapping as part of USARP. The over-all mapping program is a highly integrated effort.

The NSF–USGS Plan for Optical Aerial Mapping Photography reflects the foreseeable map requirements of USARP scientists (Figure 14) and is revised periodically to take into account increasing knowledge of the areas to be mapped and the seasonal accomplishments of the photography program.

During the past 9 years, more than 1,125,000 square miles of western Antarctica have been photographed. About 820,000 square miles of this photography cover mapworthy areas (Figure 15). The remaining 205,000 square miles cover the fringes of the mappable areas and areas considered to be cartographically featureless for medium-scale mapping. A smaller amount of photography has been obtained by the United Kingdom, Australia, Argentina, Germany, Norway, and the Soviet Union. This photography is mainly single lens, vertical, and oblique (*Antarctic Map Folio Series*, Plate 9).

Special photography flown for other USARP programs besides mapping is also available. This photography is suitable for geologic interpretation rather than for photogrammetric measurements. It has also been used for studies of penguin population, albedo studies, and ice-crevasse location studies and for other interpretive purposes. Early in the 1960's, special aerial photography was also used for an analysis of ice breakout in the McMurdo Sound area. Color photography has recently been obtained in limited areas to enhance photogeologic work and to make possible a better interpretation of geologic structure. Special photography for photogrammetric measurements was flown during a 4-year interval over a 200-mile line of targets (pass points) between Byrd Station and the Whitmore Mountains for an ice-movement study conducted by The Ohio State University. Such requests will probably continue with increased emphasis on special photography and more sophisticated sensors as better techniques are developed.

The USGS has sent engineers to Antarctica every year since 1957 to establish geodetic control for mapping. For the first few years, the men were assigned to oversnow geophysical traverses as navigators, and mapping control was established on an opportunity basis. The features to be mapped were seldom visited, and accurate identification of intersected points was difficult since aerial photographs usually were not available to the field parties. Positions were based on solar observations, and the work was not of a high order of accuracy.

The first significant step toward improving this situation occurred during the 1961-1962 field season. During this period, U.S. Army gas-turbine helicopters were made available for the exclusive use of a USGS topographic mapping party. For the first time, control engineers could move quickly to take advantage of short periods of good weather, and the high performance characteristics of the UH-1B helicopters enabled the party to land on mountain peaks with pressure altitudes up to 13,500 ft above sea level. Photographs of the area were available for detailed planning of the operation. Electronic distance-measuring instruments were used to measure distances quickly and accurately between primary control points, and features identified from photographs were intersected up to 50 miles on either side of the main traverse. During the first two seasons in which

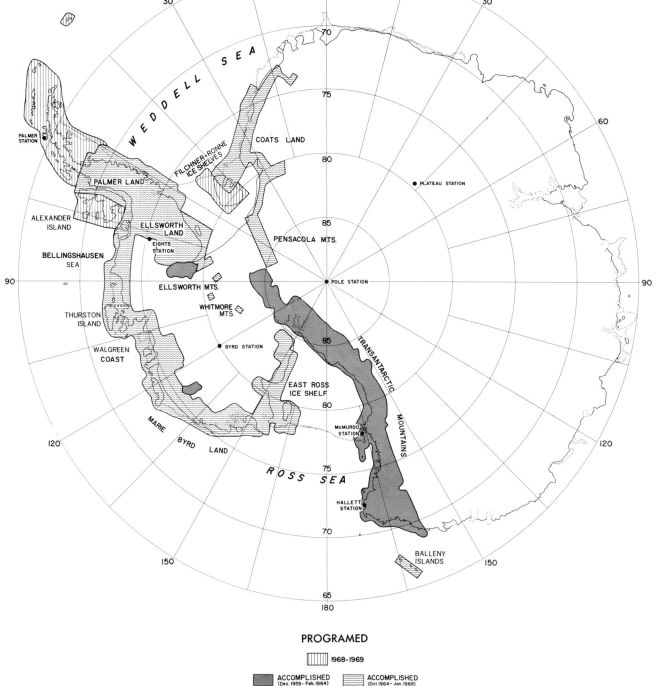

FIGURE 14   NSF–USGS plan for optical aerial mapping photography.

this method was used, USGS engineers established control for the mapping of 180,000 square miles along the Trans- antarctic Mountains while traversing over 3155 miles (Proj- ects Topo, North, South, East, and West). Similar methods have been used by USGS engineers since 1963 to control other areas in Antarctica.

ANTARCTICA

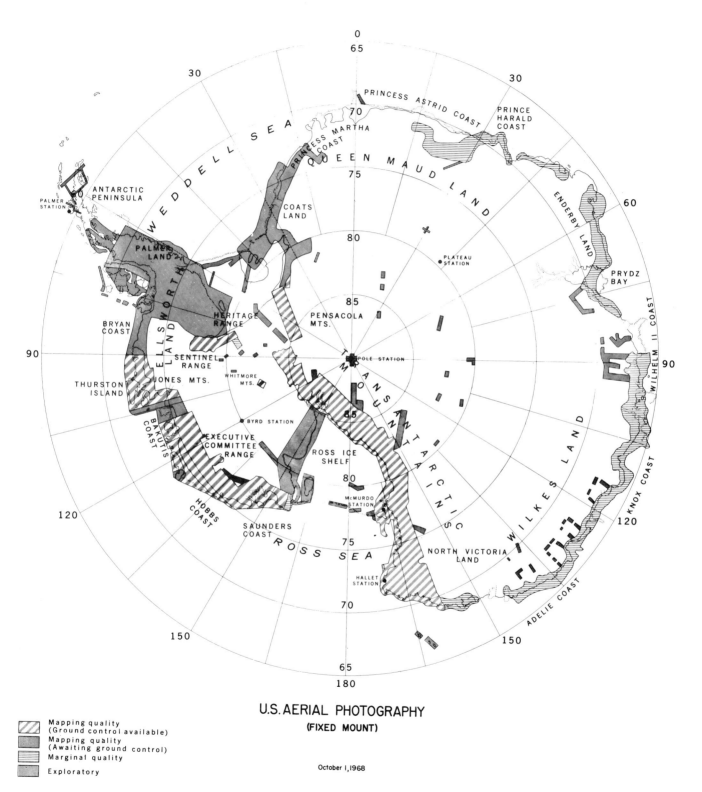

U.S. AERIAL PHOTOGRAPHY
(FIXED MOUNT)

October 1, 1968

Mapping quality
(Ground control available)
Mapping quality
(Awaiting ground control)
Marginal quality
Exploratory

FIGURE 15 United States aerial photography, Antarctica.

The current USARP plan calls for mapping the mountainous and coastal areas of western Antarctica between 158° E longitude clockwise to 8° W longitude, exclusive of the Ross and Ronne Ice Shelves. The original NSF–USGS plan called for mapping 264 maps at a 1:250,000 scale. This requirement has been reduced gradually until now the plan envisions 140 topographic maps at a 1:250,000 scale and 12 sketch maps at a 1:500,000 scale. The original plan was reduced by 124 maps because of the mapping accomplishments of other countries, the elimination of featureless areas, and the decision that scientific mapping needs in certain marginal areas could be met by the 1:500,000-scale sketch map series. The first objective of the USARP mapping program is to produce 1:250,000-scale maps with 200-m contours of all the unmapped mountainous and coastal areas of West Antarctica south of 68° S. An important by-product of this mapping is the unpublished series of 1:50,000-scale planimetric manuscripts of mountainous areas, which many USARP scientists prefer for recording the results of their early field investigations.

In support of the USARP program, the USGS has published, during the past decade, 58 topographic maps at 1:250,000 scale, covering 238,785 square miles, and seven sketch maps at 1:500,000 scale, covering 321,700 square miles (Figure 16).

A recent addition to the U.S. mapping program is the interim 1:500,000-scale, shaded-relief sketch map series. The sketch map series is designed to utilize available aerial photographs and existing, often sparse, ground control to map areas before initial penetration by USARP field parties. Most of the areas covered by the sketch map series will be mapped later as part of the standard 1:250,000-scale topographic mapping program.

The USN has published 60 nautical charts, largely of the coastal areas, at scales of 1:6250 to 1:500,000. The USN has also completed coverage of the continent with the V30-SP aeronautical charts at a scale of 1:2,188,800. Aeronautical charts (strip charts) at the scales of 1:1,000,000 to 1:3,000,000 have been published of the most frequently used routes.

Since 1954, the United Kingdom, New Zealand, Argentina, Chile, and Norway have produced topographic maps of widely distributed areas in West Antarctica. The maps vary in size, and their scales range from 1:23,150 to 1:500,000. Areas covered by these maps, with related information, are contained in the *Antarctic Map Folio Series*.

Current Mapping Programs

The areas planned for photographic coverage during the 1968–1969 season total only 169,600 square miles and include the north half of the Antarctic Peninsula, Alexander Island, and fill lines required to complete the coverage of Thurston Island, Palmer Land, Ellsworth Land, Beckner Island, and along the Coats Land coast. If the 1968–1969

photographic season is completely successful, all the aerial photography necessary for the current USARP 1:250,000-scale and 1:500,000-scale mapping programs planned for western Antarctica will be completed.

An extensive sketch-mapping program is included in NSF–USGS plans for the immediate future, in support of USARP field parties. USGS field engineers established control in the Jones Mountains and Thurston Island area of Ellsworth Land in 1968–1969; it is planned to establish control at Mt. Siple and in the Pirrit-Nash-Martin Hills area as well. It is anticipated that during the next few years teams of engineers working with other USARP field investigators will work clockwise around the continent to the Lassiter Coast and north to 68° S latitude, consistent with the 1:250,000-scale mapping plan. For approximately two years, USGS engineers and British Antarctic Survey (BAS) personnel are expected to work together to establish mapping control in the base of the Antarctic Peninsula between 68° and 73° S latitude.

Currently, the USGS is compiling 38 maps at a 1:250,000 scale covering 175,475 square miles and one sketch map at a 1:500,000 scale covering about 56,000 square miles. Scheduled for compilation during the next five years are another 45 maps at a 1:250,000 scale covering about 203,000 square miles and four maps at a 1:500,000 scale covering about 135,000 square miles. Based on the present rate of production of about eight maps yearly, it is estimated that the current program will be completed by 1982.

New Zealand's mapping activities are diminishing as the area of their interest (Transantarctic Mountains) nears complete coverage at a 1:250,000 scale. Future activities are likely to be limited to large-scale mapping in support of individual local projects. The United Kingdom's cartographic activities in the Antarctic Peninsula area are more extensive than those of Argentina or Chile. The Soviet Union established a base on King George Island in the South Shetland Islands group during 1967–1968 and, hence, is a relative newcomer to the Antarctic Peninsula area. BAS mapping, at a 1:200,000 scale, is directed at the permanent features of Coats Land and in the Antarctic Peninsula. In the southern Antarctic Peninsula area, the BAS is using aerial photography flows by U.S. Navy Squadron VX-6 to specifications prepared by the USGS for NSF. The extent to which BAS maps the southern end of the Antarctic Peninsula will depend largely on the extent of U.S. mapping. Current U.S. plans are to join the BAS maps at 68° S latitude. Regardless of how much is done by either nation, the end result will be complete coverage of the Antarctic Peninsula area and the mountainous areas of Ellsworth Land. The United States will continue to prepare maps in the Peninsula area where required in support of field studies. Because of funding problems and notable poor weather in this area, it is difficult to estimate a completion date more precise than the mid-1970's.

ANTARCTICA

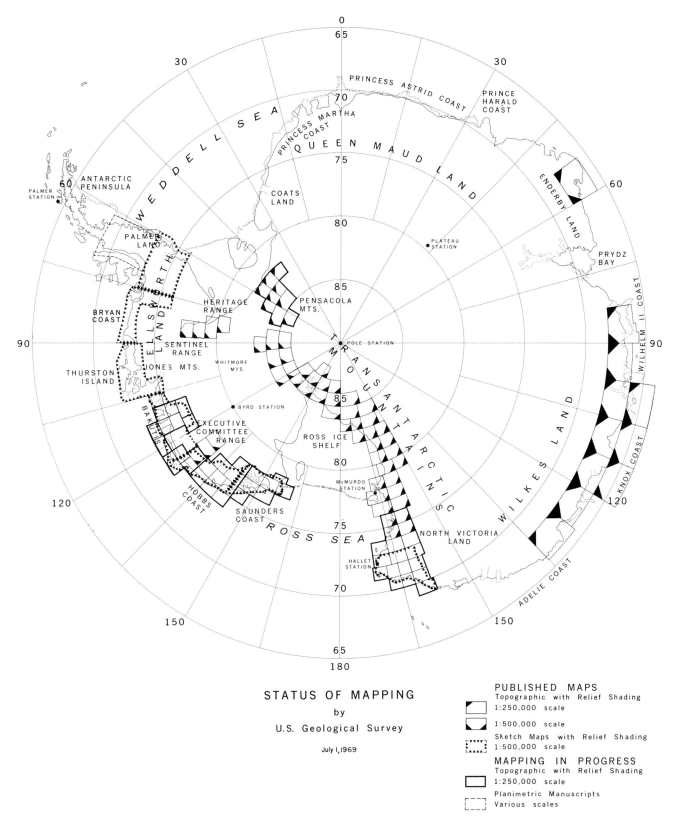

STATUS OF MAPPING

by

U.S. Geological Survey

July 1,1969

PUBLISHED MAPS
Topographic with Relief Shading
1:250,000 scale
1:500,000 scale
Sketch Maps with Relief Shading
1:500,000 scale

MAPPING IN PROGRESS
Topographic with Relief Shading
1:250,000 scale
Planimetric Manuscripts
Various scales

FIGURE 16 Status of mapping by the U.S. Geological Survey, Antarctica.

ANTARCTIC OCEANS

Recent and Current Cartographic Programs

Charting in the Antarctic Oceans has progressed much
faster than in the Arctic. The antarctic research program of
the IGY brought the first concerted international effort to
investigate the waters surrounding the continent. However,
the bathymetry of the region has been, in most cases, a by-
product of other research and logistic support operations.
Numerous nations have been active in the charting of
antarctic waters. As a result of this active bathymetric
data acquisition program, the nautical charts produced are
of relatively high quality, but bathymetric contouring of
the Antarctic has been neglected. H.O. Chart 2562 published at a scale of 1:11,250,000 is the basic contoured
chart of antarctic waters, but a tremendous amount of
data has been collected since the contours were last revised. The only other contoured chart of antarctic waters

prepared by NAVOCEANO is H.O. 6710 at a scale of
1:2,810,700. The second edition of this chart, extending
from New Zealand to Cape Adare, was printed in November 1967, but it too needs updating. There are at present
20 large-, 31 medium-, and 13 small-scale nautical charts
on issue by NAVOCEANO (see Figure 17).

At present, all charting at NAVOCEANO is in support
of Operation Deep Freeze 1968–1969. One new and five
revised editions of existing nautical charts are presently
scheduled in antarctic waters.

Geodesy

Past Programs The literature of exploration in the Antarctic Oceans is replete with positional data observed from
shipboard with navigational instruments. Geodetic activity
in the subantarctic islands has consisted principally of large
numbers of independent astronomic observations with
varying degrees of accuracy; many of these positions are

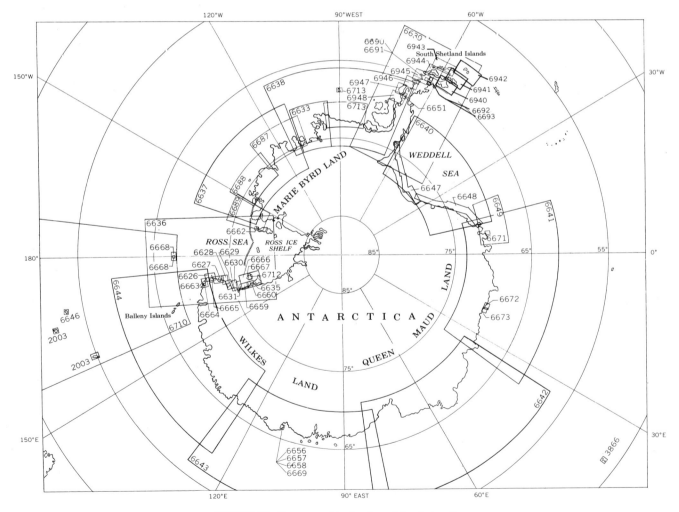

FIGURE 17 Oceanographic charting of the Antarctic.

published only to the nearest minute of latitude and the nearest degree of longitude.

In the Indian Ocean, between the years 1949 and 1956, two French naval hydrographic missions carried out two lower-order surveys by triangulation from a measured base and an astronomic position on Archipel de Kerguelen. Some 40 points with trigonometric heights were established. A height for the base was determined by precise leveling from a tide station. In 1961, when it was considered indispensable to have a good map at a reasonable scale, no usable cartography of the island existed. Plans were started at Terres Australes et Antarctiques Francaises (TAAF) in September 1961 to prepare a map of the archipelago at a scale of 1:100,000. From 1961 to 1963, the island was covered with a first-order geodetic net, which included two tellurometer baselines and two azimuths. A precise level line was run from the tide station to the base, and trigonometric heights were computed for the rest of the survey. Farther south, additional work was done on Heard Island prior to 1953 and consisted largely of determining independent astronomic positions, such as the one observed by an Australian antarctic expedition around 1950. Between 1953 and 1957, the Australians carried out some lower-order triangulation on the island.

On islands in the south Atlantic Ocean, geodetic control points were established during the period 1938-1965. On Bouvet Island, an astronomic position and elevation for a midisland point were determined by a German naval captain who visited the island as part of a German antarctic expedition during 1938-1939. On the island of South Georgia, from 1951 to 1957, several British antarctic expeditions carried out extensive triangulation and mapping control, establishing some 240 points with an accuracy, relative to each other, of about ±5 m. The trigonometric heights are said to be accurate to ±10 m. In 1961, some additional work was done in the approaches to Stewart Strait, using a triangulation survey and an uncompleted tellurometer traverse. Eleven stations were also established in the vicinity of Right Whale Bay with an estimated accuracy of ±25 m. In 1964-1965 some additional control was observed with an improvised phototheodolite. Ninety-five percent of the island is now reliably surveyed. In the South Orkney Islands, in 1965, a Royal Navy antarctic survey party, continuing work begun in 1956-1958, and using a Hydrodist for distance measurements, observed a base triangle and a five-station extension on Signy Island and Coronation Island. In 1964, a survey party from HMS *Protector* carried out the first on-shore survey activities in the South Sandwich Islands. This work included a 13-point traverse based on an astronomic position on Candlemas Island and five trigonometric points on Bellingshausen Island.

In the south Pacific Ocean, recent work in the Balleny Islands achieved an astronomic position established by a joint U.S.-New Zealand expedition, as well as aerial photog-

raphy of mapping quality by the USN for the USGS in 1966-1967. Farther north, on Macquarie Island, an Australian expedition in 1958 established a tellurometer traverse of seven stations along the east coast from Buckles Bay to Hurd Point.

Current Geodetic Programs The National Geodetic Satellite Program (NGSP) became fully operational in the Antarctic Oceans in March 1969. There is a BC-4 camera system presently on site at South Georgia Island, where it will remain until completion of the over-all Antarctic Phase in 1970 as part of the worldwide PAGEOS satellite triangulation network.

A NGSP station was installed on Heard Island in March 1969. Four other BC-4 stations will be located on the antarctic continent as will seven connecting stations as listed and shown in Figure 18. First-order astronomic positions are observed at each NGSP camera station, and survey connections are made to existing control in the vicinity. The U.S. Navy will obtain Doppler data at each of the NGSP stations.

RECOMMENDATIONS

East Antarctica

In all probability, the nations with scientific bases in East Antarctica will continue to improve and expand the mapping of the coastal and mountain regions. While U.S. activity in East Antarctica is comparatively minimal, large-scale mapping of the ice sheet compiled from aerial photographs would be very useful in ice dynamics studies. Large-scale mapping of coastal regions, revised periodically from repeated aerial photography, could be used to determine variations in the location of the ice front and in volume of iceberg discharge, major factors in establishing the antarctic ice budget. Small-scale maps compiled periodically from satellite photographs can be used to determine the seasonal and secular variations in the limits of the pack ice.

It is important to note that recommendations for future programs in East Antarctica are of necessity based on our understanding of the plans of those nations active in East Antarctica. Most of this information is extracted from the SCAR and Antarctic Treaty reports. Long-range U.S. plans for mapping in East Antarctica need to be closely coordinated with those of other nations in order to avoid duplication and be of maximum use to scientists.

We therefore recommend:

1. U.S. mapping in East Antarctica should be limited to the ice sheet and adjacent regions selected for special study by glaciologists.

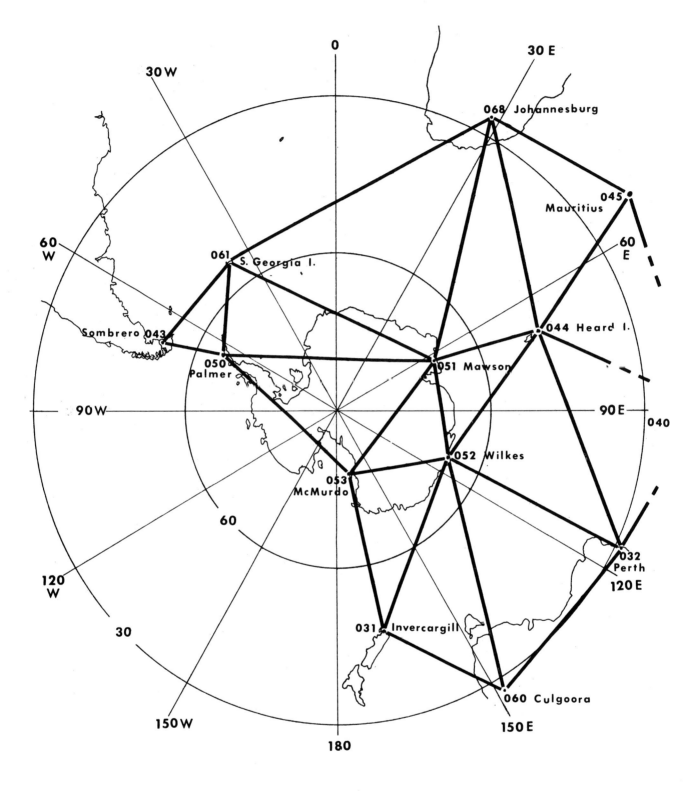

68-G&C

FIGURE 18 Stations for the National Geodetic Satellite Program (NGSP).

2. A thorough study, with periodic review, should be made by SCAR of the total cooperative scientific investigatory research program in East Antarctica, in order to avoid duplication and to realize maximum coverage of integrated activities.

West Antarctica

Geodesy   The USGS field parties have been establishing geodetic control in Antarctica for the past 10 years, and technology to support this program has progressed steadily during this period. The major use for this geodetic control has been the preparation of 1:250,000-scale maps in the mountainous areas. Glaciologists have also utilized USGS surveying ability for the determination of ice movement and strain rates. During this period, the USGS has almost completed the control for 1:250,000-scale mapping of the mountainous areas of West Antarctica. Future control activities will be directed toward the remapping of selected mountainous areas at a larger scale for special studies as needed in areas of specific geologic interest.

To provide geodetic control for glaciological studies, the present procedures and instruments are satisfactory for determining strain rates and for measuring ice movement on glaciers when adjacent to exposed rock. For measuring ice movement at isolated inland stations, the present method (repeated measurement of astronomic position) produces a weak determination.

To satisfy all geodetic control needs in Antarctica, we must develop methods for establishing control on the flat snow areas, develop the ability to advance control across the flat snow areas, or both. Because present procedures and instruments make such an effort impractical, we recommend:

1. Procedures and equipment should be developed for advancing control across flat snow areas, using specially equipped helicopters as elevated stations. The technique used would be a combination of flare triangulation and Hiran methods. For this technique, the distance-measuring component should be an autotape system, which will provide rapid distance measurements.

2. A geoceiver or other portable Doppler receiving equipment should be procured for establishing positions across vast snow flats, using the satellites monitored by the USN navigational system.

Recommendation 1 appears to be the most promising for establishing control for mapping or for referencing geophysical measurements. This technique, with further development, could be used for determining differential ice movement within extended flat areas. The second recommended technique is dependent on orbital information of satellites, and the use of this technique, in combination with the first recommended, is considered as highly desirable. The positions obtained from the satellite measurements may be considered as absolute, being referred to the orbit and thus to the entire earth. The positional uncertainties may be of the order of several meters; for differential studies, such errors would be unsatisfactory. However, for the determination of the annual rate of ice movement over broad areas, the technique should be quite satisfactory.

Cartography   We make the following recommendations:

1. A new edition of the continental map, published by the AGS in support of the USARP, should be published at least every two years until such time as the continent is covered with medium-scale mapping and there is no significant new source data to incorporate.

2. The sketch map series at a 1:500,000 scale, which provides map data prior to the initial ground penetration of an area by field parties, and the 1:250,000-scale series, which is intended to cover the mountainous and other scientifically significant areas of West Antarctica, should be carried forward at a sufficient pace to allow scientists the necessary map data at the critical stages of their investigations. The large-scale mapping of selected areas to permit more detailed studies should be implemented as needed, in support of the second phase of physical-science investigations. Earth scientists should be encouraged to state their needs prior to the mapmaking process so that the final product can be designed to meet as many requirements as possible in a program as complex as the USARP.

3. The *Antarctic Map Folio Series*, prepared by the AGS, should be continued, and the remaining folios should be published as soon as feasible. We further recommend that *Folio 3* be revised and reissued to make current the information presented therein. Such revision will establish a very useful precedent for the entire series.

4. The preparation of a series of maps should be initiated, at a scale of 1:1,000,000 with suitable contour interval, which portray the details of the physical features commensurate with the scale and which symbolize, where necessary, the features of the polar ice cap.

5. The practical uses of new satellite and airborne instruments should be carefully evaluated for their application in mapping the remaining areas of Antarctica. We single out for study such systems as radar altimetry, Vidicon imagery, camera systems of cartographic quality, side-looking radar, infrared film, and multiband sensors.

6. Aerial photography programs should be supported to the extent that photographic coverage of mountainous areas of Antarctica is completed in the immediate future.

7. Air navigation charts should be updated each austral summer when new cartographic data are available.

8. The international exchange of map material among the signatory nations of the Antarctic Treaty should receive continuous emphasis and encouragement.

Antarctic Oceans

1. A series of bathymetric charts at a scale of approximately 1:5,000,000 should be prepared as soon as possible, showing in detail the major and minor bathymetric features.

2. A bathymetric chart at a scale of approximately 1:12,000,000 should be prepared for use as a planning chart to display the general geographical relationships of both land and submarine topographic features and to serve as a base for the plastic relief model showing the ice cover, the sea floor, and the land surface.

3. A series of bathymetric charts at a scale of 1:1,000,000 and displaying a minimum contour interval of 600 ft should be compiled for use in the interpretation of physical data, and for navigation purposes.

4. There should be continued emphasis on the acquisition and international exchange of map material; future acquisition should be directed toward quality rather than quantity of data.

SYSTEMS APPLICABLE TO POLAR GEODESY AND CARTOGRAPHY

GEODESY

Terrestrial Geodesy

Classical geodetic operations for establishing horizontal and vertical control should be continued in the Arctic and Antarctic whenever feasible. Generally, such operations are in advance of economic development and not necessarily related to specific research programs. There are two basic problems relating to vertical control. First, the relationship between the sea-level surface of the oceans and the so-called sea level of the continents needs to be determined by long series of tidal measurements. The secular changes or movements of the earth's crust can be determined very accurately. In all probability, tide gauges will be established and manned by oceanographic groups, thus not requiring any specific support by the geodetic community other than the normal encouragement.

The second problem relates to the determination of elevations on the continent of Antarctica. Basically, it is the problem of determining differences of heights between intervisible points. The effects of atmospheric refraction are so great that the results of the errors accumulated by trigonometric leveling soon exceed the desired tolerance for the determination of accurate elevations.

Electronic distance-measuring equipment has been used successfully in Antarctica for establishing traverses. Trilateration may be a more practical technique, since it is easier to measure distances than angles in the environment of Antarctica. The elevations of the instrument stations would have to be determined by some other means so that the lengths could be reduced to a uniform reference surface.

Advances in the manufacture of terrestrial geodetic field instrumentation, attributed mainly to the progress made in the field of electronics, are well known. The possibility of measuring, economically, the spatial distances between neighboring stations has revived interest in the potential of precision traverses and trilateration programs as well as in the possibility of optimizing geodetic control operations by combining direction and length measurements. Leveling instruments and theodolites, with automatic compensating devices, make it possible to establish, continuously and precisely, line-of-sight or elevation circle readings with respect to local vertical, thus allowing high-order work under adverse environmental conditions, including measurements at positions with unstable ground conditions such as the ice sheets.

There is, however, little doubt that the development of geodetic data acquisition systems is well recognized, and therefore, it appears necessary only to reiterate the suggestion of using these new techniques to the fullest and to select instrumentation (including correspondingly trained crews) that is especially suited for work under antarctic conditions.

In a more general sense, attention is invited to the planning of geodetic control operations in Antarctica, as well as navigational or positioning programs in the Arctic. Such programs should be laid out in full recognition of the support that is presently available or that will become available in the near future by satellite triangulation techniques.

Satellite Geodesy

The revolutionary impact of satellites on geodesy is undisputed. Investigations of satellite orbits primarily yield results about the characteristics of the gravitational field surrounding the earth. The geometric satellite triangulation method allows the determination of three-dimensional positions of selected points on the earth's surface and can contribute to both worldwide and polar geodesy.

In the Arctic, in the northern edge of the continental land masses, stations of the Passive Geodetic Satellite (PAGEOS) World Net are located at Shemya, Aleutian Islands; Thule, Greenland; and Tromso, Norway. When the densification net in the area of North America is completed there will be at least three additional stations between Shemya and Thule on the northernmost edge of Canada (Figure 19). The location of these stations will be known to at least ±10 m in latitude and longitude, to ±12 m in height relative to the center of the earth, and to approximately

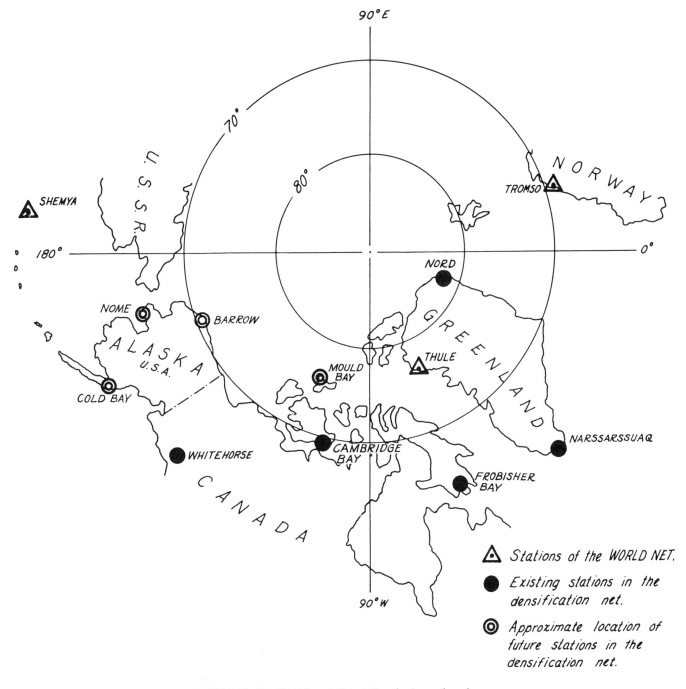

FIGURE 19 Satellite triangulation stations in the arctic region.

±5 m in all three components with respect to each other. Therefore, reliable geodetic control will be available over a 180° segment around the North Pole, on which precise navigational systems can be based. The ultimate adjustment of the classic first-order triangulation in Alaska and Canada, into the above-mentioned frame, would provide further control along the arctic shorelines consistent with respect to a World Datum as well as to a new North American

Datum as it is envisioned following the completion of the world net and densification programs.

In Antarctica, there are presently four stations of the World Net which are situated at the outer rim of Antarctica (Figure 20). The goal is to determine the three-dimensional position of these stations within the World Net to the aforementioned accuracies. When viewing Antarctica as a continent, obviously the same advantages of satellite triangula-

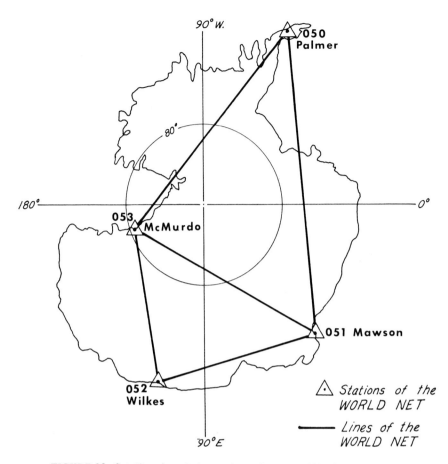

FIGURE 20   Satellite triangulation stations of the World Net in Antarctica.

tion become apparent which are derived from such densification in other continents. Considerable practical advantage would be derived, particularly in Antarctica, if a few more satellite triangulation stations were established. Because of the environmental and economic conditions, it is not likely that a systematic coverage by classic triangulation of the whole of Antarctica can be accomplished in the foreseeable future. Therefore, the availability of reasonably close-spaced frame control becomes significant, enabling the constraint of locally executed work to points that provide a consistent frame for the entire area of Antarctica. Figure 21 shows, conceptually, such a densification net. It would have been most economical to execute such a net in connection with the World Net. Such an approach appears impossible now, considering the present schedule for the World Net. However, such a plan should be given serious consideration for execution immediately after the completion of the World Net, that is, after the end of calendar year 1970. At that time, satellites, trained teams, and proven instrumentation systems should be available. The experience gained during the occupation of the world stations would also be a significant factor in planning a program most efficiently at such time.

Similarly, the application of the geoceiver, now in development in connection with USN satellites, has to be considered as an alternative method for densification. Such an approach appears particularly attractive when considering the fact that the four satellite triangulation stations in Antarctica (compare Figure 20) will be available, thus providing an existing frame of stations whose positions are tied to any new World Datum.

Finally, new technology developments with either radar- or laser ranging from satellites to the surface of the earth to approximately ±2 m (primarily to the ocean surface for determining geoid profiles) could, in connection with precise orbital tracking by geoceiver, solve the otherwise difficult problem of obtaining reliable height information across Antarctica.

PHOTOGRAMMETRY

Metric Photography

The progress made during the past decade and the continuous research and development effort in precision photogrammetry directed toward both data acquisition and data

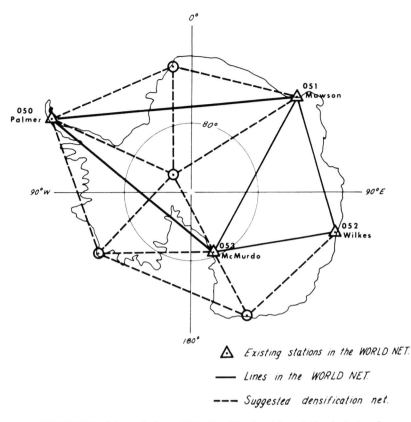

FIGURE 21 Schematic for satellite densification triangulation in Antarctica.

reduction systems encourage the consideration of aerial triangulation at least for the establishment of lower-order geodetic control. Significantly large amounts of data obtained in laboratory as well as in full-scale experiments indicate that the photogrammetric method should be capable of producing triangulation results of 1 part in 50,000 to 1 part in 100,000 of the flying height, depending on the focal length of the camera used. Such accuracies are subject to the postulation that neither systematic refraction anomalies nor scintillation effects, as they may be caused by air turbulence directly in front of the camera, impair unduly the geometric significance of the photographically recorded directions.

Therefore, thoroughly calibrated and professionally operated aerial camera systems should provide an attractive potential for providing mapping control and lower-order densification control for various projects of the antarctic programs.

The development of economical techniques to create photoidentifiable points on snow or ice from the air should be studied further with the goal of obtaining an early solution to this problem which appears, presently, to be a main obstacle to increasing the accuracy of aerial triangulation in the area of Antarctica. The application of this method offers the additional advantage of providing three-dimensional control, thus including in the determination of trigonomet-

ric elevations quantities which are difficult to obtain in Antarctica by classic surface operations.

The present development of measuring distances between the airborne camera and the ground by pulsed laser techniques provides a promising approach to maintaining uniform scale with high accuracy over extended flight lines. When considering additional solar photography, the azimuth deformation of aerial triangulation can be controlled.

When conceived in context with independently determined densification control, e.g., geoceiver or satellite-borne photogrammetry, precise aerial triangulation and photogrammetric mapping may very well be the most economical method of portraying the three-dimensional geometry of extended areas in the Antarctic with sufficient accuracy and detail.

Earth Orbital Sensors

In the past, extremely limited amounts and types of sensor information from space vehicles has been available for unclassified study. Space photographs which have been studied were obtained primarily during the Gemini Program of the National Aeronautics and Space Administration. The conditions of obtaining Gemini photographs may be described as less than favorable to the cartographic community.

Various photogrammetric analyses were performed on these photographs (stereoplotter tests and resolution tests, for example), and it was generally conceded that this photography was of little value for topographic mapping.

Probably the most important cartographic application for Gemini photographs is in the preparation of photomaps. Thousands of square miles of the earth's surface were recorded on each 80-mm focal length photograph obtained from altitudes of 100 miles and higher. These photographs were utilized in the production of extremely large-area photomosaics and photomaps. During a recent research project, a method of adding accurate cartographic grids to such space photographs was developed. This technique may be used by glaciologists for locating drifting icebergs, ice crevasses, and open water or thin ice in ice-covered areas. Oceanographers have indicated that they could be useful for locating and studying ocean currents. Small-scale, large-area photographs could be very useful to other earth scientists for studying large, regional features of the earth.

From the mapmaker's viewpoint, however, the unclassified space photographs obtained to date have been interesting but of limited metric value. Nonetheless, plans for the development of satellite-borne cartographic systems are under way. An investigation of methods of handling and processing space data, in particular the data returned from three multispectral return-beam Vidicon cameras, which may be in orbit for a year or more, is in progress. The study will assess formats and cartographic products needed by each user discipline and will determine methods by which the vidicon data may be processed to meet their needs. In further phases, the hardware and software requirements will be determined to handle the data from ERTS I (Earth Resources Technology Satellite) and process it to satisfy user needs. This study encompasses data volume, data flow, data evaluation, and storage, retrieval, and distribution systems.

Change detection has been pointed out as an important facet of the repetitive coverage to be obtained with long-duration satellites. This can be seasonal change or daily change and can be limited to specific areas or to over-all continental coverage. In any case, there is a need to develop a means for detecting, isolating, and measuring change. Cartographic studies are being pursued which may lead to a process where new and old imagery can be automatically compared and the areas of change printed out. Such a system would benefit not only specialized disciplinary investigators but also cartographers interested in revision of current editions of maps.

In seeking to relate space photography to other space sensor imagery, to aerial photo imagery, or to orthophotographic imagery, a fundamental process called image correlation and transformation must take place. With the large amount of data to be returned from satellite sensors, it is necessary to develop an automatic image-correlation and transformation system. A study to investigate current techniques and their application to such a system will be made.

The possible application of space cartographic technology to the polar regions seems promising in several respects. It seems likely that the first real test of satellite cartographic systems will occur with the launching of ERTS I. Although a formal mission plan has yet to be adopted, ERTS I will probably be a long-duration satellite (one year), placed in near-polar orbit at an altitude of about 500 nautical miles. All but a 6° circle around each pole will be observed by its sensors. The principal remote-sensing system aboard may consist of three television-type cameras, each receiving a different portion of the visible spectrum. Ground resolution attainable under the conditions stated above is expected to be about 300 ft. Other instrumentation in a long-term satellite might consist of communication-relay equipment to receive signals from surface-based sensors, record the signals, and retransmit them to ground data stations.

The advantage of using space-borne sensors is the large area view, the chance for repetitive coverage, and the accessibility of all areas on the surface of the earth to the sensor. Disadvantages of space sensors are the small-scale coverage, the relatively high initial cost, and the need for fully automated systems. As more reliable vehicles and improvements in technology develop, these disadvantages will become less important and the benefits of space sensors will outweigh them. In the next few years, the research and development of automatic data handling of software and hardware will be of great importance to the success of the early missions, and with present sensors it will be at least two years before a capable data-handling facility is developed.

Because the first in a series of earth resources satellites is expected to be launched in a near-polar orbit by 1972, consideration should be given to the utilization of satellite return-beam Vidicon imagery under the ERTS program in compilation of a planimetric supplement to the 1:1,000,000-scale map series of the Antarctic. Satellite Vidicon imagery should also be employed to monitor and map long- and short-term changes in the surfaces of the antarctic and Greenland ice caps, in coastal ice features in both the Antarctic and Arctic, and to provide synoptic up-to-date coverage for compilation of the recommended 1:5,000,000-scale map of the Arctic south to 60° N latitude.

OTHER REMOTE-SENSING SYSTEMS

Several airborne remote-sensing techniques are recommended as an aid for improvement or revision of existing topographic maps and for acquisition of new terrain data on polar regions for which adequate mapping photography is unavailable.

Radio-Echo Sounding

Topographic mapping of polar subglacial surfaces would be valuable in the cartographic representation and study of polar ice dynamics. This task, although difficult, is feasible and should be undertaken. The information needed is the glacial surface topography and the ice thickness.

Radio-echo sounding techniques have been shown to be a practical means of approximating the ice thickness over large geographic areas (Evans and Robin, 1966; Rinker *et al.*, 1966). The data are obtained as ice thickness profiles along a cross section. These techniques have been developed during the past few years and utilize low radio frequencies. Evans (1966) stated that sets operating at 30 to 35 Hz have been built to reduce absorption losses, to avoid atmospheric echoes, and to avoid communications interference. Radio-echo sounding techniques have successfully approximated the ice thickness of over 1000 m obtained on a surface traverse (Bailey *et al.*, 1964) and from a light aircraft (Evans, 1966; Evans and Robin, 1966).

Rinker *et al.* (1966) are enthusiastic about the value of radio-echo sounding, stating:

Without doubt, radio-echo sounding methods will provide a profile of bedrock through large portions of the ice sheets of Greenland and Antarctica and contribute enormously to our understanding of form and flow of ice sheets. . . . Another advantage rests in the fact that the system can be reduced to backpack simplicity for walking across a glacier or refined into a high speed airborne system recording on multichannel magnetic tape with one channel recording surface detail via a laser profiler. . . . The limitations of radio sounding techniques stem primarily from the loss of signal strength by dielectric absorption within the ice which, in turn, is temperature dependent, in that the colder the ice, the greater the thickness that can be successfully probed.

The ice-thickness information may be obtained from aircraft flying an accurately controlled grid pattern. Subglacial elevations can then be obtained by subtracting ice thickness from surface elevation.

Radar Imagery

Radar imagery mosaics should be obtained for cartographic purposes over polar land or ice-covered land masses where mapping-quality photography has been difficult to obtain because of inaccessibility, persistent cloud cover, low sun angle, or other negative atmospheric conditions. Controlled high-altitude radar imagery mosaics, of the type compiled by the U.S. Army Engineers Topographic Laboratory (1967) for the Province of Darien, Central America, are of mapping quality for 1:250,000- or larger-scale coverage and provide a uniform image over large areas without the patchwork tonal-density variations characteristic of photomosaics. In addition, surface textures and microrelief are uniformly enhanced in the better type of radar imagery, allowing

direct compilation of shaded-relief maps showing considerable topographic detail. For example, the first 1:250,000-scale topographic map of the Isthmus of Darien is presently being compiled from the radar imagery mosaic cited above. Such radar mosaics are recommended, if requested by the Danish and Icelandic governments, for Greenland and Iceland. Up-to-date complete synoptic coverage would be useful cartographically for supplying data on the ice-capped–ice-free land relationship and details on periglacial topography subject to deflation. This type of survey would be particularly valuable during the current revision and topographic mapping program being carried out in Iceland. Other arctic and antarctic land areas for which mapping photography is unavailable because of atmospheric and low sun-angle problems should also be considered as candidates for radar surveys.

Thermal Infrared, Radar, and Radio-Echo Sounding Imagery Surveys

Shoreline Configuration on Polar Areas under Ice. Both aerial side-looking radar and thermal infrared imagery surveys, utilizing optical–mechanical line-scanning devices (in the case of the infrared systems, sensitive to emitted radiation in the 3- to 14-μ wavelength region), are well suited for the task of delimiting low-lying land masses from shelf ice areas (Poulin, 1966; Leighty, 1966). Infrared techniques which can delimit snow-covered land-fast ice or bay ice are recommended for topographic map revision of shorelines where geodetic control is already available in Antarctica but where shoreline configuration is approximated by a dashed line on existing maps.

Sea-Ice Mapping Coincident infrared imagery and radar imagery surveys have been demonstrated to be useful cartographically in mapping the configuration of pack ice and recent zones of ice canopy deformation (Ketchum and Wittmann, 1966). Similarly, these methods are suitable for mapping ice pressure-ridge fractures in sea ice along the Alaskan and Canadian arctic coasts (Point Barrow to the mouth of the Mackenzie River and through the Northwest Passage to Baffin Bay) where icebreaker activities are contemplated, but where present coastal maps treat sea ice inadequately. The position of the southern limit of pack ice in the Denmark Strait (Greenland Sea area, from Cape Farewell to Svalbard) has changed more in the 1960's than previously during the present century (see Icelandic Glaciological Society, 1959–1969). Coastal shelf and land ice of southeast Greenland may be undergoing a comparable change. These problems should be treated cartographically with the aid of infrared imagery and radar imagery surveys, as well as by Ektachrome and infrared Ektachrome photography.

Polar Land-Ice Features Because air temperatures in crevasses are different from adjacent ice areas even where the crevasses are snow-covered, infrared imagery is effective in delimiting and mapping crevasse fields in Greenland and Antarctica. Prior geodetic control is undoubtedly necessary to utilize the imagery to best advantage, so infrared surveys are recommended for mapping position and trend of crevasse fields during revision of current topographic maps. Radar imagery and Ektachrome photography are recommended for synoptic small-scale coverage to determine present extent of ice caps in Iceland and periglacial areas of erosional deflation where changes in landform surfaces have occurred.

Subglacial Topography in Volcanic Areas Cartographically, little is known about subglacial volcanism in Antarctica and Iceland. In areas subject to subglacial volcanism (western Vatnajökull in Iceland, a zone from the Antarctic Peninsula across Marie Byrd Land, and another zone from Mt. Morning across Victoria Land to the Balleny Islands), subglacial topography, ice thickness, and ice features are apt to reflect the dynamics of volcanism. Thermal infrared imagery and radio-echo sounding traverses are recommended in these areas to delimit cartographically active volcanic areas and related subglacial mountain-range topography. Ice features at the surface, such as cauldron subsidence and related crevasse systems, ice-sheet perforations, outflow tunnels, and ice-dammed meltwater lakes, can be expected in these areas.

Studies on the largest Icelandic glacier, Vatnajökull, carried out in 1968 by the University Science Institute, Reykjavik, show that the highest cupola of Vatnajökull proper (Bárdarbunga) is of the arctic type as is the massive subglacial volcano Öraefajökull. There is thus a possibility of determining the ice thickness over the large Öraefajökull Caldera and the subglacial topography over this volcano's summit area.

POLAR GRAVITY PROGRAMS

Gravity data in polar regions support geodetic and geophysical studies. The geodetic significance of these data is referred to in Chapter 3. To be useful in studies of the figure of the earth, gravity data should be obtained at 5- to 10-km spacing over the region within 500 km or more from each pole. At each observed gravity station, elevations should be known to $\frac{1}{3}$ m as should the thickness of the ice and snow, and positions should be known to better than $\frac{1}{2}$ km. Such data would permit a reasonable relative geoid map to be determined for the polar regions. Such coverage would also permit the deflection of the vertical to be determined at the pole station. Gravity data combined with magnetic and seismic information would be used to develop the structure of the polar regions.

The most significant gravity survey in the arctic region made in the last decade is the project extending over the Queen Elizabeth Islands. This work was done in conjunction with the Polar Continental Shelf Project in the Canadian Arctic. Tanner (1967), Weber (1963), and Sobczak (1963) have reported on this major study and presented their interpretations of the large anomalies, both negative and positive, with a change in excess of 100 mgal.

A summary of the gravity surveys in Antarctica made prior to 1960 was published by the Committee on Polar Research (1961). Since that date, considerable work has been accomplished by the various national groups associated with the programs in Antarctica. Tardi (1964), of the International Gravity Bureau (IGB) in Paris, has published the results of the gravity measurements made during 1957–1960. The data are listed for 2200 stations. The IGB, through its *Bulletins*, carries a continuing bibliography with frequent references to gravity measurements and studies in Antarctica.

Lambert (1963, 1967a, 1967b), Secretary of the SCAR Working Group on Geodesy and Cartography, has prepared several comprehensive reports, which have included information on gravity surveys. The following sections summarize the gravity work in Antarctica of the various countries since 1960.

ARGENTINA

Gravimetric measurements were taken at "General Belgrano" station throughout 1965. Pendulum equipment has been used to establish main stations at "Decepcion" and "Esperanza," with subsidiary stations along the west coast of Graham Land.

AUSTRALIA

A U.S. scientist with the 1960–1961 ANARE summer expedition took readings at Mirny, Mawson, Davis, Heard Island, Archipel de Kerguelen, and four coastal stations in Enderby Land. A Gulf-Wisconsin pendulum apparatus was used at Mirny and Mawson, a La Coste-Romberg gravimeter at the other stations. A Mawson-Mirny-Melbourne tie was established.

The 1962 expedition took readings at 470 stations along the seismic traverse Wilkes-Vostok, at 84 stations along a traverse of 190 km southeastward from Wilkes, and at 26 stations in a gravity survey of the Windmill Islands. A 1962–1963 summer expedition established the gravity tie Wilkes-Lewis Island–Chick Island–Macquarie Island–Melbourne.

In 1963, observations were made at approximately 5-km intervals along traverses of 480 km and 160 km east-southeast and east from Wilkes, respectively. Further work was done in the Wilkes area during 1964 along 500 km of traverses over the large ice dome at latitude 66°45′ S, longitude 11°40′ E. This work was continued in 1965.

BELGIUM

The sledge parties that operated during 1959-1961 south of "Base Roi Baudouin" and in western Sφr-Rondane took readings at 30 stations, 17 of which were on rock outcrops. During November 1960, aircraft made some 80 flights over Sφr-Rondane in the course of a gravimetric triangulation survey.

CHILE

Gravimetric surveys have been made at Decepcion Island and over extensive areas of Tierra O'Higgins and the South Shetland Islands. At sea, gravity readings were taken in the course of oceanographic work in Drake Passage during the 1960-1961 and 1961-1962 seasons.

FRANCE

In 1962-1963, a Worden gravimeter was used to establish a network of 114 stations in Archipel de Kerguelen, mainly in the Peninsule Amiral, Courbet Glacier, Cook and Mont Ross regions. At Iles Crozet, eight stations were established on Ile de la Possession and one station on Ile aux Cochon. Both nets were linked to the World Network. In Terre Adélie, during the 1964-1965 season, 30 stations were occupied in the Archipel de Pointe Geologie region. These measurements were connected to the existing network on the coast of Terre Adélie.

JAPAN

The gravity value at "Syowa" was first determined by the 1958-1959 expedition and was confirmed by the 1959-1960 expedition. A gravity tie with Cape Town was established. Measurements were made at 109 points along the 1961 traverse of 890 km southward from "Syowa."

The GSI pendulum apparatus was used to establish a new gravity station at "Syowa" during the 1961-1962 season. The gravity value obtained was referred to the value at Tokyo via Cape Town. In the same season, gravity surveys were made in West Ongul Island.

Detailed reports on Japanese Antarctic Research Expedition (JARE) gravity determinations are given in the *Bulletin of the Geographical Survey Institute* for November 1960 and *Antarctic Record No. 17*, January 1963.

The JARE vessel *Fuji* used a newly designed GSI-type gravimeter for continuous observations on the 1966-1967 voyage to and from Antarctica. The accuracy of the readings is estimated to be about 10 mgal.

NEW ZEALAND

The 1960-1961 New Zealand Geological Survey Antarctic Expedition (NZGSAE) Northern Party used a Worden gravity meter to make observations at 12 points in the Barne Inlet-Cape Parr region (latitude 81°17′ S, longitude 160°35′ E). In the same season, a Victoria University of Wellington expedition carried out gravimetric traverses in the Koettlitz Glacier region.

During the 1961-1962 season, 18 stations, mostly on rock, were occupied in the mountains between Beardmore Glacier and Nimrod Glacier. In the McMurdo Sound region, stations were occupied on Black Island, Minna Bluff saddle, and Cape Crozier.

The 1962-1963 NZGSAE Northern Party carried out a gravity traverse from Cape Royds, on the west coast of Ross Island, to David Glacier in southern Victoria Land. Readings were taken at 22 stations on rock, sea ice, and land ice. In 1963-1964, the NZGSAE Northern Party made gravity measurements at 30 stations on rock, glacial ice, and inland ice along their traverse through northern Victoria Land and Oates Land.

In March 1964, a combined New Zealand-United States reconnaissance party, transported by the USCGS *Glacier,* took readings on Sabrina and Borradaile Islands (Balleny Islands).

SOUTH AFRICA

A 1961-1962 field party, using a Worden gravimeter, carried out a gravity survey from "Norway" station to the mountains of Ahlmannryggen, some 160 km southward. In the period October-December 1962, 51 stations were established at 3-km intervals along traverses in the "Sanae" area, and 97 stations at 3-km intervals were established along a traverse from "Sanae" to Ahlmannryggen. A Worden Master model gravimeter was used for this and subsequent work.

During 1963, observations were made at 101 stations, at 3-km intervals, along two geophysical traverses from "Sanae" to the Ahlmannryggen region and at 11 stations on "Blaskimen Ice Rise," which lies to the south and southwest of "Sanae."

In 1964, observations were made at 15 stations on the ice shelf (Fimbulisen) east of "Sanae." The traverse interval between stations was 3 km. Early in 1965, determinations were made in the coastal region north and northeast of "Sanae."

SOVIET UNION

From October 1960 to February 1961, a Worden gravimeter was used for observations along a traverse of some 1600 km from Mirny to "Vostok" by way of latitude 71°59' S, longitude 87°00' E, and "Komsomol'skaya." Other readings were taken during 1960 at "Lararev Ice Shelf" (224 stations), West Ice Shelf (92 stations), Shackleton Ice Shelf (5 stations), and "Pobeda" (20 stations).

During the 1961–1962 summer season, observations were made at intervals of 10–15 km along the traverse "Komsomol'skaya"–"Sovietskaya"–"Vostok"–"Komsomol'skaya."

During the period January to March 1963, gravity observations were made at 74 stations in the coastal regions of Enderby Land, between longitudes 44° E and 51° E. Gravity readings formed part of the scientific work carried out by *Ob'* during her 1962–1963 voyages.

Gravimetric observations were made along the 1963–1964 traverses "Vostok"–"Pole of Inaccessibility"–"Molodezhnaya" and Mirny–"Vostok" and along the 1964–1965 traverse, 100 km inland from Mirny.

UNITED KINGDOM

During a 1959–1960 geophysical survey by Shackleton, gravity measurements were carried out in the Scotia Sea, Bransfield Strait, and adjacent areas. A Worden gravimeter was used to obtain data at many points in the South Shetland Islands, in northwest Graham Land and off-lying islands, and at Port Stanley (Falkland Islands). The survey has been linked to the international gravity network by connecting it to a base station at Buenos Aires via Port Stanley and Montevideo. Stations have also been occupied in the South Orkney Islands, South Sandwich Islands, and South Georgia.

In 1963–1964, a reconnaissance traverse was made from Stonington Island across the Graham Land plateau to the east coast, then northwards to Foyn Coast. In addition, local detailed work was carried out in northeastern Trinity Peninsula and in the Marguerite Bay area. In the 1964–1965 season, the east-coast gravity traverse was extended northward to Hope Bay, and local surveys were made in the region of Joerg Peninsula.

During the period November 1965–April 1966 HMS *Protector* made measurements in Drake Passage, Bransfield Strait, and the South Orkney Islands area using a Graf Askania instrument. A Worden gravimeter was used for tie-ins for sea gravity measurements and repeat links between South America and the Antarctic Peninsula.

Toward the end of 1966, some of the main traverses on the east coast of the Antarctic Peninsula were flown with radio-echo sounding equipment developed by the Scott Polar Research Institute. This work should enable better estimates of ice thickness to be made.

UNITED STATES

During the 1960–1961 season, measurements were taken along three major traverses: "McMurdo" to the South Pole, "Byrd" to Eights Coast, and "Byrd" to the South Pole. In addition, gravity ties were made between Christchurch and McMurdo, "Hallett" and McMurdo, and "Byrd" and McMurdo.

The interstation gravity program was continued during the 1961–1962 season utilizing supply flights to inland stations. Several ties were made between McMurdo and "Amundsen-Scott" and between McMurdo and the new and old "Byrd" stations. Gravity values were established at the "Sky-Hi" summer station (latitude 75°14' S, longitude 77°10' W), 25 gravity stations were occupied in the McMurdo Sound area, and 142 observations were taken on Roosevelt Island. In addition, measurements were made along a traverse of 1693 km in Ellsworth Land.

During the 1962–1963 season, gravity values were determined at 202 stations along traverse routes between the South Pole and the vicinity of Queen Maud Range and the Horlick Mountains, and about 40 stations were occupied between "Byrd" and the Whitmore Mountains. Work was continued in the McMurdo Sound region; values were measured at 17 stations in Taylor Glacier Dry Valley and at 40 stations along the Victoria Land coast.

During the 1963–1964 season, 520 observations were made by a traverse party which covered 2690 km in the region between "Byrd," Whitmore Mountains, the southern ends of the Ellsworth and Pensacola Mountains and the Filchner Ice Shelf.

Gravity measurements were made along the 1964–1965 summer traverse from the South Pole station to the "Pole of Inaccessibility" (latitude 82°06' S, longitude 54°58' E).

SUMMARY

Additional gravity and astronomic measurements should be obtained at the pole station. The gravity data should be obtained with continuous recording systems, preferably more than one system at each station, to study the semimonthly earth tide. When combined with tiltmeter and latitude observations at the same site, Love's numbers can be determined and the strength of the crust inferred. Precise astronomic observations, corrected for polar motion, would be valuable for determining ice movement.

The best source of information relative to sea gravity measurements in the polar region is the compilation by Worzel (1961) of all sea pendulum gravity measurements. Charts and tabulations of data contained in the 1961 publication by Worzel indicate the limited extent of measurements of this type.

REFERENCES

Antarctic Map Folio Series (13 Folios published to May 1969), American Geographical Society, N.Y. (1964 continuing).

Bailey, J. T., S. Evans, and G. de Q. Robin, "Radio Echo Sounding of Polar Ice Sheets," *Nature, 204*, 420–421 (1964).

Beal, M. A., F. Edvalson, K. Hunkins, A. Molloy, and N. Ostenso, "The Floor of the Arctic Ocean: Geographic Names," *Arctic, 19*, 215–219 (1966).

Committee on Polar Research, *Sciences in Antarctica. Part II, The Physical Sciences in Antarctica*, Publ. 878, Nat. Acad. Sci.-Nat. Res. Council, Washington, D.C. (1961).

Committee on Polar Research, *Science in the Arctic Ocean Basin*, NAS-NRC Publ. 1086, Nat. Acad. Sci.-Nat. Res. Council, Washington, D.C. (1963).

Evans, S., "Radio Glaciology," SPRI Paper, *Scott Polar Research Institute*, Cambridge, U.K. (Nov. 1966).

Evans, S., and G. de Q. Robin, "Glacier Depth-Sounding from the Air," *Nature, 210*, 883–885 (1966).

Icelandic Glaciological Society, *Jökull, Arsrit Joklarannsöknafélags Islands* (Yearbook of the Icelandic Glaciological Society), Reykjavik, Iceland (1959–1969).

Ketchum, R. D., Jr., and W. L. Wittmann, "Infrared Scanning the Arctic Ice Pack," in *Proceedings of the Fourth Symposium on Remote Sensing of Environment*, Willow Run Labs., U. of Michigan (1966).

Leighty, R. D., "Terrain Information from High Altitude Side-looking Radar Imagery of an Arctic Area," in *Proceedings of the Fourth Symposium on Remote Sensing of Environment*, Willow Run Labs., U. of Michigan (1966).

Oceanographic Atlas of the Polar Seas, Part II: Arctic, Hydrographic Office Publ. No. 705 (1958).

Proceedings of the First Marine Geodesy Symposium, September 28-30, 1966, U.S. Govt. Printing Office, Washington, D.C. (1967).

Rinker, J. N., S. Evans, and G. de Q. Robin, "Radio Ice Sounding Techniques," in *Proceedings of the Fourth Symposium on Remote Sensing of Environment*, Willow Run Labs., U. of Michigan, pp. 793-800 (1966).

Serial Atlas of Marine Environment (17 Folios published to May 1969), American Geographical Society, N.Y. (1962 continuing).

Sobczak, L. W., "Regional Gravity Survey of the Sverdrup Islands and Vicinity," *Gravity Map Series Dom. Obs.* (Ottawa, Canada), No. 11 (1963).

Tanner, J. G., "Gravity Measurements in Canada, Jan. 1, 1963 to Dec. 31, 1966," *Dom. Obs.* (Ottawa, Canada), 36 (2) (1967).

Tardi, P. (ed.), *Rapport Sur Les Travaux Gravimetriques–Antarctique, Vol. XXXI, Part I. Annals of the International Geophysical Year, 1957-58*, Pergamon Press, New York (1964).

U.S. Army Engineers Topographic Laboratory, *Radar Imagery Mosaic of Province of Darien, Republic of Panama and Colombia*, prepared by Raytheon Corporation (1967).

Worzel, J. L., *Pendulum Gravity Measurements at Sea, 1936-1959*, John Wiley & Sons, Inc., New York (1961).

BIBLIOGRAPHY

Bermel, P. F., "The Development of Ground Control for Antarctic Mapping," paper presented at American Congress on Surveying and Mapping, Washington, D.C. Mimeographed copies available from U.S. Geological Survey, Washington, D.C. (1964).

Chapman, W. H., "Field Control for Antarctic Mapping," *Proc. Amer. Soc. Civ. Eng. J. Surveying and Mapping Div.*, 88 (SU1), 29-39 (1962).

Chapman, W. H., "Projects Topo North and South, Antarctica," paper presented at the ACSM-ASP semiannual convention, St. Louis, Mo. (1962).

Dean, W. N., "Application of Hyperbolic Radio Systems to Marine Geodesy," in *Proceedings of First Marine Geodesy Symposium, Session III*, pp. 115-123, U.S. Govt. Printing Office, Washington, D.C. (1967).

Friend, P. F., "The Growth of the North Atlantic Ocean by the Spreading of Its Floor," *Polar Rec., 13*, 579-588 (1967).

Lambert, B. P., *Report on Geodetic Surveying in Antarctica*, IAG, International Union of Geodesy and Geophysics. XIII General Assembly, Berkeley, Calif. (1963).

Lambert, B. P., "Report on Geodetic and Cartographic Activities, 1960-65," *SCAR Bull. No. 26* (1967a).

Lambert, B. P., *Report on Geodetic Surveying in Antarctica 1963-66*, IAG, Intern. Union of Geodesy and Geophysics XiV General Assembly, Lucerne (1967b).

Lee, D. R., "Daylight Star Observations in Antarctica," paper presented at American Congress on Surveying and Mapping, Washington, D.C. Mimeographed copies available from U.S. Geological Survey, Washington, D.C. (1963).

MacDonald, W. R., "Antarctica Aerial Photography Program," paper presented at the Annual Convention of the American Society of Photogrammetry, Washington, D.C. (1968).

MacDonald, W. R., "Sketch Map Series for Antarctic," in *Geological Survey Research 1968*, U.S. Geol. Survey Prof. Paper 600-B, pp. 185-189 (1968).

National Science Foundation and U.S. Naval Support Force–Antarctica, *Antarctic J. U.S.*, *1* (2) (March-April 1966).

Poulin, A. O., "Infrared Imagery in the Arctic under Daylight Conditions," in *Proceedings of the Fourth Symposium on Remote Sensing of Environment*, Willow Run Labs., U. of Michigan (1966).

Simonett, D. S., and D. A. Brown, "Spacecraft Radar as a Means for Studying the Antarctic," *CRES Report No. 61-4*, U. of Kansas (1965).

Simonett, D. S., and S. S. Morain, "Remote Sensing from Spacecraft as a Tool for Investigating Arctic Environment," *CRES Report No. 61-5*, U. of Kansas (1965).

Sobczak, L. W., J. R. Weber, N. K. Goodacre, and J. L. Bisson, "Preliminary Results of Gravity Surveys in the Queen Elizabeth Islands," *Gravity Map Series Dom. Obs.* (Ottawa, Canada), Nos. 12-15 (1963).

Southard, R. B., "Highlights of the U.S. Geological Survey Antarctic Mapping Operations," paper presented at the Conference on The History of Geographical Exploration and Scientific Research in Polar Regions by the United States, September 8, 1967.

Sykes, L. R., B. Isacks, and J. Oliver, "Seismology and the New Global Tectonics," *J. Geophys. Res.*, 73, 5855-5858 (1968).

Technical Advisory Committee on Antarctic Mapping, *Final Report of the TACAM Special Work Group* (March 1965).

"United States Antarctic Activities: Long-Range Projection, 1965–70, Appendix L, Plan for Topographic Mapping of Antarctic," *Antarctic J. U.S., 1* (3), 94–98 (1966).

Whitmore, G. D., and R. B. Southard, "United States Geological Survey Mapping for the U.S. Antarctic Research Program," *Polar Rec., 13,* 273–278 (1966).

APPENDIX A

Index Maps Showing Coverage of Greenland at Various Scales

1. Gronland, 1:5,000,000 scale showing map coverage at 1:250,000 scale. Geodetic Institute, Copenhagen, 1966.
2. Gronland, approximately 1:6,000,000 scale showing printed maps and compilation under way of 1:250,000-scale maps. Geodetic Institute, Copenhagen, May 31, 1966.
3. TOPOCOM* Holdings of Greenland Maps marked CONFIDENTIAL: Selected map coverage scales 1:48,000–1:25,000; 1:50,000 scale; 1:100,000 scale; and 1:250,000 scale.
4. TOPOCOM*, Greenland 1:250,000-scale series. Printed by TOPOCOM. No date given; series C 501.
5. TOPOCOM* Index to Maps of Greenland, 1:50,000 scale, series C 701, western coastal areas.
6. TOPOCOM* Index to Maps of Greenland, 1:50,000 scale. Only two maps of Nunatarssuag I and II. Printed by TOPOCOM.
7. USAF Index to World Aeronautical Charts at 1:1,000,000 scale. Printed by ACIC, September 1, 1966. Labeled "Arctic Region."
8. USAF Index to USAF Jet Navigation Charts—Northern Hemisphere. Current as of March 1, 1968.
9. Continental Drift—fit of continents around the Atlantic at the 3000-ft contour, as determined by Bullard, Everett, and Smith in 1965.

*TOPOCOM–U.S. Army Topographic Command (formerly the Army Map Service).

6

Polar Meteorology and Climatology

Meteorology and climatology provide a wide field for study, embracing many special topics. No attempt is made in this chapter to deal systematically with all aspects of these subjects; instead it covers those research areas which should be of particular interest in the next 5 to 10 years. A number of subjects not of primary atmospheric interest involve meteorological techniques and instrumentation, for example, ocean–atmosphere interactions; sea ice; and the heat and mass balance of glaciers. These subjects are treated in Chapters 3 and 4.

SYNOPTIC METEOROLOGY AND TROPOSPHERIC PROCESSES

SCIENTIFIC PROBLEMS

Fifty years ago or more, preliminary retrospective synoptic weather analyses were carried out in the Ross Sea. However, the southern polar region generally lagged behind the arctic regions in data collection and, consequently, in synoptic analysis and in understanding circulation processes. In the context of the Global Atmospheric Research Program (GARP), a study of polar regions appears to be at least as important as other geographical regions to a complete understanding of global atmospheric processes. Polar regions are the principal large-scale heat sinks of the earth-atmosphere system, and atmospheric phenomena associated with interaction mechanisms with the rest of the globe warrant particular attention. In the past, limitations of observational techniques and areal coverage of data have handicapped such studies, although the International Geophysical Year (IGY) program did improve the situation, except for oceanic areas. Although the possibilities for improving conventional observational systems in the polar

regions may be limited, remote and automated sensing techniques, and the use of mathematical models backed up by real observational data, offer inviting prospects.

Since the character of the northern and southern hemisphere circulations appears to be very different in such elements as wavenumber, zonal and meridional indices, and dynamic stability, the meteorologist immediately looks to geographical factors to explain these differences. With sufficient observational data, the tropospheric circulation in both large and small time and space scales can be described and analyzed. Mathematical model studies offer the possibility of reducing the time required and offer expanded possibilities for studying the effects of varying orographic and physical influences.

It has been shown that northern hemisphere stratospheric warmings are often preceded by a marked expansion in the ring of tropospheric westerlies. The analogous southern hemisphere situation has not been studied, and the whole problem of the kinetic energy budget and the transfer of energy is a significant area to be explored. This will require better data coverage and more detailed analysis.

The openness of the network in the southern hemisphere operates against a reliable spectral analysis of the velocity and temperature fields, except possibly for the stations located around the periphery of the antarctic continent. The Arctic Basin also has its own ring of stations, backed up by a good network toward the equator, which is not the case in the southern hemisphere. The gross features of the mean mass circulation and the heat and moisture balance requirements can be determined for Antarctica, but finer-scale details are highly desirable.

The difference in the character of the circulations of the two hemispheres warrants careful study. Because of the limitations of data, particularly in the southern hemisphere, definitive studies may not be possible in all cases. However, the advent of satellites and techniques for observing cloud types, cloud movement, and other indications of circulation have considerably advanced our ability to observe and understand these circulations. These techniques must be further developed and applied to synoptic analysis to overcome what will certainly be a long-continuing deficiency in observation. The horizontal sounding balloon can give new impetus to circulation studies in the southern hemisphere. Every effort should be made to advance this technique so that it may be used in the polar night. Through the use of satellite and horizontal sounding balloon data, only a minimum of ground stations need be retained to serve as reference or anchor points for the other data. Orographic considerations affecting synoptic and other features, such as oases, dry valleys, and ice-pack distribution, should be studied. Such relatively small-scale features, although they are known to show up on satellite cloud pictures, probably require more detailed study from ground-based stations or aircraft. Case studies should be carried out, based on specially collected data over limited time periods.

With respect to circulation in the northern hemisphere, a similar situation applies, except that the land masses extend well into the polar regions, and ground-based stations are numerous enough to permit reasonably reliable synoptic analysis. However, even in the Arctic more data are required for specific studies, e.g., synoptic patterns associated with orography or unique physical features and particularly the question of open water versus ice-covered water. Physical characteristics of the polar regions give rise to the possibility of studying large- and small-scale physical processes in a relatively uncontaminated and undisturbed environment, not generally available elsewhere on such a grand scale. The flat sea-level ice expanse of the Arctic Ocean offers a very different situation from the high dome of the Antarctic with its great slopes. For example, these regions offer excellent opportunities to study the formation, maintenance, and breakdown of large-scale inversions; surface stress; sastrugi patterns; the formation of ice and snow fields; areal distribution of precipitation as a function of synoptic patterns; blocking patterns; and storm tracks in respect to sea-ice cover and land–ocean distribution. Since the polar regions consist in large measure of homogeneous areas with respect to surface characteristics, relatively few stations will suffice to provide a satisfactory basis for analysis, when augmented by remote sounding techniques.

The foregoing paragraphs have emphasized the need for additional synoptic data in both polar regions and have mentioned means by which they may be obtained. However, it is important to bear in mind that many valuable data already exist which have not been properly analyzed. Data analysis is relatively inexpensive and, if pursued at universities and elsewhere, makes a valuable contribution to graduate-student education and can lead to a greater student interest in polar meteorology. Agencies funding polar research must continue to regard home-based analysis of data as an essential and high-priority part of their mission.

RECOMMENDATIONS

1. Funding agencies should give strong support to groups that are willing to investigate theoretical models of polar meteorology and climatology.

2. Until superseded by other means of observation, the three U.S. meteorological stations at McMurdo, Byrd, and Pole Stations should continue to record the basic meteorological parameters, because the process of formulating problems in synoptic meteorology of the polar regions is continuing and cannot give objective criteria for the minimum number of meteorological observing stations needed in the Antarctic.

STRATOSPHERIC AND MESOSPHERIC CIRCULATIONS

SCIENTIFIC PROBLEMS

Within the past decade or two, major features of the stratospheric and mesospheric circulations have been identified, and significant progress has been made in understanding many of their features. From both observational and theoretical studies, it is apparent that the stratosphere and mesosphere cannot be treated as isolated layers. Interactions with adjacent layers of the atmosphere, particularly the troposphere, play an essential part in shaping the flow patterns in these upper regions. Likewise, it is realized that motions within fixed geographical areas of the stratosphere and mesosphere, such as the polar regions, cannot be studied in isolation. Lateral interactions are also important in determining regional wind systems. Thus, it must be recognized at the outset that it is impossible to separate the problem of the polar stratospheric and mesospheric circulation from the problem of upper-atmospheric motions in general. Studies focused on the polar atmosphere may well contribute to a better understanding of the circulation as a whole. By the same token, it may occasionally be desirable to direct attention elsewhere in seeking solutions to polar problems. What are the significant and challenging problems of the stratospheric and mesospheric circulations which confront us at this time, and which appear ripe for investigation in view of recent scientific and technological advances? Four are suggested as follows: (a) basic zonal current systems and their seasonal variation, (b) large-scale seasonal disturbances of zonal flow, (c) tidal motions, and (d) quasi-biennial oscillations in the stratosphere.

Basic Zonal Current Systems and Their Seasonal Variations

According to our present understanding, it is important to distinguish between the circulation of the region below approximately 25 km, which is mechanically driven from beneath, and the circulation of the upper stratosphere and lower mesosphere, which is directly driven by the differential heating of ozone. The lower region is reasonably well observed, except possibly during the antarctic winter. The theory of its zonal motions and their maintenance seems to be in an acceptable state.

On the other hand, the upper region has not yet been adequately observed over much of the globe, and its motions are at best only partially explained. On the observational side, it is known that the zonal wind reverses direction in both hemispheres from easterly in summer to westerly in winter. In the northern hemisphere at both seasons, the core of the zonal currents lies in middle latitudes at a height of about 60 km. Detailed characteristics of the zonal circulation are not yet known in the southern hemisphere, where only a few rocket observations have been taken at widely separated localities and irregularly spaced time intervals. Even in the northern hemisphere, some uncertainties still exist concerning the exact nature of the zonal circulation in winter, since there are great longitudinal variations at this season and only the North American sector has been adequately sampled. To fill in the main data gaps, meteorological rocket observations are needed at several different sites in the southern hemisphere and in the Eurasian sector of the northern hemisphere, particularly in winter. At this time, the zonal circulation is known to become highly asymmetric about the pole. There is also a need for continuing nonroutine observation of wind and temperature by rocket grenade and other techniques which, though more expensive than the meterological rocket system, yield information on temperatures and densities at heights of 60 to 90 km not attainable by the rocket system.

It should be noted that occasional meteorological rocket soundings are already reported in the literature by Soviet scientists. Efforts should be made to induce the Soviets to include their rocket data in the international collection, published regularly by World Data Center A.

A minimum of three rocket stations, making 30 to 40 firings per year for a period of two or three years, is needed to define the major upper-level circulation features of the Antarctic. Possible locations are the Palmer, McMurdo, and d'Urville Stations. Cooperation with South American and French scientists would be desirable in carrying out the rocket effort. Rocket launchings should preferably be made at variable time intervals: half-monthly during the summer period of stable circulation, weekly during the winter, and possibly twice weekly during the spring period of rapid circulation change.

For antarctic soundings to be seen in proper perspective, it is important to establish a line of rocket stations along one meridian in the southern hemisphere. These stations should be separated by not more than 15° to 20° of latitude and should follow approximately the firing schedule suggested above. The beginnings of such a line already exist, thanks to the EXAMET program, a cooperative venture of the U.S., Brazilian, and Argentinian Governments. A modest increase in the number of stations and the frequency of soundings is to be encouraged.

With regard to theoretical studies, a simple model has been devised which appears to explain successfully the main features of the mesospheric circulation, including the locations and strengths of the zonal currents and their seasonal reversal. However, this model employs an assumption regarding the horizontal momentum flux (or Reynolds stresses) which may not be permissible for the winter season when large-scale disturbances are present. It is important to expand the rocket network as suggested above, so that the fluxes can be determined and the validity of this model better assessed.

It is hoped that general circulation models of the sort now being developed for the troposphere and lower stratosphere will be enlarged eventually to include upper stratospheric and mesospheric levels. Only from such multilevel, nonlinear models reaching from the ground to the lower thermosphere can one expect to gain a completely satisfactory understanding of the circulation in the regions of interest.

Large-Scale Seasonal Disturbances of Zonal Flow

A second major problem concerns the large-scale disturbances of the zonal flow which take place in winter and spring, the more spectacular instances being referred to as "sudden warmings." Temperature increases of 50°C may occur in several days in the polar stratosphere during such events. Most observers believe that the behavior of the warming phenomenon is significantly different in the two hemispheres, the majority opinion holding that strong warmings occur only prior to the return of the sun in the Arctic and only subsequent to its return in the Antarctic. There is now general agreement that the large-scale disturbances are most likely caused by interactions with the underlying atmosphere and surface. It is important to understand the effects of large topographical features on the flow patterns and differences in flow patterns in the two hemispheres.

The opinion regarding the different behavior in the two hemispheres is somewhat controversial, and the issue can only be decided by improved observations in the region between 20 and 40 km during the antarctic winter. Balloon performance must be improved so that radiosondes can reach the 10-mB level regularly. This is possible if the existing radiosonde stations use more expensive, higher-quality balloons than those presently in use. Weekly rocket soundings are needed from at least one antarctic site to observe winds and temperature at the higher levels. Radiometric observations by satellite of the 15-μ CO_2 emission should be gathered on a regular basis as soon as possible to provide temperature patterns in the lower stratosphere for the entire polar region. Power sources should be developed which will make it possible for the Global Horizontal Observation Sounding Technique (GHOST) and Interrogation, Recording, and Location System (IRLS) sounding systems to be operated during the polar night. The current design utilizes solar cells as the power source.

Renewed theoretical attacks on the large-scale winter disturbances should be carried out in conjunction with observational studies. The ultimate approach to the problem will almost certainly be through extension of present general circulation models. The problem of explaining the remarkable wintertime disturbances provides a further reason for encouraging numerical simulation experts to push their horizons upward.

Tidal Motions

Tidal motions represent a third problem deserving special attention. Recent rocket observations have revealed the existence of substantial diurnal tidal motions in the upper stratosphere and mesosphere. Already these motions appear to have been explained theoretically, but a lack of suitable rocket observations, particularly in the north polar region and in the southern hemisphere as a whole, has prevented a thorough verification of the theory.

Two relatively simple methods exist for acquiring the observations needed to define accurately both diurnal and semidiurnal tidal motions. First, special series of short-interval soundings can be taken over periods of one or two days. Second, in making routine soundings, the hour of observation at a particular station can be varied systematically from day to day so that, after a sufficient period of time, the diurnal variations can be obtained statistically. These methods should both be employed at presently established arctic stations and at future antarctic sites.

In tidal experiments, it is desirable to extend the height of present rocket wind soundings, which generally are usable only to 60 km, to 80 km, by use of special chaff or other means. It would be advantageous to have simultaneous radiometeor observations of tidal motions in the 80- to 110-km range. The latter type of observations has been lacking in the polar regions until now, though it is understood that equipment for making them is presently being installed at College, Alaska. If possible, similar equipment should be installed in Antarctica.

Quasi-biennial Oscillations in the Stratosphere

A final problem meriting investigation is the recently discovered quasi-biennial oscillation of wind and temperature in the stratosphere. It is well known that winds and temperatures in the equatorial stratosphere undergo long quasi-periodic variations with an average period of 26 to 27 months. Limited ozone and temperature observations from Australia and New Zealand and temperature observations from the Antarctic suggest that a corresponding, though smaller, oscillation occurs at middle and high latitudes of the southern hemisphere. These oscillations are of particular interest in the study of circulation differences between the hemispheres, since they seem to be ill-defined or absent in extratropical latitudes of the northern hemisphere.

Continuing worldwide measurement of stratospheric temperatures in the southern hemisphere, including the Antarctic, is needed to establish the exact nature of the quasi-biennial oscillation. The regular measurement of CO_2 emission in the 15-μ band from satellites would provide a simple and effective means of monitoring the stratospheric temperatures.

Because of the intimate connection between circulation and temperature, all the circulation problems mentioned here would benefit from more exact knowledge of three-dimensional temperature distribution and its time variation on a global scale. Remote sensing from satellites provides a means of obtaining the desired temperature information, and current efforts to develop and fly the necessary sensors in polar orbit should be supported.

RECOMMENDATIONS

1. Special quality balloons should be used in the polar winter to improve the performance of routine radiosonde measurements.

2. The meteorological rocket network should be expanded to give adequate coverage in the northern hemisphere by encouraging greater Soviet participation in the rocket network program and to give limited coverage in the southern hemisphere by establishing a network of three rocket stations in Antarctica and a north–south line of stations in South America.

3. For the purpose of making statistical studies of tidal motion in polar regions, the hour of launch of meteorological rockets should be systematically varied in such a manner that approximately equal numbers of soundings are available for at least four equally spaced hours of the day.

4. Special chaff, or some other economical technique, should be used to make rocket measurements of tidal motions in the 60- to 80-km region.

5. Radiometeor equipment should be installed in both

polar regions for measuring winds in the 80- to 110-km region.

6. Measurement of stratospheric and mesospheric temperatures should be made by remote sensing from meteorological satellites in nearly polar orbits.

CLIMATOLOGY

SCIENTIFIC PROBLEMS

Four major research areas may be identified as likely to be of particular importance in polar climatology in the next 5 to 10 years; they are the mass budget of Antarctica, micrometeorology, surface winds, and paleoclimatology.

Mass Budget of the Antarctic

A quantitative analysis of the mass budget of Antarctica is one of the major problems of polar climatology, but it is more appropriately considered as a part of glaciology (see Chapter 4).

Micrometeorology

Studies of the transfer of momentum and heat in the lowest layers of the atmosphere under extreme conditions of stability and instability can be conveniently carried out in polar regions. Extreme stability is found over the polar land masses, particularly at the high Plateau of the antarctic continent, while extreme instability is realized with less regularity at the coasts, where cold air flows over open water areas.

The first report on measurements obtained with the 100-ft micrometeorological tower at Plateau Station, located at 79° S and at 3500 m elevation, indicates that new and intriguing results can be expected. Two or three years will probably be needed for evaluation of the data obtained. It might be advisable to leave the bulky tower where it now stands, with the intention of returning to Plateau to use it again, if and when the results of the present work make it desirable to do so.

Surface Winds

The concept of a "katabatic wind," when applied to the surface winds in Antarctica and Greenland, needs clarification. Over the gentle slopes of antarctic inland ice, poleward of the coastal escarpments, the surface wind regime is strongly affected by the thermal wind due to the existence of a sloped inversion layer. Analysis of wind data at the surface and at the top of the inversion leads to a quantitative determination of the frictional deflection angle and of the ratio between surface and geostrophic surface wind. Hence, it is possible to derive the prevailing surface wind direction and strength for any place on the Plateau for which the topographic contour lines are known.

Paleoclimatology

Improving core technology, stratigraphic methods, and isotope analysis will rapidly increase our knowledge of antarctic paleoclimatology in the next decade. Selection of new drilling sites in Antarctica should be related to their location within important drainage areas.

The Arctic Ocean, and particularly the Atlantic sector of the Arctic, has been a region of great change during climatic variations of the past century. The same region is also the center about which the Pleistocene ice sheets accumulated. It is probably a key area for interpretation of climatic history. Palynological and glaciological field studies also indicate that there have been significant climatic changes in the area throughout the past 10,000 years. We need to establish patterns and synchroneity of these changes and their relationships to the general circulation.

A thorough study of the arctic heat budget and atmospheric circulation has been made with particular reference to climatology (Fletcher, 1966). The findings of this report represent a practicable and valuable research program. Careful thought has gone into the report, and it will have a great influence on this subject in the coming decade.

Some interesting research programs on paleoclimatology are (a) survey of organic accumulations consisting of peat bogs, lake sediments, and the like and palynological analysis; (b) palynological analysis of Greenland and antarctic ice cores and examination of Greenland cores for charcoal falls from Canadian forest fire episodes; (c) examination of the organic accumulations in the presumed areas of initiation of continental ice sheets for evidence of incipient glaciation during various times in the past ten millenia and correlation of such arctic lowland evidence with glacial advances in the montane areas; and (d) climatic and circulation conditions of the antarctic "dry valleys."

RECOMMENDATIONS

1. Funding agencies should give priority to continuing grants of several years' duration for home-based analysis of climatological data.

Research on problems of climatology and related fields requires field programs in the polar regions. Data collection cannot be fully satisfying by itself, and much can be done with observational evidence that already exists. It is important, therefore, that sufficient funds be made continuously available for data evaluation, which may require several years. Assurance of continued support could lead to more involvement with the important problems and thus to a higher quality of research work.

2. The findings of the Lake Arrowhead Study (Fletcher, 1966) should be accepted as defining the probable directions of rewarding research projects in arctic climatology for the next 5 to 10 years.

HEAT BALANCE

SCIENTIFIC PROBLEMS

Early heat-balance studies generally dealt with the balance for a whole hemisphere for the year, for seasons, or for midseason months. They did not include the south polar region; insufficient and inaccurate data did not permit detailed studies of the Arctic. The International Geophysical Year and subsequent observational programs in both hemispheres have resulted in a number of recent heat-balance studies. Polar meteorological field work, with very few exceptions, has not included specific observations for the study of the heat balance. Such knowledge as exists comes from analysis and subsequent synthesis of large numbers of inhomogeneous data.

The goal of meteorology must be to explain the atmospheric thermodynamic system as a whole. Being major heat sinks, the polar regions must be understood in order to gain better knowledge of the ways in which the atmosphere operates. Information about certain specific phenomena is needed in order that better details may be introduced into theoretical models. These are reviewed under the following seven headings.

Shortwave Radiation

Absorption of solar radiation by the atmosphere and at the surface is probably the largest uncertainty in polar heat budgets. It is likely that the turbidity of the polar atmosphere is considerably greater than previously suspected. Scattering and absorption by cloud droplets is generally insufficiently understood. As a minimum requirement, measurements of solar radiation intensity from aircraft are needed above, in, and below the stratus layer. Aircraft traverses can also give areal average values of surface albedo, its change with season, and circulation patterns.

Most of the effect of clouds on solar radiation occurs at midsummer, and variations in summer cloudiness from year to year are more important to the global radiation budget in the polar regions than in lower latitudes.

Long-Wave Radiation

The study of radiative transfer in clouds is particularly important in the polar regions where the long-wave terms dominate the heat budget. Present synoptic reporting of clouds is inadequate for purposes of radiation studies; to improve this situation, simultaneous measurements should be made from the ground and from aircraft. At one station such as Point Barrow, Alaska, or Resolute, N.W.T., the physical properties of clouds should be observed by cloud radar and from light aircraft. These observations should be related to surface visual observations of clouds and to direct and diffuse solar radiation as well as atmospheric thermal radiation. The results may serve as a base for new additions to the synoptic cloud reporting code, established on the relationships between physical observations and optical appearance.

Surface Conditions

The average ice thickness in the Polar Ocean may be about 2 m, although a greater thickness of from 3 to 4 m has usually been assumed. More ice than suspected may go into ice ridging, which would increase the mean thickness. More information on sea-ice thickness and amount of ridging can be obtained by aircraft and helicopter surveys in connection with surface observations, as well as by submarine. Aircraft observations have indicated that there may be roughly 10 percent more open water than previously assumed (about 5 percent at the end of the summer). Both terrestrial radiation and turbulent heat loss increase enormously over open water; it is important that the amount be ascertained in both polar regions. Aerial photography and infrared radiation measurements from low-flying aircraft are needed in conjunction with satellite observations, which do not yet give the required detail under all sky conditions.

Atmospheric Advection

Direct computation of heat advection can be made across a certain latitude circle, say 65° N, based on daily surface and upper-air charts. The problems of obtaining such data are discussed in the first section of this chapter on Synoptic Meteorology and Tropospheric Processes.

Turbulent Heat and Moisture Exchange

There is a need for better knowledge of the turbulent boundary layer heat flux under extreme conditions over land, ice, and snow surfaces, as well as under extremely unstable conditions (see Micrometeorology, page 143). It is important to find out how quickly the exceedingly high exchange rates over small leads decrease when the size of the open-water area increases.

Oceanic Transport of Ice and Water

Various estimates of the area of ice exported from the Polar Ocean are in good agreement; however, we need better estimates of average ice thicknesses. Improved estimates are also required of water exchange through the channel between Greenland and Svalbard as well as of water temperatures.

Other Problems

The influence of meteorological activity on the various energy budget terms must be known, but such studies can only be made at the present time with theoretical, numerical models of the earth–atmosphere energy balance. Many valuable investigations can be made at relatively modest levels of effort. Large semipermanent research programs are rarely the best approach; there is probably a sufficient number of permanent or semipermanent stations in the Arctic and Antarctic at present, except perhaps on the floating ice.

The value of radiosondes for radiation research can be enhanced greatly by simultaneous horizontal probes accomplished by properly instrumented aircraft, which have many advantages over fixed surface stations. Such aircraft must be available at the time and place decided by the scientist concerned with the research program. Increased use of submarines in Arctic Ocean research is desirable but may not be available in the immediate future. The main requirement at present is to make existing observations available in forms suitable for research purposes.

RECOMMENDATIONS

1. Instrumented aircraft flights in the Arctic Basin should continue to be provided by the appropriate agencies.

Properly instrumented aircraft will be the most important single tool in heat-balance research in the Arctic Basin for the next few years. Measurements should include (a) solar radiometric observations at various levels in stratus clouds combined with cloud-particle measurements, (b) thermal radiation measurements above and below clouds, and (c) photography to determine open-water areas and other surface characteristics.

2. A ground station, equipped with cloud-sensing radar, should be established in the Arctic to permit visual cloud studies to be made in conjunction with instrumented aircraft flights. It is probable that special groups of the synoptic cloud observation code can be devised which will

greatly improve the value of routine cloud observations for heat-balance studies.

ATMOSPHERIC CHEMISTRY

SCIENTIFIC PROBLEMS

Arctic and antarctic regions are important in the study of atmospheric chemistry because of their remoteness from many sources of minor atmospheric constituents. Much of the earth's surface in those regions is covered with ice and snow, and there are long periods of daylight and darkness. Especially in the southern hemisphere, the remoteness makes possible improved estimates of relative tropospheric lifetimes of certain trace constituents such as sulfur dioxide and sulfates. Such studies can be made on a historical basis by analysis of ice samples from different depths.

Very long periods of sunlight and darkness have interesting implications with regard to photochemistry. During long periods of sunlight, sulfur dioxide from any source might be expected to be oxidized fairly rapidly to form sulfates; during long periods of darkness, there would be little such oxidation, and any sulfate present would have to be part of sea salt or be transported for long distances. A number of analyses of the ice and snow at various depths have shown that the Greenland Ice Cap contains an order of magnitude more sulfate than other tropospheric constituents such as chloride, sodium, calcium, and potassium. Concentrations of Na, Mg, K, Ca, Cl, and N have been measured in ice in the vicinity of King Baudouin Base ($70° $ S, $24° $ E) and Pole Station ($90° $ S). Numerous analyses have been made of the tropospheric polar atmospheres for both trace gases and particles. Studies at the South Pole have shown that a six-month phase difference exists between maxima for ozone concentrations and maxima for radioactivity; this contrasts with a one-month difference in the middle latitudes of the northern hemisphere.

Aerosol samples in the Arctic and in the vicinity of McMurdo Sound in the Antarctic contain much greater relative concentrations of sulfate than do midlatitude samples. Since the Antarctic is believed to have a center of subsidence at about midcontinent, this might tend to bring down particles from the stratospheric "sulfate layer." Another explanation invokes tropospheric transport of Aitken nuclei into polar regions and their subsequent coalescence into larger, detectable aerosol particles. Alternatively, Aitken nuclei could be produced by local oxidation of sulfur dioxide.

The following investigations are likely to be important in the next 5 to 10 years:

(a) The high concentrations of sulfates in the polar aerosol raises a question of whether their source is stratospheric or tropospheric. If the origin is stratospheric, the dominant downward mixing in the winter would cause sulfate concentrations in the winter to exceed those in the summer.

(b) The very low concentrations of particles of tropospheric origin in the polar atmospheres make them ideal places for searching for extraterrestrial particles.

(c) Does the horizontal folding which E. F. Danielsen believes occurs at the so-called tropopause breakline produce injections of tropospheric air at about the 100-mB level in polar regions? If this occurs, how rapidly does this air travel into polar regions and with how much mixing? It would be helpful to make soundings to at least 60,000 ft, using tracers such as water, ozone, sulfur dioxide, and methane.

(d) Are the concentrations of trace gases and particles in the polar troposphere more nearly constant with regard to both time and space than they are in midlatitudes? This would be true if, as is now generally believed, downward mixing between the stratosphere and troposphere occurs mainly in midlatitudes.

(e) Is there a net downward movement of trace substances, such as ozone, and radioactive particles, throughout certain seasons or all year in the polar regions? Is this transport the result of subsidence or eddy diffusion?

(f) An interesting possibility for investigating both vertical and horizontal atmospheric motions in polar regions involves the presence of active volcanoes in both the Arctic and the Antarctic. The fume from even mild eruptions has been visually traced for thousands of miles; aircraft employing chemical techniques for detecting and tracing the fume can extend these possibilities.

(g) The reason for the phase difference between ozone and radioactivity concentrations at the South Pole is not known.

Some questions which were accorded high priority in the IGY and the subsequent decade seem less important to current research interests. Routine carbon dioxide measurements in polar regions can no longer be justified on grounds of atmospheric research. Ozone measurements by themselves, both on the ground and from balloon sondes, have probably been sufficiently well explored. However, ozone is an important tracer, and carefully conceived programs in which ozone concentration is related to concentrations of other gases and substances, or to meteorological parameters, may be of value for testing hypotheses about atmospheric circulations.

RECOMMENDATIONS

1. Funds should be made available for the development of suitable automatic unmanned chemical sampling stations, including development of the station-transducer

interface and engineering the transducers for reliable unattended operation.

Well-posed and directed questions about atmospheric chemistry exist, instruments capable of measuring minute concentrations are being developed, and aircraft capable of chemical sampling in polar regions have generally been available when required. However, an unsatisfied need remains for long-term series sampling, particularly during the polar night. The high cost of routine chemical sampling in polar regions by human observers probably cannot be justified, but automatic stations capable of chemical sampling and transmitting data to the continental United States may be feasible at reasonable cost.

THE GLOBAL ATMOSPHERIC RESEARCH PROGRAM IN THE POLAR REGIONS

The Global Atmospheric Research Program (GARP) is addressed to the single goal of extended prediction of global circulations. The program has grown out of a recognition on the part of leading atmospheric scientists that recent advances in geophysical fluid dynamics, together with development of high-speed digital computers and earth satellites, provide the scientific and technological base which is necessary for prediction beyond a few days of atmospheric circulation patterns. GARP has been endorsed by the United Nations, the World Meteorological Organization (WMO), and the International Council of Scientific Unions (ICSU); encouragement and support have come from many individual nations. In a variety of ways, the United States has shown interest in and support of GARP, while at the same time reserving judgment on budgetary levels of assistance.

The international aspects of GARP are the responsibility of the ICSU–WMO Joint Organizing Committee for GARP, while the U.S. national aspects are centered in the National Academy of Sciences' U.S. Committee for GARP (USN-GARP), which was established on March 1, 1968. The Environmental Science Services Administration (ESSA) has been designated as the lead government agency for GARP and the associated World Weather Watch (WWW). Literature relating to GARP is extensive, but two reports are of special significance (Committee on Atmospheric Sciences, 1966; The Global Atmospheric Research Programme "Stockholm Report," 1967).

While focus on the objective of extended prediction is regarded as essential to success of the program, GARP is not intended as an umbrella under which all atmospheric research can be fitted, and other research objectives should be pursued independently of GARP. At the same time, GARP should contribute enormously to many other research programs. One may look forward to a post-GARP era when atmospheric sensing and transmission systems will provide research data in numbers and quality far beyond anything we now regard as feasible.

Of the earth's surface, 8.2 percent is strictly polar and 13.3 percent lies poleward of 60° latitude; on the other hand, 60.2 percent is contained within the tropics. This fact had an important influence on the strong emphasis of GARP programs on the tropics. Because polar regions form the atmospheric heat sink, an areal comparison between tropic and polar regions as a basis for determining GARP program emphasis may not be altogether relevant. Unless careful consideration is given to special problems of polar meteorology, such as limitations of logistical support and six-month night, much valuable data from polar regions may not be available to GARP.

We attempted at first to distinguish between the possible contribution of polar meteorology to GARP and the possible benefits from GARP for strictly polar problems. We concluded that, in our present state of knowledge, this distinction is not meaningful. No differentiation between the requirements of GARP and the requirements of polar meteorology is therefore made in this chapter.

Predicting global circulation for extended periods involves representing the distribution of net radiative flux, solar minus emitted infrared, with some accuracy. The region of the polar night affords the largest values of net outgoing flux. The design of a global observing system must take special account of this, even though the area concerned is no greater than about 5 percent of the total surface area of the earth. Extended prediction will require that numerical models correctly represent major large-scale energy transformations. This may involve predicting the large-scale rate of subsidence in the polar stratosphere, which may require measurements of the distribution of temperature and ozone, as well as wind velocities.

Observations in the polar regions that are needed for GARP may face problems that require special attention. These problems are:

(a) Design concepts for constant density balloons are based on use of solar energy, rendering these ballons useless in regions of the polar night.

(b) The accuracy of humidity observations at the surface and in the free atmosphere is inadequate for important problems concerned with water-vapor transport, precipitation, and evaporation in polar regions.

(c) The network of manned stations reporting surface- and upper-air data in the polar regions is insufficient, and the cost of substantially augmenting the present network is unreasonably high.

RECOMMENDATIONS

To provide upper-air data of the quality and distribution needed for GARP, we recommend the following:

1. A development program should be undertaken to provide the GHOST balloon system or its successor with a power supply which will permit operation in regions of the polar night.

2. Vertical soundings in the lowest 500 mB should be made by dropsondes launched from reconnaissance aircraft designed as flying laboratories. They should carry out programs which might include air sampling, measurement of surface radiation temperatures, optical observations of the upper atmosphere, and soundings. During periods of intensified GARP observations, these flights should be carried out daily; less frequently at other times.

3. Strong support should be given to good proposals for remote measurement from satellites of water vapor in the lowest 500 mB. The radio-occultation method may prove to be feasible for this purpose. Measurements must be made in conjunction with radiation observations and temperature soundings already under development for GARP.

4. The development of a reliable automatic unmanned weather station should be funded as a matter of urgency. The feasibility of such a station is well within current technology. Development costs should be acceptable when considered over a reasonable time period in light of the extreme cost of manned stations in polar regions, expecially during winters. The station should be capable of reporting about 20 weather elements on each pass of a satellite, which should be capable of reading out data and commanding the station. This requires a data capacity far less than that of the automatic geophysical observatory presently under development at Stanford University and should consequently be less costly (Jenny and Lapson, 1968). To obtain maximum value from such a development, simultaneous attention must be given to the development and testing of sensors for remote automatic measurement of humidity, wind velocity, presence of ice particles and clouds, and snow depth. Requirements for an automatic buoy station are closely related, and development should be undertaken with both requirements in mind.

AUTOMATION, LOGISTICS, AND DATA

The most important advance of the next 5 to 10 years is likely to be the application of new technologies to polar meteorology and climatology. Satellite and balloon developments are already planned under GARP. These may be combined with automated ground stations and aircraft flying laboratories to give satisfactory synoptic coverage of the two polar regions and simultaneously relieve logistic problems and costs by reducing the need for manned surface stations.

There is evidence that much of the necessary logistical support for our recommended programs in the Arctic may already exist, particularly with regard to aircraft. Steps should be taken to ensure optimum use of these expensive facilities.

There is also evidence that some of the data required by research workers have already been obtained but are not fully used, either because they are not processed in a suitable manner or their whereabouts is not widely known. The problem is similar in some respects to the logistical support problem and may be resolved by similar steps. Other data from both polar regions are readily available but not fully used. Such material is invaluable for home-based programs, particularly at universities, which have an educational role and serve to bring new research workers into polar research. Support for such programs is an essential complement to field programs and must continue to be given high priority.

It is important to avoid the danger of subordinating research to logistics. This has sometimes happened in the past, often with disappointing results, and is unnecessary. Facilities, transportation, logistical and administrative support should be available for small, independent, short-term research efforts which aim to solve specific problems with limited observational programs.

The high cost of logistic support in the polar regions and recent advances in numerical modeling dictate a change of emphasis in the traditional relationship between theory and observation in meteorology and climatology. More effort is needed in theoretical modeling of atmospheric processes, and related processes at ocean and glacier surfaces, to ensure that expensive observational programs are properly directed toward specific scientific objectives.

RECOMMENDATION

Along with the Panel on Upper Atmosphere Physics, we recommend the following:

1. An *ad hoc* group should be convened, within the National Research Council, including representatives of all government agencies with arctic interests, for the purpose of (a) seeking appropriate priorities for scientific observations on missions undertaken for other than scientific purposes, (b) to inform the scientific community and other interested groups of facilities and new opportunities for arctic research, (c) to identify needs for facilities, (d) to assist in the full utilization of existing data, including determination of its availability and processing requirements, and (e) the formulation of national goals for arctic research.

REFERENCES

Committee on Atmospheric Sciences, National Academy of ences–National Research Council, *The Feasibility of a Global Observational and Analysis Experiment* (Referred to as the "Charney Report"). NAS–NRC Publ. 1290, p. 23, National Academy of Sciences–National Research Council, Washington, D.C. (1966).

Fletcher, J. O., ed., *Proceedings of the Symposium on the Arctic Heat Budget and Atmospheric Circulation*, Lake Arrowhead, Calif., Jan. 31 to Feb. 4, 1966, Memo. No. RM-5233-NSF, The RAND Corp., Santa Monica, Calif. (1966).

Jenny, J. A., and W. F. Lapson, *Feasibility Study on an Automated, Unmanned Geophysical Observatory for Operation in Antarctica,* Tech. Rep. No. 3433-1, Radioscience Lab., Stanford U. (1968).

The Global Atmospheric Research Programme (GARP), *Report of the Study Conference Held at Stockholm, 28 June–11 July 1967, Jointly Organized by the ICSU/IUGG, Committee on Atmospheric Sciences and COSPAR and Co-sponsored by WMO* (Referred to as the "Stockholm Report") (1967).

BIBLIOGRAPHY

Aldaz, L., "Surface Air Radioactivity and Ozone at Amundsen-Scott (90°S) Antarctica," *Nature*, *215*, 722–723 (1967).

Badgley, F. I., "Heat and Water Budget of the Arctic," in *Science of the Arctic Basin*, NAS–NRC Publ. 1086, Nat. Acad. Sci.–Nat. Res. Council, Washington, D.C. (1963).

Cadle, R. D., W. H. Fischer, E. R. Frank, and J. P. Lodge, Jr., "Particles in the Antarctic Atmosphere," *J. Atmos. Sci.*, *25*, 100–103 (1968).

Draig, R. A., *The Upper Atmosphere: Meteorology and Physics,* Academic Press, Inc., New York (1965).

Fletcher, J. O., "Ice Extent on the Southern Ocean and Its Relation to World Climate," Rep. No. RM-5793-NSF, The RAND Corp., Santa Monica, Calif. (1969).

Fletcher, J. O., *The Heat Budget of the Arctic Basin and its Relation to Climate*, Rep. No. R-444-PR, The RAND Corp., Santa Monica, Calif. (1965).

Kellogg, W. W., "Chemical Heating above the Polar Mesopause in Winter," *J. Meteorol.*, *18*, 373–381 (1961).

Lamb, H. H., "On Climatic Variations Affecting the Far South," in *Proceedings of the WMO/SCAR/ICPM Symposium on Polar Meteorology*, Geneva, September 5–9, 1966; *WMO Tech. Note No. 87*, 428–453 (1967).

Lettau, H. H., and W. Schwerdtfeger, "Dynamics of the Surface-Wind Regime over the Interior of Antarctica," *Antarctic J. U.S.*, *2* (5), 155–158 (1967).

National Academy of Sciences–National Research Council, "Glaciology in the Arctic," Report of the Glaciology Panel, Committee on Polar Research, *Trans. Amer. Geophys. Union*, *48*, 759–767 (1967).

Vowinckel, E., and S. Orvig, "The Heat Budget over the Arctic Ocean," *Arch. Met. Geoph. Biokl.*, *14*, 303–325 (1966).

Vowinckel, E., and S. Orvig, "Climate Change over the Polar Ocean," *Arch. Met. Geoph. Biokl.*, *15*, 1–23 (1967).

Wexler, J., and M. J. Rubin, "Antarctic Meteorology," in *Science in Antarctica, Part II, The Physical Sciences in Antarctica*, NAS–NRC Publ. 878, Nat. Acad. Sci.–Nat. Res. Council, Washington, D.C. (1961).

Witte, J. J., "Airborne Measurements of Cloud Particle Distribution and Infrared," M.S. Thesis, U. of Washington, Dept. of Atmospheric Sciences (1968).

World Meteorological Organization, "Polar Meteorology," in *Proceedings of the WMO/SCAR/ICPM Symposium on Polar Meteorology*, Geneva, September 5–9, 1966, *WMO Tech. Note No. 87*, Geneva (1967).

7

Upper-Atmosphere Physics in the Polar Regions

The polar upper atmosphere is dominated by effects of energetic particles precipitating into it as a direct or indirect result of solar activity. These effects cannot be considered out of the context of other atmospheric regions where they occur, even though these may not be at polar latitudes. Since the upper atmosphere is accessible to satellites and other space vehicles, effects occurring even thousands of kilometers from the earth's surface are observable and are intimately connected with those effects that can be detected from polar ground stations. In this chapter, therefore, we define the polar regions as follows: For those phenomena (in the E region and above, together with precipitation effects in the D region) where geomagnetic control is dominant, the polar regions include those geomagnetic dipole latitudes greater than 60°. For those phenomena (in the D region and below) where direct solar influence predominates, the polar regions include geographic latitudes greater than 60°. It is recognized that areas are frequently included in the polar regions because of logistic problems which they have in common (e.g., the entire Antarctic region).

Reference is made throughout this chapter to various regions of the upper atmosphere. The D region is defined as extending up to 90 km altitude and can generally be regarded as the region where most of the absorption of radio waves takes place and where negative ion chemistry may be important. The E region is defined as extending from 90 to 160 km altitude and is a region where the ionization is primarily molecular. The F region is the region above 160 km altitude; its ionization is primarily atomic. The magnetosphere is a name given to the entire medium surrounding the earth, where the terrestrial magnetic field is a dominant factor in controlling the motion of ionization, namely, from about 150-km altitude out to its boundary with the solar wind.

This chapter covers solar and galactic cosmic rays, auroral phenomena, photochemical effects, and upper-atmosphere dynamics. Progress in each field is reviewed, and recommendations are made for future work. The recommendations result from the discussion of outstanding problems in each area of the polar upper atmosphere. Programs are recommended to solve the outstanding problems that the Panel feels warrant maximum attention during the next 5 to 10 years. Specific methods for solving the problems are mentioned in the program recommendations as far as these methods exist and as far as they are known to the members of the Panel. Where such methods do not exist or are not known to the panelists, the program recommendations contain what are considered to be realistic statements of the requirements to be met by new methods which should be developed.

While properties of the upper atmosphere are quite similar in the arctic and antarctic regions, upper-atmosphere observations in Antarctica do more than merely repeat similar observations in the Arctic. In the last decade, it has become obvious that the polar regions of the upper atmosphere are not truly identical in behavior. A north–south asymmetry may exist in galactic cosmic rays and in magnetically conjugate observations. Unusually high whistler rates are found in the general region of the Palmer Peninsula of Antarctica. Sudden stratospheric warmings occur prior to the return of the sun in the Arctic and subsequent to its return to the Antarctic; and observations from the southern hemisphere are vital to an understanding of the biennial oscillation in stratospheric temperatures.

In addition to the asymmetries between the atmospheric properties in the northern and southern polar regions, the alternation of permanent daylight between the poles can be useful. For example, observations of polar cap absorption (PCA) events require a sunlit ionosphere to avoid domination by electron attachment of the processes involving free electrons. Continuous monitoring of PCA events at high latitudes is impossible from only one hemisphere.

In many studies, the geographic longitude of the point of observation becomes important because of the separation of the geomagnetic and geographic poles. Unlike the drifting ice cover of the Arctic Ocean, all longitudes in Antarctica are freely available for scientific work. In particular, the Amundsen-Scott South Pole Station is favorably situated for nighttime studies of phenomena occurring near local noon, geomagnetic time.

GALACTIC AND SOLAR COSMIC RAYS

Galactic cosmic rays consist of a flux of completely ionized nuclei of many elements, dominantly protons and alpha particles, together with energetic electrons and gamma rays. Their energies range from a few MeV to some 10^{13} MeV, with an average energy of ~10^3 MeV. It is known that these particles are generated outside the solar system. In their propagation toward the earth, solar–terrestrial conditions can significantly modify their characteristics, with the dominant effects at lower energies: the low-energy particles can reach the earth only in the vicinity of the polar cap.

Solar cosmic rays are nuclei generated most spectacularly in great solar flares, which may give rise to particles with energy from ~10^{-1} MeV to ~10^5 MeV. However, on numerous occasions, smaller flares and active solar regions may emit appreciable fluxes of lower-energy nuclei. The total energy flux during large solar events may exceed the galactic cosmic-ray background by many orders of magnitude.

The unique character of observations of these phenomena in the polar regions lies in the fact that the geomagnetic field acts both as a momentum spectrometer and as a complicated system of charged-particle "lenses." Thus, only in the polar regions can one detect inside the magnetosphere the lowest-energy particles in these phenomena. Conversely, by study of directionality and momentum spectra of such particles over the polar regions, one can probe the far-distant reaches of the magnetosphere and indeed of the interplanetary system itself. Furthermore, only in the polar regions are the directions of viewing appreciably inclined to the equatorial plane.

PROGRESS IN THE FIELD

Solar Cosmic Rays

Although the history of solar cosmic rays dates back over 25 years, detailed particle measurements on such events only began following the great outburst of February 23, 1956. As a result of these events, the earlier concept of ex-

tremely rare solar particle outbursts has given way to a description in which the time interval between major events is to be reckoned in months rather than years, and the particle energies are most typically in the tens and hundreds of MeV rather than in the GeV range. It is suspected that the sun emits weak fluxes of low-energy particles more or less continuously.

Satellites can make rapid latitude surveys of solar cosmic-ray events in the polar regions, where such events are confined. Because of their ability to measure the original particles themselves, satellites have made some important and unique discoveries. For example, a clear-cut distinction of solar cosmic rays in different energy ranges has been demonstrated in the polar plateaus (Pieper et al., 1962). This distinction can be used to test theories of the magnetospheric configuration and particle propagation within it (Reid and Sauer, 1967). Additional studies have shown both the long-term and short-term temporal and spatial changes in the latitudinal distribution of fluxes of different energies (Pieper et al., 1962; Paulikas et al., 1966). These results may be meaningfully applied to the explanation of limited ground-based or rocket- or balloon-borne measurements of solar cosmic rays, their atmospheric effects, and the ionization and luminosity (polar glow) that they produce. Satellite studies also proved the usefulness of the McIlwain L-coordinate system in ordering of the data and the clear violation of Störmer cutoff theory.

Many new aspects of solar, interplanetary, and terrestrial phenomena have been revealed by balloon and rocket observations in connection with solar flare outbursts. For example, the relative abundances of nuclei in these solar cosmic-ray events, as derived largely from balloon and rocket measurements in the polar cap, are being used for an assessment by astrophysicists of the hydrogen–helium ratio in the sun itself (Biswas and Fichtel, 1965). Briefly, some of the significant results concern: (a) the time history and energy spectra of solar particles at 1 AU; (b) the presence and variability of alpha particles and heavier nuclei in the solar cosmic-ray beam; (c) the lowering of geomagnetic rigidity cutoffs following the impact of solar plasma on the terrestrial magnetic field; (d) the identification of related terrestrial effects such as the polar-glow aurora and ionospheric anomalies at mesospheric heights.

Since before the International Geophysical Year (IGY) ground-based ionospheric observations, using such techniques as very-high-frequency (vhf) forward scatter and riometer measurements of cosmic-noise absorption, have constituted one of the major sources of information on solar cosmic-ray fluxes (Bailey, 1964; Reid, 1967a). Although accurate information on particle fluxes and spectra can now be obtained directly from satellites, the ionospheric techniques continue to supply information that cannot be obtained with satellites. For example, satellites in orbits close to the earth sample the particle flux above a given location only at intervals of ~90 min. Changes in flux often cannot be uniquely described as either spatial or temporal, owing to the rapid motion of the satellite. Ground-based observations, carried out continuously at a fixed location, are an essential complement to satellite observations in helping to resolve such ambiguities. In addition, they provide information on the structure and properties of the lowest region of the ionosphere, where the incoming particles produce their greatest ionizing effects.

Investigation of ionized molecular nitrogen optical emissions (e.g., at 3915 A) from the atmosphere during the solar-particle events has shown that the radiance of the night sky at this wavelength can be used as a good measure of the total incident energy during these events (Brown, 1964; Sandford, 1967). Some observations of emission from the second positive bands of molecular nitrogen have suggested that electron excitation of these bands is not the only process involved in the emission (Gadsden, 1961; Dalgarno, 1967). Possibly, excitation by fast hydrogen atoms or electron excitation of vibrationally excited nitrogen is occurring.

Solar-particle events in which the energies are sufficient to propagate their effects to sea level are relatively rare but exceedingly important. Only two such events have occurred during the present cycle since the high-counting-rate neutron monitor network has been in operation in both polar regions. Solar particles of sufficiently high energy can reach very high latitudes only through a prior diffusion process in interplanetary space, since there are no impact zones in the polar regions for direct travel from the sun. Comparison of data recorded at both poles reveals whether large-scale anisotropies exist and provides important information about the propagation process. For example, the event observed in January 1967 was unusual in that it represents the first example of the arrival at the earth of particles produced by a flare on the far side of the sun (Baird et al., 1967). Especially in the analysis of solar-particle events, the availability of data from the neutron monitors at high altitudes in the polar regions, such as the South Pole, is exceedingly valuable. This is due to the reduced atmospheric cutoff as well as to narrow asymptotic cones.

The above observations have contributed to the understanding of the theory of propagation of solar cosmic rays through the interplanetary medium and have given some information on the nature of this medium between the sun and the earth. The four main features of solar cosmic-ray events (i.e., intensity–time variations, solar east–west effect, direction of the initial anisotropy, and time decay of this anisotropy) suggest that the particles diffuse anisotropically from the sun to the earth, being strongly guided by the interplanetary magnetic field. The diffusive processes are caused by fluctuations of this field; the effective diffusion coefficient can be related to the power spectrum of the fluctuations of this field.

Galactic Cosmic Rays

The energy spectra and composition of the nucleonic and electronic components of the primary cosmic radiation have been measured down to about 10 MeV, i.e., to energies accessible only over the polar cap. In particular, the modulation of these characteristics over the solar cycle has been studied to some extent, although many more measurements remain to be made. While there has been considerable theoretical progress in this field, many significant problems still remain.

The use of the extremely high-counting-rate neutron monitors has led to a better description of the anisotropies of galactic cosmic rays, particularly in the 1- to 10-GeV energy range. In particular, it has been shown that the quiet-day diurnal variation appears to be consistent with corotation of the particles with the sun, although there is still a problem concerning the amplitude of the variation (McCracken and Rao, 1965). The presence of a semidiurnal variation has been detected. This has been interpreted in terms of a variation across the ecliptic plane (Ables et al., 1965), although it is possibly due to atmospheric modulation by inadequate correction of the semidiurnal pressure variations affecting ground-based measurements.

Detailed observations of anisotropies during Forbush decreases have been made in attempts to understand the expansion of de-energization of galactic cosmic rays in interplanetary space over the earth during geomagnetic storms (Ables et al., 1967). Regular balloon flights over the past decade from Mirny and Murmansk have shown an apparently large north–south anisotropy (Vernov et al., 1968), which has also been detected over limited periods by ground-based measurements with neutron monitors in the polar caps (Nagashima et al., 1968).

OUTSTANDING PROBLEMS

Solar Cosmic Rays

Many details of solar cosmic-ray propagation through the magnetosphere remain unsolved. For example, there is a need for examination of the time delays between the appearance of solar protons and solar alpha particles, at selected energies between 100 keV and 100 MeV, outside the magnetosphere—also their appearance at various latitudes and local times over the polar cap in both hemispheres as a function of, for example, season and storm intensity. This can yield conclusive magnetospheric models and distinguish simply between "open" or "closed" magnetospheric tail models (e.g., is access to the midnight meridian as opposed to the midday meridian of the polar cap consistent with the dispersion down a long magnetospheric tail, or do all particles have essentially direct access to both regions?).

The detailed relationship between particle fluxes and spectra and the magnitude of the ionospheric effects is still largely uncertain. Previous attempts to attack this problem have been confined to one or two specific events and have not led to general agreement. There is a distinct need to obtain direct correlations between satellite, rocket, and balloon measurements of the particle properties and ionospheric measurements carried out at a location immediately below the satellite.

The indications already obtained of occasional nonuniformity of proton precipitation (Reid and Sauer, 1967) need to be investigated further. This can be done best by a combination of satellite, rocket, and balloon observations and ionospheric measurements at a suitably located network of ground stations. The results can have important implications for our understanding of the interconnection between the outer geomagnetic field and the interplanetary magnetic field.

Twilight effects observed in the lower ionosphere during PCA events are a potentially rich source of material on which to base theories of the ion chemistry and physics of the mesosphere. A detailed study of these effects at several locations and during events with several different proton spectra would be highly productive.

In this area, as in other fields of geophysics, a great deal of progress is likely to come about through a multidisciplinary approach. The combination of ground-based ionospheric observations with optical measurements and direct particle and ionospheric observations by balloons, rockets, and satellites will undoubtedly be a fruitful source of information.

Many theoretical problems are still unresolved, including the production of the solar cosmic rays, their storage near the sun, their propagation through interplanetary space, and the modification of geomagnetic cutoffs during magnetically disturbed periods.

Galactic Cosmic Rays

The dominant problems in understanding the solar cycle modulation appear to lie in theoretical studies. However, continued balloon measurements in the critical energy range of 100 to 500 MeV per nucleon are vital to testing future theoretical developments.

An apparent disagreement exists between different groups of workers on the extent of solar modulation of galactic electrons. This is a particularly sensitive test of possible modulation mechanism, and its magnitude must be determined accurately. This can be achieved by balloon or satellite measurements in the polar regions. Another sensitive test of modulation mechanisms is study of particles of different charge–mass ratios and with different (unmodulated) energy spectra. In regard to anisotropies, dominant areas to be studied are north–south anisotropy (if it exists); anisotropies associated with Forbush decreases; "anomalous" amplitude of the normal diurnal variation which presently

appears to be approximately 30 percent less than predicted; and semidiurnal variations and their causes. Each of these phenomena may be associated with effects above and below the ecliptic plane and, therefore, perhaps may be related to an over-all modulation of the cosmic rays. Thus, ground-based observations in both polar regions are crucial for studies of the three-dimensional spatial characteristics of the interplanetary medium.

Data from polar stations are also required to provide clues to the nature of the mechanism that causes the large day-to-day variability of the diurnal variation and the role of transient intensity fluctuations in producing this effect. Furthermore, the behavior of the recently discovered (Duggal et al., 1967) changes in the annual mean daily vector from year to year remains to be established, and the intercomparison among data from many stations is essential for these studies. The study of transient north–south anisotropies deserves considerable attention during the coming years, and efforts should be made to investigate the small long-term axial asymmetry that might exist.

RECOMMENDATIONS

1. Existing programs of riometer and vhf forward-scatter observations at high magnetic latitudes should be continued, with active consideration being given to the relocation of sites or establishment of new sites to optimize the interdisciplinary aspects of the study. In the case of vhf forward-scatter observations, an experiment aimed at measuring the height of the scattering region, under a variety of conditions in polar regions, would be of great value in interpreting the observations in quantitative terms. Programs of very-low-frequency (vlf) vertical sounding, such as the existing program at Byrd Station, should be actively encouraged.

2. Techniques that presently yield only qualitative information on solar cosmic-ray events, such as measurement of phase and amplitude of signals from distant low-frequency (lf) and vlf transmitters, should not be abandoned yet. They are capable of yielding information on weak, and often long-lasting, effects that are below the threshold of other techniques. Every effort ought to be made to understand the mechanism and magnitude of these effects and their compatibility with the more quantitative observations.

3. Coordinated experiments involving both ionospheric and particle measurements should be carried out during solar particle events. The combination of results from such experiments with observations by a suitable network of ground stations and by polar-orbiting satellites would undoubtedly provide answers to many of the unsolved problems.

4. Measurements by neutron supermonitors and meson telescopes should be continued.

5. A relatively simple set of solar cosmic-ray detectors

should be flown in a series of polar-orbiting satellites for long-term monitoring. More sophisticated instruments that can measure protons and alphas over many energy intervals between ~100 keV and ~100 MeV should be flown in one or more satellites to permit more detailed scientific studies. These instruments should have sensitivities down to a 1 particle cm⁻² sec⁻¹ with directional capabilities.

6. Continued and more detailed balloon-borne observations of changes in spectra of all measurable components of the galactic cosmic radiation (protons, ^{3}He, ^{4}He, C, N, and O nuclei, as well as electrons and positrons) are required if a solution to the modulation problem is to be found. Information is particularly needed in the 100- to 1000-MeV energy range.

AURORAL PHENOMENA

Auroras and associated phenomena occur mainly along both the auroral *oval* (Akasofu, 1966) and the classical auroral *zone* (Hartz and Brice, 1967). On the occasions of auroral substorms they spread into the polar caps and into lower latitudes. The auroral light is caused by bombardment of the upper atmosphere by charged particles, mostly electrons and protons, with the greatest contributions from particles with energies of a few kilovolts.

However, during auroral substorms, almost every measurable phenomenon of the polar upper atmosphere is greatly modified and displays unique characteristics. The atmosphere is heated, expands, and is ionized, thereby affecting radio-wave propagation and transmission. It has intense electric currents (auroral "electrojets"), electromagnetic field perturbations, and other phenomena. These phenomena are summarized in Figure 22 (O'Brien, 1965).

Because auroral phenomena are largely confined to polar regions, polar research is vital to study of these phenomena. Auroral phenomena in the polar regions can be regarded as ultimately and intimately linked with solar–terrestrial interactions and with the magnetospheric plasma "laboratory." Understanding of these phenomena, while of both pure and applied research interest at present, will become of increasing interest to future applied research. Such polar research lends hope to the belief that scientists may utilize these studies in fundamental research into plasma phenomena, treating the entire magnetosphere as a vast natural plasma laboratory. If magnetospheric processes such as auroras can be understood, they may provide clues to other plasma phenomena; for example, those that have until now prevented the practical harnessing of fusion plasma processes.

The importance of polar-cap and auroral studies is perhaps most simply illustrated by Figure 23, contrasting the picture of the earth in interplanetary space envisaged in the 1950's and earlier with that now commonly accepted. It is clear that the polar features are the ones most altered. The

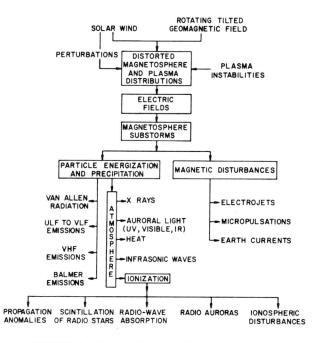

FIGURE 22   Organization chart of auroral phenomena.

significance of the polar region is that much of the energy generated in the magnetosphere is guided toward, and dissipated in, the polar upper atmosphere.

PROGRESS IN THE FIELD

In the realm of auroral phenomena, it is convenient to review progress over the past decade (i.e., since the IGY); this space-associated decade has seen extraordinary developments in these studies.

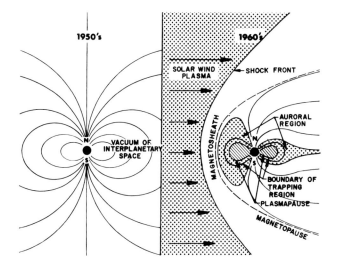

FIGURE 23   The earth in interplanetary space 1950 to 1968.

Auroral Particle Fluxes

In 1957, McIlwain proved conclusively that bright auroral forms are caused by bombardment of the upper atmosphere by electrons with energies of a few keV, with accompanying more stable precipitation of proton fluxes. O'Brien (1967) used satellite data to show that these particles originated at altitudes above a few thousand kilometers. Recently, Reasoner *et al.* (1968) have found that the proton–alpha ratio in the energetic auroral ions (viz., 50:1) is comparable to that in the solar wind. They deduce that the particles that bombard the auroral atmosphere were once lower-energy constituents of the solar atmosphere or solar wind. However, the energization process remains unknown.

Rocket and satellite measurements of particles and balloon-borne studies of x rays from auroral electrons have complemented each other and have revealed that the particle fluxes are dynamically variable and occasionally periodic in time. Periodicities have been found over the range from approximately 100 sec down to a few milliseconds. Such periodic fluctuations may be likened to "wavelike" behavior, and in a few isolated studies a temporal and spatial wave–particle correlation has been discovered. Preliminary measurements, particularly with balloon-borne detectors which are best suited for the purpose, have found a strong local-time control of the characteristics of the particle periodicities, but the reasons are not understood.

Rockets and satellites have studied the pitch-angle and energy distributions of the primary auroral particles. The pitch-angle distributions of precipitating electrons and protons show a tendency to approach isotropy over a wide range of intensities and energies. Electron and proton spectra have been measured over the range 50 eV to 1 MeV and are found to be highly variable in space and time. Increasingly sophisticated instrumentation has been employed to extend the observational studies, but no coherent pattern of particle behavior has yet emerged.

It has been clearly demonstrated that auroral-particle precipitation is continuously present, that its average intensity increases with increasing geomagnetic activity, and that its intensity may range at any auroral location over a factor of a million or more. Furthermore, it has been shown that the average worldwide dissipation of the energy of auroral particles is of order 10^{18} erg sec^{-1} during auroral substorms, or some 1 percent of the energy brought to the magnetosphere by the solar wind.

Auroral Luminosity

Temporal and spatial variations in auroral luminosity have been studied extensively, and major characteristic patterns of auroral substorms have been derived by Akasofu (1964, 1966). These describe, but do not as yet explain, the microscopic behavior of visible auroras. Recently, it has become increasingly clear that the substorm manifests itself in many aspects of particle precipitation other than visible auroral activity.

An extensive analysis of IGC and IQSY data has revealed that auroras appear along the oval belt which encircles the dipole pole. This oval band is called the auroral oval and is eccentric with respect to the dipole pole. Its center is displaced toward the dark hemisphere by about 3°. As a first approximation, the auroral oval is fixed with respect to the sun–earth line, and the earth rotates once a day under the oval. It is the auroral oval, not the auroral zone, along which auroras appear and auroral primary particles precipitate. In addition to this oval band, precipitation of energetic particles occurs along the classical auroral zone, mainly in the morning sector.

The auroral oval is not only the region that auroras occupy at a particular instant but also the region along which major polar geophysical phenomena associated with auroral primary particles occur. An intense electric current, the polar electrojet, also flows along the auroral oval and causes geomagnetic disturbances.

Studies of large-scale auroral activities over the entire polar region during the last several years have revealed that auroras are intermittently and sporadically activated all along the auroral oval. The activation originates in the midnight sector of the auroral oval, and its effects spread violently in all directions, causing various characteristic displays in different local time sectors. The sequence of such auroral events in the entire polar region during the passage from auroral quiet through the various active phases to subsequent calm is called an auroral substorm. Each auroral substorm has a lifetime of approximately 1 to 3 hours and consists of two phases—the expansive phase and the recovery phase. During medium magnetic storms, substorms occur once every few hours.

Aerial photographs of auroral displays at magnetically conjugate locations during equinoctial nights have shown that, at least occasionally, they are strikingly similar in conjugate regions. This gives evidence that at least some auroras are caused by electrons that were accelerated at very high altitudes, rather than merely locally.

Smaller-scale characteristics of auroras, such as the rapid motions of auroral rays, are as yet not explained. Experimental studies of the microscopic behavior of auroral structure have been advanced considerably by the use of high-sensitivity television cameras, which have conclusively demonstrated that wavelike changes in auroral luminosity (e.g., auroral rays) can move with horizontal velocities up to about 200 km sec^{-1}.

Theoretical studies have demonstrated that, on occasion, "atmospheric feedback" effects can affect the microscopic, or local, auroral displays. For example, it has been shown that the magnetic field associated with the auroral electrojet may so perturb the trajectories of precipitated particles, which originally caused the intense ionization in the electrojet itself, that oscillations with periods of tens of seconds may occur locally in the precipitation processes.

High-sensitivity photometers have been utilized to study and distinguish between auroras produced dominantly by electrons or by protons. Proton auroras appear to be relatively stable, steadily advancing toward the equator prior to midnight and then back again, with only an extensive surge across the sky at times of auroral breakup. Generally, they are intense enough to be barely visible and surround the auroral oval of the bright visible auroras which are produced by electron bombardment.

Spectroscopic Studies

Increasingly refined experimental techniques have permitted detailed studies of spectroscopic auroral features (Vallance-Jones, 1965). For example, temperatures of the upper atmosphere can be almost routinely monitored by spectroscopic analysis of the rotational-band structure of light emitted by N_2^+.

Scanning spectrometers at the University of Alaska have shown that the central region of an auroral arc emits both 5577 A (from atomic oxygen) and 3915 A (from ionized molecular nitrogen) in addition to a surrounding "mantle" or glow at 3915 A. Furthermore, theoretical analysis of both ground-based spectroscopic data and rocket data has shown that dissociative recombination involving O_2^+ takes place, since less than 10 percent of the intense OI (5577 A) line can be excited by direct electron impact.

Observations in the infrared have been made from the ground and from balloons, e.g., excitation of the 10830 A helium line has been observed. Somewhat more extensive investigations of the aurora for ultraviolet regions of the spectrum have been carried out using rockets and satellites; radiation at wavelengths below ∼3000 A is not detectable in any other manner. While theoretically predicted uv emissions have been measured, the causes of the relative intensities of several uv emissions are not yet understood. However, it is clear that a relatively large percentage of auroral light is radiated in the uv. In this context, ground-based measurements of the intensity of visible light, e.g., 3915 A of N_2^+, can be used to estimate total particle energy input to the atmosphere. Sparse spectroscopic studies of daytime auroras have been made using balloon-borne detectors.

Ionization

Precipitating auroral particles cause atmospheric ionization, which is of interest for several reasons. First, the actual structure of the ionization can greatly modify radio-wave propagation as well as the absorption of vlf and other radiation. Second, the characteristics of the ionization can be used to deduce the characteristics of the precipitated parti-

cles (Bailey, 1968). For example, use of the riometer for study of daytime auroras has been very extensive. Indeed, synoptic studies of riometer recordings have shown the precipitation pattern of energetic electrons over large areas of the polar region. When combined with more conventional nighttime studies of auroras, a picture of worldwide auroral morphology can be constructed, as was done recently by Hartz and Brice (1967).

Valuable investigations of the physics of the ionosphere can be made from ionization studies. For example, the success of the two-stream plasma instability theory of Farley (1963) in explaining the small-scale irregularities in the equatorial electrojet has led several others to consider the applicability of a similar theory to auroral irregularities. Radio studies of auroral ionization have also provided data on the motion of ionospheric irregularities. McDiarmid *et al.* (1961) have shown that, by simultaneous measurements of precipitating electrons and the resultant ionization, one can deduce effective recombination coefficients for the D region.

Geomagnetic Disturbances

As is apparent from Figure 23, the regions most susceptible to geomagnetic disturbances are those in the polar and auroral latitudes, where the geomagnetic field lines reach far into space and are strongly perturbed by solar-wind variations and solar–terrestrial interactions. Ground-based magnetometers and riometers are among the most useful devices with which to correlate other auroral data.

The dominant geomagnetic disturbance observed in the auroral region is that caused by the auroral electrojet, an intense electric current presumed to be confined largely within auroral forms. Worldwide patterns of the morphology of the electrojet have been derived from limited ground-based measurements of geomagnetic disturbances. It is still not known to what extent the electrojets complete their circuit within the ionosphere as distinct from up magnetic field lines and inside the high-altitude magnetosphere.

Included in the context of geomagnetic disturbances are phenomena associated with periodic or sporadic hydromagnetic waves or emissions, as well as associated earth currents induced by these effects. Extensive observations have led to classifications of the numerous types of observed phenomena, as well as the latitude variation of their conjugate interrelations (Wescott, 1966). At low, subauroral, magnetic latitudes conjugate behavior seems to be consistent, but in the auroral and polar regions no clear-cut relation has yet been established.

Quasi-static Electric Fields

The existence of quasi-static electric fields (Boström, 1967) in the ionosphere is inferred from the presence of ionospheric currents, and to some extent from ionospheric drifts. In the auroral region, the ion-cloud studies of Haerendel *et al.* (1967) have indicated that indeed there may be electric fields of ~100 mV m^{-1} normal to the magnetic field, although the component parallel to the magnetic field appears negligible in the ionosphere. Rocket studies of particles by Mozer and Bruston (1966) have been interpreted as indicative of electric fields parallel to the magnetic field. There have been preliminary attempts at measuring the fields directly with probes; however, it must be admitted that the experiments to date have been largely exploratory, and few definitive conclusions can be drawn from them.

The observed radial drift of whistler ducts is consistent with east–west electric fields of about 0.3 mV m^{-1} in the equatorial plane at $L \sim 4$. This value is not inconsistent with the above values measured in the ionosphere itself.

Atmospheric Effects

Two of the effects of auroras on the neutral atmosphere are heating and wave generation. Heating of the neutral atmosphere can arise from kinetic energy brought in by primary auroral particles and from joule heating by currents arising from electric fields and hydromagnetic waves. The kinetic energy of the incoming primary auroral particles is eventually lost in part by visible and ultraviolet radiation from the precipitating region and in part by heating the ambient atmosphere. While some measurements have been made on the ultraviolet spectrum of auroras by Barth (1967), there is still uncertainty about the ratio of the energy that goes into heating, and only rough estimates of the heating arising from particle fluxes can be made.

The heating by hydromagnetic waves of frequencies less than 10 Hz in the upper atmosphere at midlatitudes has been calculated by Sorenson (1968). He finds that during magnetic storms there is insufficient energy by several orders of magnitude to account for the observed changes in density and temperature. Whether this is true in the auroral zone, and whether ionospheric electric currents are effective in heating the neutral atmosphere by joule heating, is still not clear.

It is of interest that ion temperatures from 2000 K to 6000 K have been measured in the auroral zone by a satellite at a height of approximately 500 km by Knudsen and Sharp (1967), implying considerable energy input into the medium at these altitudes from some source.

Two types of waves are apparently generated by auroral processes. These are infrasonic waves, which have been measured at ground level, and traveling ionospheric disturbances. The infrasonic waves have been studied at College, Alaska, by Wilson and Nichparenko (1967) and have been observed to be radiated by rapidly moving auroral forms associated with substorm activity. Periods are of the order of 80 sec, amplitudes up to 10 dyn cm^{-2}. The traveling ionospheric disturbances have been measured at several locations and consist of wavelike movements in the F-region ionization which appear to propagate in the form of internal gravity waves from sources in the auroral zones. Periods are from approximately 1 to 3 hours, and vertical movement is approximately 10 km.

Wave Emission and Propagation

Extensive data taken during and following the IGY and IQSY show that unusually high whistler rates (1–100 per minute) are detectable in the general area of the Antarctic Peninsula and Eights Station, permitting virtually continuous monitoring of the plasmasphere (Helliwell, 1965). Using Byrd Station data, whistler propagation paths out to the magnetopause on the day side of the earth have been identified, thus giving access by whistlers to this remote tenuous region of the magnetosphere. The high rates are attributed to the low local atmospheric noise level and the high concentration of lightning sources in the conjugate region. Very-low-frequency experiments on satellites have revealed a number of new phenomena, such as nonducted electron whistlers, proton whistlers, and lower hybrid resonance noise (Carpenter, 1966; Carpenter and Smith, 1964; Carpenter and Stone, 1967). Corresponding advances in theory have led to new tools for measuring the concentration of electrons and ions using satellite-observed whistlers. In many satellite passes to high latitudes, all vlf signals, including whistlers, are suddenly cut off in the region just above the plasmapause (about $L = 4$), suggesting the possible presence of a belt of D-region absorption with a relatively sharp lower-latitude boundary.

Extensive study of whistlers recorded at Eights Station shows that nearly all nose whistlers show a sharp high-frequency cutoff at one half the minimum gyrofrequency on the path, often associated with triggered emissions. This result gives strong support to the prediction (Smith and Angerami, 1968) of a half-gyrofrequency cutoff due to propagation effects and suggests in addition that wave-propagation interactions may also be involved.

Eights Station whistler data have led to the identification of the plasmapause as an essentially permanent three-dimensional field-aligned boundary in space. Inside this shell, often very sharply defined, is located a plasma in diffusive equilibrium with electron concentrations of greater than 100 cm^{-3}. A region of depressed concentration with values of the order of 1 cm^{-3} lies outside the shell. The plasmapause has been found to move to lower L-values with magnetic disturbance. Individual whistler ducts are found to drift inward together during a polar substorm, implying the presence of a large-scale east–west electric field of about 0.3 mV m^{-1} at 4 earth radii. This discovery provides a basis for developing a new method for measuring electric fields in the magnetosphere.

Satellite vlf data from OGO-2, Alouette 1, and Injun 3 and electron concentration data from Explorer 20 have demonstrated the existence of a temporally persistent but spatially limited form of hiss associated with field-aligned irregularities near the auroral oval. Measurement of the spectrum of vlf hiss using the OGO-2 satellite and the ground recordings at Byrd Station has shown that incoherent Cerenkov radiation may qualify as a mechanism for producing auroral hiss. Observations with the OGO-1 satellite at high altitude indicate that the source of generation of emissions on closed field lines lies in the vicinity of the equatorial plane (Heyborne, 1966).

The regular observation of artificially stimulated emissions at Eights Station and elsewhere demonstrate the feasibility of carrying out whistler-mode wave–particle interaction experiments using man-made signals. Furthermore, these experiments have already provided new results regarding the characteristics of discrete emissions which must be explained by an acceptable theory. Theoretical work on the relationship between whistler-mode radiation and trapped particles in the Van Allen belts has advanced our understanding of the mechanism producing the continuous low-level particle precipitation in the polar as well as in the midlatitude regions (Kennel and Petschek, 1966). Application of the cyclotron resonance interaction between streaming electrons and coherent waves has led to new ideas for the explanation of narrow-band triggered emissions.

Some attempts have been made to measure variable electric fields directly with rocket- and satellite-borne probes. While some satellite measurements are indicative of substantial fields in the vicinity of the auroral zones, there are uncertainties associated with, for example, spacecraft potential, probe plasma sheath, and impedance, so that the results should be treated as preliminary, showing the need for more sophisticated studies.

OUTSTANDING PROBLEMS

A need exists for continued theoretical and experimental study of a great number of auroral problems. Many of the achievements of the past decade have been such that they have brought us to the point where we can begin to pose and solve definitive problems.

Coordinated Approach

A single unifying auroral problem is attainment of complete understanding of the whole sequence of auroral phenomena, to include the time when particles of the solar wind are captured in the magnetosphere, accelerated, and transported through it until they finally plunge into the auroral atmosphere. On the way there may be complex wave–particle interactions dominated by, but in turn affecting, the local thermal environment beyond the plasmapause. Once the particles plunge into the atmosphere, they cause the atmosphere to be heated and ionized and to emit light, much of it at uv and far ir and microwave wavelengths as yet unmeasured. The ionization may provide an optimum path wherein the auroral electrojet flows, though its driving potential is still unknown. A complete understanding of the over-all energy balance in all these processes poses one of the outstanding problems which can be solved only by coordinated studies of given auroral events. In particular, either with rocket payloads or with coordinated aircraft, ground, balloon, rocket, and satellite instruments, measurements should be made of:

(a) pitch-angle distribution, intensity, and energy spectra of precipitated electrons and protons over the energy range of ~10 eV to ~1 MeV;

(b) temperature and density of electrons, ions, and neutral atoms in the auroral region with particular attention to gradients;

(c) the complete spectrum of emitted light, ranging from the xuv into the far ir;

(d) ulf through vhf waves; their intensity, spectrum, polarization, and propagation directions with separation of E and H components;

(e) current flow and electric fields in the magnetosphere including the polar ionosphere;

(f) fine structure and motions of visible auroras by techniques such as TV photography.

While logistics problems of such a coordinated program are great, this approach is essential to a thorough understanding of the interaction of auroral particles with the atmosphere.

Auroral studies in both polar regions should be continued and extended in order to examine further conjugate phenomena, the extent and variations of conjugately coherent regions, and thence the ultimate acceleration mechanism responsible for auroral particles.

Electric Fields

It is important to carry out a greater number of sophisticated measurements of electric fields in the auroral region. In a similar context, some methods need to be devised to determine whether the auroral electrojet completes its circuit path within the polar ionosphere or whether it extends up magnetic field lines to close in the magnetosphere.

Ground–Satellite Coordination

Polar geophysical data cannot be improved by simply increasing the number of geophysical stations by random choice of the sites. A substantial improvement of our knowledge of polar geophysical phenomena can be made only by a systematic and organized observational effort, keeping in mind the eccentricity of the auroral oval.

An obvious way to monitor the activity along the eccentric oval is to set up a few well-organized north–south chains of stations. A chain of stations can thus monitor the activity over the entire polar region at a selected longitude. Without such a chain, a study of polar geophysical phenomena by polar-orbiting satellites would remain partially inconclusive. Ground stations provide a framework with which one can compare satellite data obtained in a spatial and temporally variable coordinate system. In addition, each technique can measure some phenomena that are undetectable by the other. It would indeed be a serious failure for various space efforts to ignore an equivalent sophistication of ground efforts from the above point of view. By intercalibration of the two techniques it may be possible to infer quantitatively the progress of the magnetospheric substorm from ground observations.

In this general connection, it has often been noted that the altitude of a satellite in a synchronous (geostationary) orbit lies close to the altitude at which dipole field lines from the auroral zone cross the equatorial plane. This fact can be utilized by locating a synchronous satellite in the magnetomeridian plane of two conjugate ground stations in the auroral region, thereby allowing direct monitoring of effects occurring near the outer extremity of the field line connecting the stations. Two ground stations well located for such a study are Byrd and Great Whale River.

Ionospheric Physics

Study is needed of the relationship between plasma instabilities and the formation of the small-scale irregularities in ionization that give rise to such phenomena as auroral radar echoes at vhf. As a natural extension of this problem, the relationship between auroral ionization, currents, and electric fields requires detailed investigation. In particular, the connection between the auroral electrojet and the visible and radio structure of the aurora is far from clear. Detailed correlation between the magnitude of such radio effects as auroral absorption and the properties of the primary fluxes of particles creating the ionization remains in an unsatisfactory state. An increase in our knowledge in this area can lead to an improved understanding both of the physics of the lower ionosphere and of such properties of the primary particles as their spatial fine structure.

The large-scale morphology of auroral precipitation during individual substorms needs further study, particularly at latitudes below those of the auroral oval, where the visible and magnetic effects are most intense. At these "suboval" latitudes, the precipitating electrons are generally more energetic than those responsible for most of the visual effects, and the precipitation is most readily recorded by radio techniques.

Jet Aircraft in Auroral Studies

The usefulness of a high-speed plane in polar geophysical studies has recently been well demonstrated. Excellent conjugacy of the aurora was observed in the two hemispheres by two jet aircraft flying simultaneously at geomagnetically conjugate areas. A detailed study of the latitudinal distribution of various atmospheric emissions was also conducted along flights across the auroral oval by a jet aircraft. The mobility inherent in a jet aircraft should be seriously considered in future studies of polar geophysical phenomena, particularly because a large part of the polar regions is inaccessible by ordinary means. Employment of jet aircraft should be reserved for specific purposes and events. For example, during an intense geomagnetic storm, a well-instrumented aircraft flying along a geomagnetic meridian line can investigate relationships between the three circumpolar luminosities: the auroral oval excited mainly by electrons, the proton aurora excited mainly by protons, and the midlatitude red arc of unknown excitation. The value of the flight will be greatly increased if it can be coordinated with the passage of polar-orbiting satellites.

Relationships between the auroral region and the internal structure of the magnetosphere need much further study. By inference, the area encircled by the auroral region coincides approximately with the region of the polar cap absorption. Geomagnetic field lines which originate in the area encircled by the auroral region traverse the tail region of the magnetosphere and thus guide solar protons toward their "feet" from the end of the tail. A properly instrumented aircraft can investigate this relationship in detail by flying across the auroral region. Instead of such energetic particles, photoelectrons from the geomagnetically conjugate points possibly could provide a clue to the same problem, since photoelectrons can reach the conjugate point only when the field lines along which they are guided lie in the trapping region of the magnetosphere.

Electrodynamics of the Polar Magnetic Substorm

In the analysis of polar magnetic substorms, it was formerly thought that the observed geomagnetic disturbances were produced by a current system flowing in a spherical shell concentric with the earth—namely, the ionosphere. This procedure tacitly assumed that div $i = 0$ in the ionosphere, where i denotes the current intensity. The assumption that the current is entirely confined to the ionosphere should be carefully examined. We know that the storm-time trapped-particle belt is greatly asymmetric, and a possibility exists that the polar electrojet could be an ionospheric part of an asymmetric ring-current system.

The correct electric current distribution within the magnetosphere, including the ionosphere, needs to be constructed. If this can be successfully accomplished, a study of the polar magnetic substorm will become a powerful tool to infer the electric field in the magnetosphere. Inversely, direct or indirect measurements of the electric field in the ionosphere by rockets and satellites will be useful in inferring the ionospheric component of the current system associated with the magnetospheric substorm. Satellite observations of the polar magnetic substorm will also be extremely useful in constructing the three-dimensional current system.

Wave Generation and Propagation

Specific problems associated with wave propagation include identification of the source of the absorption of vlf waves in the trough region above the plasmapause and study of the effects on ray paths of the plasmapause and other field-aligned irregularities in the high-latitude ionosphere. A more complete description of the location and drift of the plasmapause and its characteristics is needed, as well as studies of its mechanism of formation, coupling of thermal and near-thermal plasmas between the ionosphere and the magnetosphere, and location of the regions of generation of the various kinds of emissions.

Some outstanding problems associated with vlf emissions are (a) precise quantitative description of emission spectra, (b) correlation of emissions with energetic particle fluxes, and (c) a workable nonlinear theory of magnetospheric wave–particle interaction that will describe whistler-mode particle-scattering processes as well as the generation of high-intensity narrow-band emissions. A useful tool for these studies would be a high-power, vlf ground facility that could launch electromagnetic waves into the magnetosphere to study the characteristics of propagation and to stimulate various kinds of emissions. Another valuable technique would be a satellite-borne transmitter which would stimulate emissions and sound the magnetosphere at frequencies above and below the electron gyrofrequency. Fine-scale auroral absorption measurements should also be made using narrow ($\sim 1°$) beams as well as the wide-beam arrays used to date.

Energetic Particles

One of the principal problems associated with energetic particles is that of the mechanism of acceleration of auroral particles. Detailed studies are required to disclose the precise role played by wave–particle interactions and plasma instabilities, not only along lines connecting to the auroral oval but poleward and equatorward as well. The importance of longitudinal electric fields needs clarification. The regions over which the mechanisms prevail must be established, i.e., ionospheric versus equatorial. In addition, more attention should be given to the clear separation of temporal and spatial effects and the clarification of sudden commencement precipitation.

Considering the dynamics of the charged particles, detailed particle trajectories need to be established, with particular emphasis on characteristic periods, lifetimes, or both. Also needing study are the entry of solar wind particles into the magnetosphere; whether point, L-shell, or area conjugacy applies in conjugate precipitation; and definitive field tracing, particularly on the question of open or closed lines. Careful study should be made of the complete energy budget to include the solar wind, local fields, and both trapped and precipitated particles.

RECOMMENDATIONS

1. For the study of auroral phenomena, consideration should be given to the establishment of ground-based unmanned geophysical observatories to be used in conjunction with satellites.

2. Support of a jet aircraft instrumented and available for auroral studies should be continued.

3. The possibility should be explored of developing a satellite vlf transmitter suitable for magnetosphere sounding and emission stimulation in low-altitude polar and synchronous-altitude equatorial orbits. Coordinated satellite measurements of energetic and thermal particles should be made on the same satellite; various correlated measurements should be made at the conjugate points on the ground.

4. A vlf transmitting facility should be set up at about $L = 4$ to produce efficient excitation of propagation paths near the plasmapause.

5. Artificial injection of identifiable particles into the ionosphere should be examined as a means of probing electric fields and magnetospheric morphology.

6. A geomagnetic north–south chain of geophysical stations should be set up and sustained in order to monitor auroral activity over the entire range of polar latitudes for at least one magnetic longitude.

7. Coordinated rocket and satellite measurements of auroral particle fluxes, plasma, the emitted radiation, and electric and magnetic fields are encouraged.

PHOTOCHEMICAL EFFECTS

This section covers photochemical aspects of the upper atmosphere, i.e., the effects of the sun's radiation, as distinct from the effects of incident energetic particles. The latter are responsible for most of the peculiar and unusual features of the polar upper atmosphere; this section can be considered as dealing with the extrapolation to polar latitudes of the essential features of the undisturbed midlatitude upper atmosphere. Taken in this sense, the area can be subdivided into three broad topics:

(a) Problems of the quiet ionosphere in polar regions (the disturbed ionosphere associated with particle bombardment has been considered in the two preceding sections);

(b) The problem of chemical composition of the polar upper atmosphere;

(c) The problem of polar airglow.

These three fairly distinct topics cannot easily be treated separately. They are to some degree interdependent, and the area will be taken as a single entity in describing recent progress and formulating recommendations.

RECENT PROGRESS

Progress in the study of photochemical effects at midlatitude within the last few years has been fairly rapid, but little attention has been given to the possible impact of some of these advances on our understanding of the polar upper atmosphere.

Magnetosphere

Measurements of magnetospheric electron densities by nose-whistler dispersion at high latitudes have shown the existence of a sharp drop in the electron density at about $L = 4$, beyond which the magnetospheric plasma is no longer relatively cool (Carpenter, 1966). This transition level, termed the plasmapause, has been discussed earlier in connection with our current understanding of auroral effects. It provides a convenient way in which the polar magnetosphere (lying beyond the plasmapause) may be distinguished from the remainder (lying within the plasmapause).

F Region

The network of vertical-incidence ionosphere sounders established during the IGY has been continued through the IQSY as recommended in the previous review of the Committee on Polar Research (1961). Detailed morphological studies of the data obtained from this network have shown the existence of strong universal-time variations in the F2 region.

Satellite studies of the electron density at 1000 km and below using the topside-sounding technique (Thomas *et al.* 1966; Nelms, 1966) have presented for the first time a synoptic picture, with high resolution in latitude, of the electron density in the upper F region, indicating the presence there of the plasmapause alluded to above. It is at present uncertain to what extent the location and properties of the plasmapause are associated with particle-precipitation effects. Extremely low electron densities are frequently observed in the topside F region beyond the plasmapause (Hagg, 1967).

Very-low-frequency measurements also carried out by topside-sounder satellites have yielded striking evidence for differences in ionic composition between polar regions and midlatitudes (Barrington *et al.*, 1965). In the neighborhood of 1000 km, the fractional abundance of atomic oxygen ions is much larger at high latitudes, and that of atomic hydrogen ions correspondingly much lower, leading to the conclusion that the polar upper atmosphere has a relatively high plasma temperature. While not completely understood theoretically, this high temperature may be connected with the high plasma temperatures deduced for the magnetosphere beyond the plasmapause.

Electron temperatures in the F region have been studied from the ground by the Thomson scatter technique at Prince Albert, Saskatchewan (Maynard and DuCharme, 1965) and from satellites at various altitudes (Brace *et al.*, 1967). High variable electron temperatures have been seen, perhaps associated with heating by charged particles with energies much higher than the thermal plasma.

E Region

Very little information on polar E-region electron-density distributions is available other than that continuing to come from ground-based ionosonde networks. The few rocket flights that have been made into the undisturbed E region have primarily revealed properties of sporadic E and of the electron-temperature structure (Smith, 1966). The latter shows variations, by a factor of two or three, from one rocket flight to another.

Theoretical and experimental work on sporadic-E layers at midlatitudes has shown the importance of both wind shears and metallic ions for layer formation. At polar latitudes, however, the wind-shear mechanism is inhibited by the nearly vertical magnetic field, and the influx of metallic species from meteors is quite different from that at midlatitudes, so that the picture is not so clear.

D Region

Much of the information about electron densities in the disturbed polar D region has come from riometers and vhf forward-scatter experiments, but the quiet D region does not contain sufficient ionization for these techniques to give much useful data. Few rocket measurements have been made of undisturbed D-region electron densities at high latitudes. However, the partial-reflection technique has its greatest applicability when the D region contains marked inhomogeneities capable of scattering radio waves and has been applied extensively by workers in Canada (Belrose *et al.*, 1964) and Norway (Thrane *et al.*, 1968). While the data obtained by this technique are laborious to analyze and sometimes difficult to interpret, they have established the existence of a high degree of variability in the winter D-region electron density, quite distinct from the anomalously high electron density seen on some winter days at temperate latitudes and apparently correlated with stratospheric warmings (see Chapter 6).

Perhaps the most important advance in recent years, as far as the D region is concerned, is the realization of the overwhelming importance of minor constituents of the neutral atmosphere in determining the ionic composition and, hence, the electron density. Such species as O, O_3, N, NO, NO_2, H, OH, H_2O, and CO_2, all of which are trace constituents in terms of number densities, must be taken into consideration in attempting to understand the ion chemistry and physics of the mesosphere; the effects of these minor constituents have been reviewed recently by Reid (1967b). Many of these species have relatively long lifetimes against removal by chemical reactions, and their global distribution is likely to be strongly influenced by the circulation pattern of the atmosphere. In polar regions, the situation is likely to be quite different from that in temperate latitudes, since solar illumination can be completely absent for long periods of time, and the circulation may well have a totally different character (see Chapter 6).

Mass-spectrometer rocket flights carried out at midlatitudes have shown that the positive-ion composition is extremely complex, with water-derived species and metallic ions playing an important role (Narcisi and Bailey, 1965). Although no data are yet available from polar regions, there is no reason to believe that the situation there will be any less complex, though the relative numbers of the different species may well differ considerably from those present at lower latitudes.

The negative-ion composition in the mesosphere is even more uncertain than that of the positive ions. Indirect inferences from ground-based radio observations with riometers and vhf forward scatter at high latitudes (Reid, 1961) and rocket measurements of twilight electron densities at midlatitudes (Bowhill and Smith, 1966) have shown that the dominant negative-ion species is likely to be of high electron affinity, requiring ultraviolet light for efficient photodetachment. However, techniques for observing the full spectrum of negative-ion species are still in their infancy. Laboratory measurements of negative-ion reactions (Fehsenfeld et al., 1967) have indicated the possible importance of such species as NO_2^-, NO_3^-, and CO_3^-, but the application of these results to the mesosphere remains a rather speculative step. In the polar regions, there are unique problems associated with the absence of solar illumination during the polar night, when the production of negative ions must continue through particle bombardment.

Airglow

Knowledge of the morphology of nightglow emissions at high geographic latitudes is in an unsatisfactory state. This is largely due to the great observational difficulty in separating the airglow contribution from that arising from auroral processes, i.e., associated with particle precipitation. As a broad generalization, ground-based studies have contributed little to interpretation of airglow processes at high latitudes; there are a few data from satellite-borne photometers which have been combined with simultaneous data from particle counters to yield nightglow information. No regular dayglow observations have been made at high latitudes.

Recently, data have become available from twilight observations of resonant scattering of sunlight from metallic ions (principally sodium and lithium) in both Alaska and Antarctica. Preliminary analysis shows that the distribution of atomic sodium in the atmosphere at the South Pole differs markedly from that at middle latitudes.

OUTSTANDING PROBLEMS

Magnetosphere

The nature of the ionization structure of the magnetosphere outside the plasmapause, and its relationship to local electric fields and possible wave–particle interactions, needs to be explored, as do the effects of magnetospheric convection on the ionization density and temperature structure. Even the existence of the plasmapause itself is not yet fully understood. A closely related problem is that of the extremely low electron densities and high plasma temperatures observed in the polar topside ionosphere.

F Region

It is known from Thomson scatter measurements at midlatitudes that abundant photoelectrons stream along the magnetic field lines (Geisler and Bowhill, 1965). The importance of these photoelectrons to the energy budget of the high-latitude magnetosphere and F region needs investigation. The maintenance of the F region through the polar night presumably involves transport of ionization, but its details are not yet understood.

The frequent occurrence of small-scale irregularities in the polar F-region electron density is now well established as a result of both ground-based ionosonde and topside-sounder satellite results. The detailed structure and the mechanism of formation of these irregularities require further investigation.

E Region

The prime problem in the electron-density structure in the undisturbed polar E region is that of its electron temperature. If the fluctuations observed by rocket measurements are indeed real, they must be produced by variations in some form of energy input to the plasma, which is not yet understood. Eclipse measurements have shown only a minimal solar influence on the electron temperature, so the most likely candidate appears to be some form of particle influx.

The structure and mode of formation of polar sporadic-E layers requires further investigation, although the formation of "night-E" and the r-type sporadic-E layer by direct energetic-particle ionization seems established (Bailey, 1968). As mentioned above, the influence of wind shears on long-lived metallic ions successfully explains many of the properties of sporadic-E layers at temperate latitudes, but the efficiency of this mechanism decreases as the magnetic field becomes more nearly vertical. There is some evidence, however, that sporadic-E layers with temperate-latitude characteristics can occur in polar regions, and this point appears to be well worth further study.

D Region

The electron-density structure of the polar D region is likely to be strongly influenced by the neutral and ionic composition. An understanding of the ion chemistry of the undisturbed D region is essential to the achievement of a better understanding of the ionization economy of the disturbed D region.

Particularly important in this connection are atomic oxygen, ozone, water vapor, and nitric oxide; knowledge of the distribution of these constituents would also have an important bearing on the problem of the high temperature of the polar winter mesopause (see Chapter 6), which may be at least partially due to the release of chemical energy by recombination of subsiding atomic oxygen from the lower thermosphere (Kellogg, 1961; Young and Epstein, 1962).

RECOMMENDATIONS

1. High priority should be given to study of the D and lower E regions of the polar ionosphere by the use of techniques of rocket exploration which have been proven successful at lower latitudes. Specific problems include:

(a) Measurements of electron-density profiles at selected seasonal and local times, and during special phenomena, such as sporadic E.

(b) Determination of the distribution in latitude and altitude of the more important minor constituents of the neutral atmosphere at all seasons. Of particular importance are atomic oxygen, ozone, water vapor, and nitric oxide, all of which probably play an important part in determining the ion chemistry of the mesosphere.

(c) Determination of the positive and negative ionic composition by direct mass-spectrometer measurements. Important seasonal differences are likely to exist due to the peculiar solar-illumination conditions in polar regions, and major differences may well exist between the arctic and antarctic regions.

(d) Determination of the altitude profile of neutral and ionic composition and temperature in the thermosphere, especially during the long polar nights.

2. The rocket measurements should be carefully integrated in both space and time with ground-based and satellite measurements. For example, D-region sounding using both partial reflection and vlf pulse techniques should be encouraged. A sufficient network of ionosondes should be maintained to monitor the key features of variability of the polar ionosphere, but this network might well include a smaller number of ionosondes than that currently in operation.

3. An adequate Thomson scatter facility should be constructed at a high magnetic latitude to permit studies of E- and F-region electron density and thermal structure.

4. At least some satellite experiments for the study of ionization properties in the magnetosphere and high-altitude ionosphere should be specifically oriented toward understanding the physics of the F region and magnetosphere in and beyond the plasmapause. In particular, problems of fine structure in ionization and of the extremely low electron densities in the polar upper F region require special attention.

5. The morphology of airglow emissions at high latitudes should be studied, with a careful separation of auroral effects. The possibility of combining particle detectors and photometers in one satellite package points to satellite-borne observations as the way of satisfactorily studying this morphology, despite difficulties in calibration and interpretation. Measurements of winds and turbulence in the E region are vital to the interpretation of such an airglow survey.

UPPER-ATMOSPHERE DYNAMICS

The field of upper-atmosphere dynamics is taken to include all those phenomena in which motion in the atmosphere affects its structure. It is discussed from the point of view of its importance to the transfer of energy on a macroscopic scale within the atmosphere. The motions involved cover a wide range of dimensional scales, the smallest being eddies that are too small to be easily observed from a distance and the largest being circulations of global extent. The small-scale eddies collectively produce effects on the structure of the atmosphere through eddy transport of heat and atmospheric constituents. Next on an increasing scale of sizes are internal gravity waves, which are responsible for some observed features of the field of motion, and which may be an important mechanism for the transfer of energy from lower to higher levels in the atmosphere. Finally, there are tides and large-scale circulation in the form of meridional cells and horizontal, planetary scale waves which transfer heat energy and angular momentum in the upper atmosphere over the whole globe.

From a polar research viewpoint, interest in upper-atmosphere dynamics is largely concerned with the ways in which conditions are different over the polar regions compared with lower latitudes. The following questions apply to each scale of motion: (a) Is the pattern of small-scale eddy transport over the polar regions the same as that at low latitudes, and does it change systematically with season? (b) Can the observed large fluctuations in the vertical temperature structure of the polar mesosphere during winter be ascribed to internal gravity waves? (c) What is the tidal wind pattern over the polar regions, and how does it vary with season?

The large-scale circulation problem cannot, of course, be considered on a restricted geographical basis. However, it must be expected to bear a strong relationship to some of the most pronounced features of the polar upper atmosphere, such as the maintenance of the very low temperatures in the polar mesosphere during summer and the related formation of noctilucent clouds, the production of a helium bulge over the winter polar region, the concentration of ozone in the polar stratosphere during winter, the establishment of vast differences in temperatures of stratospheric air masses at high latitudes in winter, and the migration of these air masses.

RECENT PROGRESS

Only recently has there been any significant progress in recognizing that there are unique polar effects in atmospheric dynamics. These include the development of a helium bulge over the winter polar region (Keating and Prior, 1967) and its explanation in terms of dynamics (Johnson, 1967). Associated with this has been recognition of the role of large-scale circulation and adiabatic heating in maintaining the warm thermosphere over the winter polar region and the inverse effect involving cooling over the summer polar region and the consequent displacement of the temperature maximum from high to low latitudes.

Recent systematic probings of the structure of the high-latitude mesosphere (Theon *et al.*, 1967) have led to the inference of very strong upward motion in summer (Prabhakara, 1968). This could be responsible for the transport of water vapor to the polar mesopause and the resulting formation of noctilucent clouds, a unique phenomenon of the polar upper atmosphere. The same observations have revealed an equally unique phenomenon of the winter polar mesosphere—large wavelike fluctuations of temperature with height. Hines (1965) has advanced the theory that these temperature fluctuations might indicate the upward and poleward propagation of gravity waves.

The development of radiometric techniques for the mea-

surement of upper-atmosphere temperatures from satellites has recently provided a powerful tool for mapping the occurrence and migration of stratospheric warmings, especially in Antarctica. Stratospheric warmings are a long-recognized feature of the polar winter atmosphere. The continued application of this observational technique may provide the answer to some of the still outstanding questions concerning this phenomenon. Finally, one of the most exciting recent developments has been the recognition of an association between these stratospheric warmings and D-region ionospheric effects (Shapley and Beynon, 1965).

OUTSTANDING PROBLEMS

Eddy Transport

Since eddy transport produces a strong, even dominant, effect influencing the structure of the upper atmosphere, largely in the region 60 to 110 km, it is important that the pattern of eddy transport be known. Of particular importance is the variation in the vertical of the average vertical component of eddy mixing. The pattern or profile should be known at polar latitudes as well as at temperate latitudes; however, satisfactory techniques to perform these observations do not exist. For a considerable time in the future, the observations will have to rely on indirect techniques such as the study of motions of chemicals released in the atmosphere. It is important that we improve our knowledge of the relationship between the observed motions and the inferred eddy transport. Also, since the existence of twilight varies drastically with season at polar latitudes, it is imperative for the purpose of these observations to develop techniques that are independent of solar illumination.

Gravity Waves

Gravity waves are a very important phenomenon because they provide a means of propagating energy upward in the atmosphere. Recent observations indicate that this, or a similar form of energy propagation, takes place primarily at high latitudes in winter. The resulting heat input into the upper atmosphere appears modest. Internal gravity waves are probably responsible for the generation of turbulence and the consequent eddy transport in the upper atmosphere, although the detailed mechanism of conversion from internal wave energy to turbulent energy is not understood. The energy source for internal gravity waves is in the circulation of the lower atmosphere, where there is an abundance of energy, but the source mechanism has not yet been explored. Gravity waves associated with mountain lee waves or with the jet streams may perhaps propagate to mesospheric or even thermospheric altitudes.

These observations will also be very difficult to make. Studying the motions of chemical releases from rockets combined with rocket measurements of temperature, pressure, and wind seems to be most feasible at this time. Because of the limitation on the number of observations, it will be important to choose the observation sites prudently and to correlate the observations with each other as well as with observations of the larger-scale circulation at lower altitudes, since the source of energy may be found there.

Tides

Tides are another form of internal gravity waves, but with a different mechanism of excitation. Although gravitational excitation is the normal mode of excitation for tides, it is usual to consider also as tides those motions induced by diurnal thermal heating. The latter are more significant than the former in the dynamics of the upper atmosphere.

Two aspects of the diurnal tidal problem can be considered more or less separately: those motions induced by heating in the troposphere and ozonosphere and those induced by heating in the thermosphere. The former give rise to motions in the mesosphere and lower thermosphere and have been analyzed by Lindzen (1967) and Reed et al. (1966). According to Lindzen, away from levels where there is direct excitation, the major perturbations in the thermodynamic structure of the upper atmosphere due to this tide are expected to occur at low latitudes. Reed found a strong meridional tidal wind component blowing across the poles in the upper stratosphere and mesosphere. The effect of this wind component on the structure of the polar atmosphere has not yet been explored.

Motions induced by heating in the thermosphere are not very well defined. Kohl and King (1967) have calculated the motions expected to be produced by the diurnal bulge in the thermosphere. They conclude that a general pattern of flow must exist from the general region of the temperature bulge to the temperature minimum, and that this flow extends also over the polar regions.

The role of the tidal meridional wind in the polar stratosphere and mesosphere and its effect on large-scale polar circulation must be explored. The role of tidal motions in generating turbulence needs to be known at both polar and temperate latitudes. For example, it is possible to imagine a situation in which tidal motions are the main source of energy for generating turbulence, and where the tidal motions are confined to low and temperate latitudes, so that no turbulence is generated in the lower thermosphere over the polar regions.

Large-Scale Circulation

The major features of large-scale circulation in the thermosphere are still to be established. There are arguments that indicate what some of these features should be, but they have not been established by actual observation. Concerning the polar regions, there are several major questions: Is there a general inflow into the winter polar region at thermospheric levels and an associated downward motion and adiabatic heating to compensate for the lack of solar heating? Is there a corresponding outflow from the summer polar region and an associated adiabatic cooling to displace the temperature maximum from high latitude, where it should be expected on the basis of solar heating, to low latitude, where it is observed?

Global observation of the thermospheric temperature distribution must be considered a key to the knowledge of the general circulation. The general pattern of upper thermospheric temperature over the globe is known, mainly from satellite drag data. No polar anomalies are recognizable in the relatively crude data that are available. However, it is hardly conceivable that some characteristic atmospheric phenomena should not exist where the sunlight has been cut off, and data much more accurate than those now available are needed to show this. Only after accurate data have been acquired can an understanding develop of the driving forces for the circulation.

Large-scale circulation in the stratosphere and mesosphere is of as fundamental importance to the state of that region as it is in the troposphere. Especially in the polar regions, large-scale circulation is related to the maintenance of strong thermal gradients with longitude; the possible poleward transport of heat and angular momentum through transient, planetary scale, horizontal eddies; the downward transport of atomic oxygen in winter; and the poleward transport of ozone in winter. Newell (1966) has postulated that the upper stratosphere acts as a "heat engine," while the mesosphere acts as a "refrigerator." Despite recent progress, much of this picture is still very sketchy and rather speculative, more or less substantiated by extremely sparse observations.

Global observations of the temperature structure (and possibly ozone distribution) are necessary in the stratosphere and mesosphere from satellites. These observations must be augmented by frequent and coordinated rocket soundings of temperature, pressure, density, winds, and composition (especially ozone) at many longitudes in the polar regions.

Atmospheric Composition

One anomaly in polar-region composition may be inferred from satellite drag data: the helium bulge over the winter polar region. This probably results from an inflow of air into the polar region to compensate for the heat deficit there, and the inflow is relatively rich in helium because of its large-scale height above the turbopause. The downward losses do not involve such a preferential effect for helium; therefore, helium accumulates and produces the bulge. This explanation requires confirmation by direct compositional measurements, and it must be determined whether a similar effect is observable for hydrogen.

Another polar composition question is that of atomic oxygen. The few data that exist indicate that the atomic oxygen concentrations over the winter polar region remain about equal to the low-latitude values, even though the dissociating sunlight is not present. Presumably the concentrations are maintained by large-scale inflow into the polar regions. It is possible that the atomic oxygen concentrations are even enhanced above their low-latitude values, just as in the case for helium. Better information is needed on the concentrations, and the concept that the concentrations are maintained by large-scale inflow requires testing. The losses downward also require evaluation, and these may affect the ozone concentrations over the winter polar region. It is possible that the recombination losses can be monitored by airglow observations.

Two other considerations are most applicable to the dynamics of the polar mesosphere in connection with composition studies. One is the distribution of minor constituents (ozone, water vapor, and nitric oxide) up to the mesopause. These constituents play an important role in the energy-exchange processes, and they are indicative of transport phenomena. Eddy transport in connection with minor constituent distribution has been described recently by Hesstvedt (1968), and it is desirable that this theoretical concept be verified experimentally. The other consideration concerns noctilucent clouds. Noctilucent clouds are not only a most striking phenomenon unique to high latitudes and not fully explained yet, but they also can serve as a most appropriate source to provide information on wave motions in the mesosphere. Extensive surface-based observations have been made of noctilucent clouds in the northern hemisphere and recently also at high southern latitudes. Rocket techniques were also developed and flown successfully to analyze the nature of cloud particles. Based on some of these observations is the speculation that the noctilucent clouds may disappear or be suppressed during and after the occurrence of auroras. The energetics and dynamics inherent in such a relationship, if they exist at all, certainly warrant further investigation.

Neutral and Ionized Atmosphere Interactions

Some D-region ionospheric effects are associated with rapid warmings of the stratosphere or with a sudden breakdown in the polar vortex; both are high-latitude phenomena. Cause and effect have not been clearly identified here. It is possible that dynamical effects in the lower atmosphere lead to a breakdown of the polar vortex, and the effects of this breakdown are felt even in the lower thermosphere, where vertical velocities result from the breakdown. The change in warming and concentration due to the vertical velocity would affect D-region chemistry.

Sechrist (1967) has speculated that the wavelike temperature fluctuations in the winter high-latitude mesosphere are related to corresponding wavelike structures in the D-region ionization. The relation would be established via the temperature dependence of the recombination rate of NO molecules.

Simultaneous rocket soundings must be made of the electron concentration in the D region, the temperature structure of the neutral atmosphere, and the composition of the neutral and ionized atmosphere.

RECOMMENDATIONS

1. The global pattern of atmospheric composition needs measurement, preferably at an altitude near 200 km. This should be done with a mass spectrometer in a circular-orbit satellite to avoid undesirable confusion between altitude and latitude; the orbit should be nearly polar to cover the regions of greatest interest. Helium and argon concentrations over the polar regions relative to low latitudes would give indications of meridional transport at altitudes just above the turbopause. The atomic and molecular oxygen concentrations relative to nitrogen concentration would give an indication of recombination heating and ozone in the lower thermosphere. It would also be advantageous to make direct measurements of temperature, for example, by measuring the spin modulation of the nitrogen response in a satellite.

2. Global observations of temperature and ozone in the stratosphere and mesosphere should be made by remote sensing from satellites in nearly polar orbits; theoretical models relating these observations to the large-scale circulation should be improved.

3. The frequency and geographic coverage, especially in the polar regions, of rocket soundings of temperature, pressure, density and winds in the upper stratosphere, mesosphere, and lower thermosphere should be expanded, following the pattern of the Meteorological Rocket Network, in order to calibrate and supplement satellite measurements applicable to the large-scale circulation. These rocket measurements will also fulfill the purpose of investigating small-scale motions such as gravity waves.

4. Data need to be collected on winds and diffusive spreading of vapor trails over the polar regions to develop a comprehensive picture of winds and eddy diffusion. The release mechanisms used in rockets require optimization for diffusion measurements, and better models must be developed relating the observed trail formations to eddy transport. These observations should be supplemented by ground-based radiometeor observations from suitable locations in the polar regions. The radio technique operates over a much smaller altitude range but provides a much better statistical sample than the rocket soundings. Observations of noctilucent clouds, both of their morphology with

ground-based techniques and of their structure with rocket-borne techniques, should be made in conjunction with the above-mentioned measurements, since noctilucent clouds will give information on horizontal wavelengths of motions in the mesosphere while chemical releases will give a better indication of vertical wavelengths.

5. Rocket measurements of composition, especially of O_3, O, and NO, in the lower thermosphere and mesosphere in polar regions are highly desirable. Techniques now exist to measure O_3 up to 60 km in the polar night and O above 100 km. It will be difficult to extend the measurement of O_3 to higher altitudes and of O to lower altitudes. For this reason we cannot recommend a concrete observational program at this time. If appropriate techniques were to become available, such a program would be strongly recommended because of the important role which the variation of these constituents plays in large-scale, as well as small-scale, dynamics and in interactions between the neutral and ionized atmosphere.

LOGISTICS

In all preceding sections of this chapter, observations of high-latitude phenomena are called for; logistic problems arise in making these observations simply because the best places from which to observe the polar atmospheres are in high geographic latitudes. These high latitudes are not heavily populated, and available locations with usable support are few in number and often poor in access. Normal habitation in the Arctic provides several well-used sites for geophysical studies; transport into these places is usually a matter of commercial arrangement. Nevertheless, in spite of the relative ease of establishing a series of observations from a site in the Arctic, it should be remembered that a need exists for smaller sites between the larger centers of population.

In the Antarctic, extra problems of transport and support arise; the National Science Foundation and the U.S. Naval Support Force, Antarctica, have provided outstanding logistic support for work in Antarctica.

UNMANNED AUTOMATIC OBSERVATORIES

At the present time, the support facilities at polar observing sites involve semipermanent occupation of living quarters. Consideration should be given to the establishment of automatic observatories which are attended only once or twice a year. A valuable extension in spatial coverage of high-latitude phenomena would result from the situation in selected locations of observatories involving all-sky cameras, photometers, magnetometers, riometers, vlf-elf receivers, and micropulsation detectors.

In the case of experiments involving locations where either space or manpower is limited, strict attention should be paid to the time scale of the proposed observations. This involves quite definite identification of experiments in which long-term monitoring measurements are to be taken and experiments involving a specific period during which measurements are to be made. It is recommended that the schedule of experiments be fairly rigorously adhered to, particularly when the situation is such that the presence of one experiment at a station necessarily excludes another.

At present, the data from observations during the winter in Antarctica are available in detail only at the end of the winter season; this typically involves delays up to almost a year before the project scientist has the data for close examination. There is the danger in a malfunction remaining undetected for an entire year, involving a serious loss of observing time and implicit effort. There is a very real need for many more channels of communication with scientific equipment in Antarctica to achieve rapid access to data, with the target of achieving real-time transmission.

The unmanned automatic observatory with real-time communication link has nearly all the observational capabilities of a manned station, as has been demonstrated by various observatory satellites. The experience gained from manned stations has provided enough information to enable the observatories and sensors to be interfaced to the local environment. In addition, an unmanned automatic observatory in the polar regions can provide vastly improved data-acquisition capabilities. Data can be transmitted from the field site to the experimenter's laboratory in real time using synchronous satellites. This confers several advantages on a research project. First, the researchers can stay together as a team rather than sending one or more of their members to the field station to collect the data. Second, research on the data can start almost as soon as the measurement has been taken instead of having to wait for 12 to 18 months for shipments of paper charts and magnetic tapes to be returned from the Antarctic. Finally, real-time data acquisition, coupled with a command capability via the same satellite telemetry link, makes possible modification in the experiment parameters in response to the observations. Thus the onset of a polar substorm, as evidenced by some change in a particular sensor, could be the signal for increasing the data rates on certain key experiments or activating others which normally would not be operating.

By employing modular design, it becomes relatively easy to make changes in the experiment configurations from year to year; as a practical matter, this is not possible at the present antarctic stations. Another advantage of the unmanned automatic observatory is the inherent mobility of such a design. A station, housing 20 to 30 experiments, could be moved by a C-130 aircraft to any other site of interest. The cost of building, installing, and operating an unmanned geophysical observatory of the reliability and complexity of a typical spacecraft appears to be less than that of a comparable manned observatory, if the period of operation is at least five years.

ROCKET AND AIRCRAFT SUPPORT

In the discussions on Galactic and Solar Cosmic Rays, attention was drawn to the desirability of a rocket launcher at a very high geomagnetic latitude. The Panel believes that launchers for small rockets should be available at high latitudes, both geographic and geomagnetic, coupled with simultaneous balloon launch capability. The use of an aircraft for auroral and airglow studies over the Arctic should be continued and extended to winter flights in Antarctica.

FACILITIES AND LOGISTIC SUPPORT IN THE ARCTIC BASIN

The Panels on Meteorology and Climatology and on Physics of the Upper Atmosphere believe that much of the logistic support required for its programs may already be available but is not being used to full advantage. There are also examples of needed data which are not fully utilized because their existence is not widely known or because they have not been processed in a desirable manner. (See Chapter 6.)

There is a need for an Arctic Research Planning Group whose objectives would be: (a) to seek appropriate priorities for scientific observations on missions organized for other than scientific purposes; (b) to inform the scientific community and other interested groups of facilities and new opportunities in arctic research; (c) to identify areas in which new facilities are required; (d) to aid in the full utilization of existing data in special cases where information about the existence of the data or suitable processing are lacking.

RECOMMENDATIONS

1. The most desirable moves for improving logistics in the next 10 years of upper-atmosphere research in polar regions appear to be: (a) the use of small sounding rockets in Antarctica, (b) the establishment of small, automatic stations in a selected pattern in both the Arctic and the Antarctic, (c) improvement of data-transmission capabilities toward real-time acquisition (this includes capability for high-data-rate readout from polar satellites), and (d) improvement of logistic coordination and data exchange in the Arctic.

2. Along with the Panel on Meteorology and Climatology, we believe that an *ad hoc* group should be convened within the National Research Council, including representatives of all government agencies with arctic interests, for the purpose of (a) seeking appropriate priorities for scientific observations on missions undertaken for other than scientific purposes, (b) informing the scientific community and other interested groups of facilities and new opportunities for arctic research, (c) identifying needs for facilities, (d) assisting in the full utilization of existing data including the determination of its availability and processing requirements, and (e) formulating national goals for arctic research.

REFERENCES

Ables, J. G., K. G. McCracken, and U. R. Rao, "The Semidiurnal Anisotropy of the Cosmic Radiation," in *Proceedings of the Ninth International Conference on Cosmic Rays*, Inst. of Phys., London, Vol. 1, pp. 208-212 (1966).

Ables, J. G., E. Barouch, and K. G. McCracken, "The Cosmic Radiation Anisotropy as a Separable Function of Time and Radiation," *Planet. Space Sci.*, 15, 547-555 (1967).

Akasofu, S.-I., "The Development of the Auroral Substorm," *Planet. Space Sci.*, 12, 273-282 (1964).

Akasofu, S.-I., "Electrodynamics of the Magnetosphere: Geomagnetic Storms," *Space Sci. Rev.*, 6, 21-143 (1966).

Bailey, D. K., "Polar-Cap Absorption," *Planet. Space Sci.*, 12, 495-541 (1964).

Bailey, D. K., "Some Quantitative Aspects of Electron Precipitation in and near the Auroral Zone," *Rev. Geophys.*, 6, 289-346 (1968).

Baird, G. A., G. G. Bell, S. P. Duggal, and M. A. Pomerantz, "Neutron Monitor Observations of High-Energy Solar Particles during the New Cycle," *Solar Phys.*, 2, 491-501 (1967).

Barrington, R. E., J. S. Belrose, and G. L. Nelms, "Ion Composition and Temperatures at 1000 km as Deduced from Simultaneous Observations of a VLF Plasma Resonance and Topside Sounding Data from the Alouette I Satellite," *J. Geophys. Res.*, 70, 1647-1664 (1965).

Barth, C. A., "The Spectrum of the Ultraviolet Aurora," paper presented at the Birkeland Symposium, Sandefjord, Norway (September 1967).

Belrose, J. S., L. R. Bode, and L. W. Hewitt, "Physical Properties of the Polar Winter Mesosphere Obtained from Low-Frequency Propagation and Partial Reflection Studies," *Radio Sci.*, 68D, 1319-1323 (1964).

Biswas, S., and C. E. Fichtel, "Composition of Solar Cosmic Rays," *Space Sci. Rev.*, 4, 709-736 (1965).

Boström, R., "Currents in the Ionosphere and Magnetosphere," paper presented at the Birkeland Symposium, Sandefjord, Norway (September 1967).

Bowhill, S. A., and L. G. Smith, "Rocket Observations of the Lowest Ionosphere at Sunrise and Sunset," in *Space Research VI*, Spartan Books, Washington, pp. 511-521 (1966).

Brace, L. G., B. M. Reddy, and H. G. Mayr, "Global Behavior of the Ionosphere at 1000-Kilometer Altitude," *J. Geophys. Res.*, 72, 265-283 (1967).

Brown, R. R., "On the Relationship between Polar-Glow Aurora and Solar Cosmic Ray Fluxes," *J. Atmos. Terrest. Phys.*, 26, 805-809 (1964).

Carpenter, D. L., "Whistler Studies of the Plasmapause in the Magnetosphere, 1, Temporal Variations in the Position of the Knee and Some Evidence on Plasma Motions near the Knee," *J. Geophys. Res.*, 71, 693-710 (1966).

Carpenter, D. L., and R. L. Smith, "Whistler Measurements of Electron Density in the Magnetosphere," *Rev. Geophys.*, 2, 415–442 (1964).

Carpenter, D. L., and K. Stone, "Direct Detection by a Whistler Method of the Magnetospheric Electric Field Associated with a Polar Substorm," *Planet. Space Sci.*, 15, 395–397 (1967).

Committee on Polar Research, *Science in Antarctica, Part II, The Physical Sciences in Antarctica.* NAS-NRC Publ. 878, Nat. Acad. Sci.–Nat. Res. Council, Washington, D.C. (1961).

Dalgarno, A., "Atmospheric Reactions with Energetic Particles," in *Space Research VII.* (R. L. Smith-Rose, ed.) North-Holland Publishing Co., Amsterdam, pp. 849–861 (1967).

Duggal, S. P., M. A. Pomerantz, and S. E. Forbush, "Long-Term Variation in the Magnitude of the Diurnal Anisotropy of Cosmic Rays," *Nature*, 214, 154–155 (1967).

Farley, D. T., Jr., "Two-Stream Plasma Instability as a Source of Irregularities in the Ionosphere," *Phys. Rev. Lett.*, 10, 279–282 (1963).

Fehsenfeld, F. C., A. L. Schmeltekopf, H. I. Schiff, and E. E. Ferguson, "Laboratory Measurements of Negative Ion Reactions of Atmospheric Interest," *Planet. Space Sci.*, 15, 373–379 (1967).

Gadsden, M., "The Relative Intensities of Some Nitrogen Bands in Auroral Spectra," *J. Atmos. Terrest. Phys.*, 22, 105–121 (1961).

Geisler, J. E., and S. A. Bowhill, "Exchange of Energy between the Ionosphere and the Protonosphere," *J. Atmos. Terrest. Phys.*, 27, 1119–1146 (1965).

Haerendel, G., R. Lust, and E. Reiger, "Motion of Artificial Ion Clouds in the Upper Atmosphere," *Planet. Space Sci.*, 15, 1–18 (1967).

Hagg, E. L., "Electron Densities of 8–100 Electrons cm^{-3} Deducted from Alouette II High-Latitude Ionograms," *Can. J. Phys.*, 45, 27–36 (1967).

Hartz, T. R., and N. M. Brice, "The General Pattern of Auroral Particle Precipitation," *Planet. Space Sci.*, 15, 301–329 (1967).

Helliwell, R. A., *Whistlers and Related Ionospheric Phenomena*, Stanford University Press, Stanford, Calif. (1965).

Hesstvedt, E., "On the Effect of Vertical Eddy Transport on Atmospheric Composition in the Mesosphere and Lower Thermosphere," *Geofys. Publ. Geophys. Norv.*, 27 (4), (1968).

Heyborne, R. L., "Observations of Whistler-Mode Signals in the OGO Satellites from VLF Ground Station Transmitters," *Research Rept. No. SEL-66-094*, Radioscience Lab., Stanford, Calif. (1966).

Hines, C. O., "Dynamical Heating of the Upper Atmosphere," *J. Geophys. Res.*, 70, 177–183 (1965).

Johnson, F. S., "Developments in Upper Atmospheric Science during the IQSY, Symposium on the Years of the Quiet Sun—IQSY," *Proc. Nat. Acad. Sci.*, 58, 2162–2174 (1967).

Keating, G. M., and E. J. Prior, "The Distribution of Helium and Atomic Oxygen in the Exosphere" (abstract), *Trans. Amer. Geophys. Union*, 48, 188 (1967).

Kellogg, W. W., "Chemical Heating above the Polar Mesopause in Winter," *J. Meteorol.*, 18, 373–381 (1961).

Kennel, C. F., and H. E. Petschek, "A Limit on Stably Trapped Particle Fluxes," *J. Geophys. Res.*, 71, 1–28 (1966).

Knudsen, W. C., and G. W. Sharp, "Ion Temperatures Measured around a Dawn-Dusk-Auroral-Zone Satellite Orbit," *J. Geophys. Res.*, 72, 1061–1072 (1967).

Kohl, H., and J. W. King, "Atmospheric Winds between 100 and 700 km and their Effects on the Ionosphere," *J. Atmos. Terrest. Phys.*, 29, 1045–1062 (1967).

Lindzen, R. S., "Thermally Driven Diurnal Tides in the Atmosphere," *Quart. J. Roy. Meteorol. Soc.*, 93, 18–42 (1967).

McCracken, K. G., and U. R. Rao, "A Survey of the Diurnal Anisotropy," in *Proceedings of the Ninth International Conference on Cosmic Rays*, Inst. of Phys. London, Vol. 1, pp. 213–218 (1965).

McDiarmid, I. B., I. C. Rose, and E. Budzinski, "Direct Measurement of Charged Particles Associated with Auroral Zone Radio Absorption," *Can. J. Phys.*, 39, 1888–1900 (1961).

Maynard, L. A., and E. D. DuCharme, "A New Technique for the Measurement of the Electron/Ion Temperature Ratio at High Altitudes," *Can. J. Phys.*, 43, 2088–2092 (1965).

Mozer, F. S., and P. Bruston, "Auroral-Zone Proton-Electron Anticorrelations, Proton Angular Distributions, and Electric Fields," *J. Geophys. Res.*, 71, 4461–4467 (1966).

Nagashima, K. S., P. Duggal, and M. A. Pomerantz, "Cosmic Ray Anisotropy in Three-Dimensional Space," *Planet. Space Sci.*, 16, 29–46 (1968).

Narcisi, R. S., and A. D. Bailey, "Mass Spectrometric Measurements of Positive Ions at Altitudes from 64 to 112 Kilometers," *J. Geophys. Res.*, 70, 3687–3700 (1965).

Nelms, G. L., "Seasonal and Diurnal Variations of the Distribution of Electron Density in the Topside of the Ionosphere," in *Electron Density Profiles in the Ionosphere and Exosphere.* (J. Frihagen, ed.) North-Holland Publ. Co., Amsterdam, pp. 358–386 (1966).

Newell, R. E., "A Review of Eddy Fluxes in the Stratosphere and Mesosphere," in *Les Problemes Météorologiques de la Stratosphère et de la Mesosphère*, Presses Universitaires de France, Paris, pp. 81–129 (1966).

O'Brien, B. J., "Auroral Phenomena," *Science*, 148, 449–460 (1965).

O'Brien, B. J., "Energetic Charged Particles in the Magnetosphere," in *Solar-Terrestrial Physics.* (J. W. King and W. S. Newman, ed.) Chapter IV, Academic Press, London (1967).

Paulikas, G. A., S. C. Freden, and J. B. Blake, "Solar Proton Event of February 5, 1965," *J. Geophys. Res.*, 71, 1795–1798 (1966).

Pieper, G. F., A. J. Zmuda, C. D. Boström, and B. J. O'Brien, "Solar Protons and Magnetic Storms in July 1961," *J. Geophys. Res.*, 67, 4959–4981 (1962).

Prabhakara, C., "Feasibility of Determining Atmospheric Ozone from Outgoing Infrared Energy," *Trans. Amer. Geophys. Union* (in press).

Reasoner, D. L., R. H. Eather and B. J. O'Brien, "Detection of Alpha Particles in Auroral Phenomena," *J. Geophys. Res.*, 73, 4185–4198 (1968).

Reed, R. J., D. J. McKenzie, and J. C. Vyverberg, "Diurnal Tidal Motions between 30 and 60 km in Summer," *J. Atmos. Sci.*, 23, 416–423 (1966).

Reid, G. C., "A Study of the Enhanced Ionization Produced by Solar Protons during a Polar Cap Absorption Event," *J. Geophys. Res.*, 66, 4071–4085 (1961).

Reid, G. C., "Ionospheric Effects of PCA Events," in *Space Research VII.* (R. L. Smith-Rose, ed.) North-Holland Publ. Co., Amsterdam, pp. 864–883 (1967a).

Reid, G. C., "Ionospheric Implications of Minor Mesospheric Constituents," in *Space Research VII.* (R. L. Smith-Rose, ed.) North-Holland Publ. Co., Amsterdam, pp. 197–211 (1967b).

Reid, G. C., and H. Sauer, "Evidence for Nonuniformity of Solar-Proton Precipitation over the Polar Caps," *J. Geophys. Res.*, 72, 4383–4389 (1967).

Sandford, B. P., "Polar-Glow Auroras," in *Space Research VII.* (R. L. Smith-Rose, ed.) North-Holland Publ. Co., Amsterdam, pp. 836–848 (1967).

Sechrist, C. F., Jr., "A Theory of the Winter Absorption Anomaly at Middle Latitudes," *J. Atmos. Terrest. Phys.*, 29, 113–136 (1967).

Shapley, A. H., and W. J. G. Beynon, "Winter Anomaly in Ionospheric Absorption and Stratospheric Warmings," *Nature*, *206*, 1242–1243 (1965).

Smith, L. G., "Rocket Observations of Sporadic E and Related Features of the E Region," *Radio Sci.*, *1*, 178–186 (1966).

Smith, R. L., and J. J. Angerami, "Magnetospheric Properties Deduced from OGO I Observations of Ducted and Nonducted Whistlers," *J. Geophys. Res.*, *73*, 1–20 (1968).

Sorenson, W. R., "Investigation of Possible Ionospheric Heating by Hydromagnetic Waves," *J. Geophys. Res.*, *73*, 287–294 (1968).

Theon, J. S., W. Nordberg, L. G. Katchen, and J. J. Horvath, "Some Observations on the Thermal Behavior of the Mesosphere," *J. Atmos. Sci.*, *24*, 428–438 (1967).

Thomas, J. O., M. J. Rycroft, L. Colin, and K. L. Chan, "The Topside Ionosphere. II. Experimental Results from the Alouette I Satellite," in *Electron Density Profiles in the Ionosphere and Exosphere*. (J. Frihagen, ed.) North-Holland Publ. Co., Amsterdam, pp. 322–357 (1966).

Thrane, E. V., A. Haug, B. Bjelland, M. Anastassiades, and E. Tsagakis, "Measurements of D-Region Electron Densities during the International Quiet Sun Years," *J. Atmos. Terrest. Phys.*, *30*, 135–150 (1968).

Vallance-Jones, A., "Optical Measurements of Auroras," in *Auroral Phenomena*. (M. Walt, ed.) Stanford University Press, Stanford, Calif., pp. 20–38 (1965).

Vernov, S. N., A. N. Charackhchyam, T. N. Charackhchyam, and Yu. J. Stozhakov, "The Results of Simultaneous Measurements of the Cosmic Ray Intensity over the Antarctic and Arctic," in *Proceedings of the Tenth International Conference on Cosmic Rays*, Calgary, 1967, Special issue, *Can. J. Phys.*, *46*, 823–824 (1968).

Wescott, E. M., "Magnetoconjugate Phenomena," *Space Sci. Rev.*, *5*, 507–561 (1966).

Wilson, C. R., and S. Nichparenko, "Infrasonic Waves and Auroral Activity," *Nature*, *214*, 1299–1302 (1967).

Young, C., and E. S. Epstein, "Atomic Oxygen in the Polar Winter Mesosphere," *J. Atmos. Sci.*, *19*, 435–443 (1962).

8

Polar Astronomy

INTRODUCTION

Although the polar regions offer some unique advantages to the observing astronomer, very little attention has been given to the establishment of polar observatories. The remoteness and earlier logistic inaccessibility of the polar regions partly account for the lack of polar observing stations. In addition, earlier astronomical research was not particularly oriented to benefit from the peculiar advantages offered by the polar stations, for example, the long uninterrupted stretches of observing time and the exceptionally dry climate so essential for infrared observations.

Logistical systems are now capable of supporting remote polar facilities. The well-established polar research stations at Thule, McMurdo, and the South Pole now provide well-supplied environments of a permanent nature. Modern cold-weather technology has made great strides in the last decade so that diverse types of equipment have been made to operate under polar conditions.

The time thus appears ripe for an evaluation of the astronomical research programs that could be undertaken in polar regions. One of the two major advantages of such locations is the duration of uninterrupted observing periods for the study of the evolution of long-lasting events. Given adequately clear weather, observing periods over many diurnal cycles (24-hour periods) can be achieved in the summer and winter seasons, whereas the average present midlatitude observatory may enjoy only 12–15 hours of uninterrupted observing at best. An order-of-magnitude increase in the length of the observing period should thus be possible at a polar site, stretching uninterrupted observations from a duration of, say, 10 hours to over 100 hours.

In this connection, it may be instructive to examine the longitude and latitude distributions of present-day observa-

tional facilities in the northern and southern hemispheres (Figures 24 and 25). Although these data refer mainly to 1960 and 1966 compilations (Kuiper and Middlehurst, 1960; Panel on Astronomical Facilities, 1966) and a number of major telescopes are in the process of being built or planned, they are representative of established relative telescope strengths in the northern and southern hemispheres. Certain cooperative observing programs in solar and variable-star research have from time to time been established to overcome the brevity of the available continuing observing period for a single station. As seen in Figure 25, the present-day longitude coverage by midlatitude stations is not ideal. Furthermore, any such network of stations inevitably gives a heterogeneity to the observing data because of the mixing of individual station errors.

When one looks at the distribution in latitude (Figure 25) the well-known deficiency in southern observatories is clearly brought out, with 13 southern stations as against 103 northern ones. What is more significant in the present context is the pronounced lack of truly high-latitude stations; only one minor station (Turku, Finland, 61° N) exists north of 60° N and only one (Mt. Johns University Observatory, New Zealand, 45° S) south of 37° S.

The second outstanding advantage of polar locations lies in the exceptional dryness of the arctic atmosphere because of the extremely low temperatures (the annual average at the South Pole is −58°F). This corresponds to an average of 0.04 mm of precipitable water, which is one to two orders of magnitude less than in dry midlatitude locations. The polar dryness in winter corresponds favorably with the water vapor content in air masses overlying high-altitude aircraft (40,000 ft). One would expect that infrared observations could be carried out in polar areas in spectral regions hitherto inaccessible from the ground.

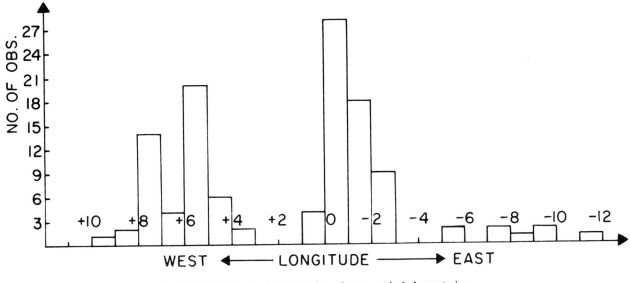

FIGURE 24 Longitude distribution of astronomical observatories.

Clearly, problem configurations should be sought that enable us to profit fully from these special advantages of polar locations, and it is the main purpose of this chapter to collate and summarize a number of these. It is feasible in terms of observing requirements to divide the possibilities into three different categories: solar research, planetary research (moon, planets, and comets), and stellar research.

SOLAR RESEARCH

In the summer half of the year, attention naturally turns to solar phenomena, and it is apparent in modern solar research that many solar surface phenomena should be studied in their long-term evolutionary aspects by using photometry, polarimetry, and spectrophotometry. Particularly note-

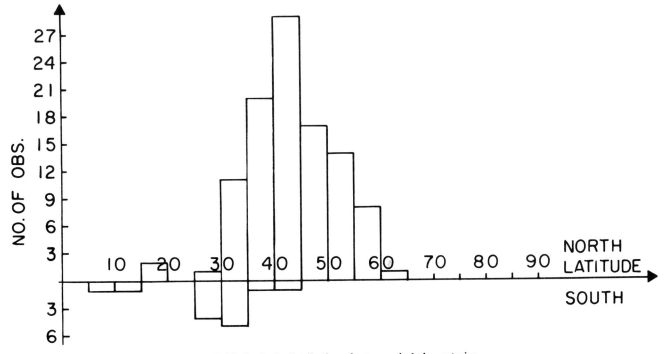

FIGURE 25 Latitude distribution of astronomical observatories.

worthy in this respect are recent time-lapse studies of solar granulation patterns and supergranulations, sunspot pores, and flares. In this rapidly growing field of research, which probably holds the key to important aspects of solar variability and activity cycles, there is presently a strong need for long time-sequence studies over several diurnal periods. An example of such studies is the time-lapse movie of solar supergranulation which represents 65 hours of uninterrupted observations taken with a 12-inch telescope at Thule Air Base, Greenland (Rogers, 1968).

Often an interesting dynamic phenomenon on the sun cannot be followed in its entire course of evolution just because the sun may go below the horizon of the particular location in question. With the clearly demonstrated longitude gaps in the distribution of observatories, there is often no station available to continue the study of the particular phenomenon where the first station left off. Admittedly, the solar global network of modest-sized observing facilities shows a better coverage in longitude than their stellar equivalents, but the coverage is far from optimal. The midlatitude coordinating observer has to contend with both longitude gaps and inclement weather, while the polar observer is dependent only on the weather conditions to maintain an unbroken long period of observation. Furthermore, a long uninterrupted polar observation series at a given station would have the additional advantage of complete homogeneity in the data. In a long time-lapse study, any midlatitude global network inevitably juxtaposes many observations with different local station errors and instrumental errors.

Time studies of the creation and disintegration of sunspots would also appear rewarding. Long time sequences of the granulation and supergranulation patterns should, in their microstructure, tell us what particular conditions are conducive to the creation of a sunspot pore and what agents are responsible for the decay of sunspots and the redistribution of the remnants into the granular patterns.

High-resolution pulse-counting spectrophotometry can now be simply undertaken with the new generations of Fabry-Perot pressure scanning spectrometers that are becoming available (Orsay Conference Proceedings, 1967). These completely self-contained units can be installed in cylindrical vessels, only 4 ft long and 2 ft in diameter, which are easily transportable to and operational in remote locations. While they do not supplant more conventional high-resolution grating spectrographs, they are far more rugged and compact.

Thus, a number of solar spectrophotometric research problems can be undertaken at a polar station during different phases of the long-term evolution of dynamic features in the sun. The Fabry-Perot spectrometers, operating in the magnetometer mode, could also study, in detail, long-term aspects of solar velocity and magnetic-field configurations such as in the umbra and penumbra of sunspots.

The peculiar polar advantages to infrared studies will not benefit solar as much as stellar research. Nevertheless, infrared spectroscopy and observations in integrated infrared light of the corona and sunspots could profitably be undertaken. Fourier spectroscopy in the new infrared windows would be of particular interest.

In another observational field, one should not disregard the possibilities of solar and planetary radioastronomical work in parallel with the long-term optical studies of various solar dynamic phenomena. Although midlatitude radio observers are not hampered by weather conditions, the lack of circumpolarity does restrict their observing times.

PLANETARY RESEARCH (MOON, PLANETS, AND COMETS)

While the observations of the sun are, of course, restricted to the summer half-year, other solar system components—the moon, the planets, and comets—can be observed at certain times in both the summer and winter periods.

The possibility of observing the moon continuously through large segments of a lunation may offer some good opportunities for more systematic studies of intensity, color, and polarization variations of lunar surface features. A continuous surveillance on lunar volcanic activity would be of interest.

Likewise, the long-term monitoring of planetary photometric and spectroscopic behavior could be undertaken. The variations in the atmospheric or surface parameters with phase of illumination for the inner planets could be studied as could solar-flare-induced effects. Continuous photometric and spectroscopic work could also be carried out on Jovian and Martian disk features. The next favorable opposition of Mars requires extensive observations from southern latitudes.

One notes the recommendation by the Panel on Planetary Astronomy (1968) for the establishment of a worldwide photographic planetary patrol that is appropriately distributed in longitude. The Panel advocates the erection of one or two new reflectors in the 24–30-inch class at appropriate sites to complete the patrol.

Another recommendation by that Panel stresses the need for vigorously pushing infrared spectroscopy of the planets by new techniques such as Fourier spectroscopy, preferably with observations from airplanes above the tropopause. In this connection, the extreme dryness of the South Pole site should again be pointed out. During five months in the wintertime, the mean surface temperature at the South Pole is so low ($\simeq -60°C$) that the amount of precipitable water ($20 \mu m$) approaches that of the air mass overlying an aircraft flying at an altitude of 40,000 ft in midlatitudes. Thus, Fourier spectroscopy in the new polar infrared windows could well be carried out from the ground at a polar station.

Cometary studies could also be profitably undertaken in terms of continuous surveillance of the evolution of dynamic features in the cometary coma, nucleus, and tail as a function of the passage around the sun, particularly at perihelion. These objects probably hold the key to our understanding of the early history of the solar system, and a detailed spectroscopic study of their structure and constituents should yield much valuable information. In spite of the existence of astronomical observatories over most of the globe, they are still far from successful in even the simple photography of cometary forms on a 24-hour basis (Whipple, 1967).

The frequency of individual events in meteor showers and the deposition rates of micrometeorites might be profitably studied under polar conditions.

Finally, it appears that improved values for the precession constants from complete circumpolar star tracks (unaffected by differential refraction) could be obtained from observations at a South Pole site.

STELLAR RESEARCH

As emphasized earlier, the very low polar temperatures and the altitude (9200 ft at South Pole) make for extremely dry air conditions, which should imply that ground-based polar observations of infrared radiation from stellar sources could be undertaken in regions hitherto inaccessible from the ground.

The experience of Neugebauer and Leighton (1968) shows that infrared observations in wavelength regions beyond 2 μm can be carried out in the daytime. Thus, extensive stellar infrared observing programs could be undertaken during both the summer and winter seasons. In the rapidly growing field of infrared astronomy, we shall only point to some of the numerous possible research programs, which could be studied advantageously in the new polar infrared windows.

Fourier spectroscopy of cool stars ($T \lesssim 3000$ K) would appear particularly feasible, since the bulk of stellar radiation is emitted in wavelengths beyond 1 μm, and in these regions numerous molecular band systems exist which are largely uncharted in their details.

In the integrated infrared light of cool variable stars, circumstellar grain emissions in the regions 3 to 10 μm could well be looked for, with particular attention to the variability and polarization of the emissive features. The results would have significance for the understanding of grain formation processes with relevance also to interstellar matter.

For work in the visual spectral regions, some of the more significant advantages of long observing periods lies in the field of variable-star research. The last decade has seen a number of occasions where a global network of observing stations in the northern hemisphere has been established

out of existing facilities for the continued study of a particular eclipsing system at the time when it is entering an eclipse. Several long-period eclipsing variables, like 32 Cygni, VV Cephei, 31 Cygni, and ζ Aurigae show atmospheric eclipses the total phase of which lasts for months.

In the case of the system ζ Aurigae, a total eclipse occurs every 972 days (on the average) and lasts for 38 days. Immediately preceding and following this total phase there are partial atmospheric eclipses which last for 1½ days. Such partial eclipses provide potentially a wealth of detailed knowledge about the atmospheric structure of the primary giant star, as the light of the secondary star shines through it in the partial phases. In this connection, the Fabry-Perot spectrometer would be eminently suited to the precision study of stellar line profiles. A polar telescope equipped with this auxiliary instrument can be operational (weather permitting) during the entire partial phase and would provide observational material of a homogeneity unsurpassed till now.

As Wilson (1960) put it:

One serious difficulty in the photometric study of the eclipses of ζ Aurigae is that the duration of partial eclipse is too long to be covered by any single observer. Hence, it has become necessary to combine measures by a number of individuals, sometimes made under adverse conditions and therefore of varying degrees of reliability; the judgment of the analyst necessarily affects the conclusions.

A recent example of an international cooperative observing program of an eclipsing system is the program on SX Cas initiated in 1965 (Koch, 1965). This is a system of an A and a G giant star which eclipse every 36 days. Clearly, a polar telescope by itself over a winter season could build up a substantial body of homogeneous data.

The whole field of close binaries requires around-the-clock coverage in terms of light curves, which preferably should be coordinated with observations of the spectral behavior of the eclipsing system. The periods range from a few days (or even less) up to a month or more. In recent years, more and more interest has focused on these objects on account of the important evolutionary implications such studies may have in terms of mass loss and eventual nova phenomena.

In this connection, any nova or supernova picked up by the presently established global surveillance network (Zwicky, 1967) at midlatitude could be continuously followed throughout the early phases of light rise and decline. Such data are needed to enlarge our present understanding of the early stages of development of these objects.

In the field of ultrashort variables (periods less than one day), a long period of uninterrupted observations would yield a number of unambiguously consecutive light curves which would be eminently suited for a study of changes in period and shape from one light curve to the next. Now, very often an observer is not able to cover a complete light curve in one observing session (especially if it is close to a diurnal cycle), and the observer is forced to superimpose observations from different light cycles to yield one "master cycle" thereby smoothing out any individual cycle-dependent effects (Merrill, 1967).

Undoubtedly, other programs would be undertaken once polar observational facilities are established. In the southern hemisphere, as seen in Figure 25, any new station will add greatly to the research potential of that hemisphere. For example, to have access, over the exceptionally long polar observing periods, to the Magellanic Clouds for comparative "galaxology" or to the brightest globular clusters like 47 Tucanae and Omega Centauri would, by itself, entail much valuable work.

STATIONS AND INSTRUMENTS

The research opportunities, some of which were discussed in the preceding sections, that are favorably afforded by polar locations appear numerous enough to warrant the establishment of at least one astronomical observatory. It is, of course, important to establish such an observatory at a site where one has reasonable assurance of relatively long periods of clear weather in order to benefit from periods of long continuous daylight or night. In this respect, weather conditions along the coastal perimeter of Antarctica are rather poor. However, as seen in Figures 26-28, the South Pole itself bears comparison with any observing site of average acceptable quality. It certainly stands out very favorably among the other antarctic stations. Its altitude, 9200 ft, should provide high transparency, and the location on an exceptionally extended plateau might provide quite feasible seeing conditions. The climate at the South Pole is desert-like in precipitation, and the winds are moderate, especially in the summer (annual average 8 m sec^{-1}, see Figure 27). The data on temperature and wind conditions have been taken from Jenny and Lapson (1968).

In the arctic regions, location at the North Pole is precluded. However, it would appear that the past weather records of Camp Century, Greenland (now abandoned) at 77° N latitude should be looked into, since it was located rather similarly to the South Pole station at an altitude of 6500 ft some 150 miles inland on the Greenland icecap. Also, the weather conditions at Thule (77° N) and Alert, Ellesmere Island (82° N) should be evaluated, while the records of the station "Eismitte" (71° N, altitude 9800 ft) should be indicative of conditions in the interior of the Greenland icecap.

From these preliminary considerations, the South Pole station offers interesting possibilities which should be explored. It is strongly recommended that some form of preliminary seeing evaluations be made with telescopes that are small but of high optical quality. For solar seeing tests, repeated visual observations in Kiepenheuer's scale (Kiepen-

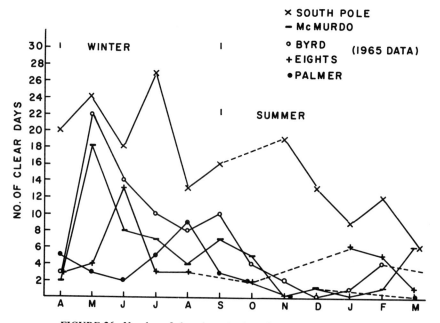

FIGURE 26   Number of clear days at selected antarctic stations.

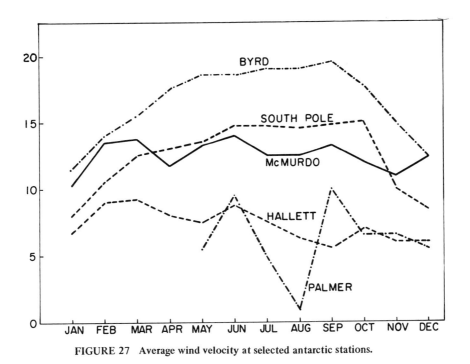

FIGURE 27   Average wind velocity at selected antarctic stations.

AVERAGE MONTHLY TEMPERATURE – DEGREES

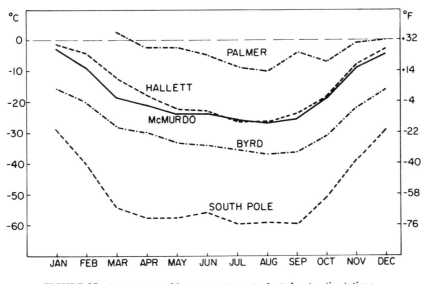

FIGURE 28   Average monthly temperature at selected antarctic stations.

heuer, 1963) should be made. Nighttime seeing can also be visually evaluated with the Danjon's diffraction ring scheme (c.f., Stock, 1963).

While the South Pole station should be chosen primarily for its exceptional geographic location, it is obvious that truly poor seeing conditions would severely curtail some of

the research tasks outlined in this report, particularly those in solar and planetary research. Since solar and planetary altitudes above the horizon can never be appreciably more than 23 deg, the seeing conditions for these objects may be considerably worse than for stars at higher altitudes.

Experience at Thule (Rogers, 1968) has shown that the

astronomical conditions there are occasionally quite good and implies the same for other desert-like arctic regions. However, these periods of good seeing may be restricted, and a year-long study of daytime and nighttime seeing conditions at South Pole Station is strongly urged and should be initiated as soon as possible.

The results of the seeing tests will condition the observing programs to be selected. For example, if night testing shows indifferent seeing but excellent transparency, it might be advisable to consider only photometric programs; if the reverse is true, photographic and spectrographic observations can be much more heavily emphasized.

In the matter of instrumentation, it is probably too early to settle on any one aperture. Certainly the expense and effort involved would rule out a very small instrument, say 12 inches or less for the major telescope. On the other hand, the setting up of a polar observatory is an experiment in which many things may go wrong and in which it may not be possible to correct serious trouble for six months or more. This factor argues against the implementation of a large telescope, say 36 inches or greater, and the preferred aperture probably should be in the 16- to 30-inch range.

One point is obvious: a conventional telescope operated in conventional ways will not be useful when working at temperatures of the order of $-80°$F, at an altitude of 9200 ft (effective altitude considerably higher because of the dryness), in part because of strain on the observer. Assuming that problems such as lubricants for moving parts at this temperature are solved, three alternatives appear possible:

(a) The telescope drive should be of excellent quality or an automatic guider should be included and the auxiliary equipment automated as fully as possible. A dual-head photometer might be conceived, where the observer's chief function during most of the night would be to keep the stars centered. Properly coded data may be automatically recorded. Under this approach, the observer would need to remain in the dome for only five to ten minutes of each hour.

(b) The telescope could be completely automated using television techniques, so that the observer could carry out his functions from a heated room. This is now possible; however, it may be extremely expensive and difficult to maintain in an operable state.

(c) One or more mirrors could be used to conduct light indoors where it could be collected and analyzed. Various coelostat or siderostat arrangements might be considered, although considerable modification of either would be needed for 24-hour tracking. The problem of the effects of the temperature differential between the outside and inside temperatures at the opening where the light is to enter the inside room is a very real one and will need careful study.

Finally, in the matter of operating personnel, it seems obvious that the kind of programs carried on at the Kitt Peak and Cerro Tololo National Observatories, where visitors come for durations of a few weeks to carry out their programs, will not work at a polar station except for the few summer months. Not only is to-and-fro traffic in the winter impossible, but any serious malfunctions of equipment may render it inoperable for long periods. The answer may lie in specially trained observers who will carry out the programs as required but who will have secondary nonastronomical programs which could be carried out in any long cloudy intervals or if for other reasons the astronomical programs are not possible.

RECOMMENDATIONS

Two main advantages of a polar observatory are (a) exceptionally long uninterrupted periods of observing time and (b) exceptionally dry atmosphere for infrared observations. A multitude of observing programs can be formulated in solar, planetary, and stellar research that would benefit uniquely from these advantages.

Among the presently established permanent polar stations, the South Pole appears to offer exceptional advantages in terms of periods of clear weather and low water-vapor content in the atmosphere. We therefore recommend the following:

1. Preliminary seeing tests should be initiated at the present South Pole Station. The seeing observations should be coupled to the continual meteorological observations at that site.

2. Present advances in arctic mechanical technology should be evaluated for the operation and maintenance of medium-sized (24–30 inch) telescope facilities in polar environments.

REFERENCES

Jenny, J. A., and W. F. Lapson, Stanford Electron. Lab. Tech. Rep. No. 3433-1 (1968).

Kiepenheuer, K. O., in *Proceedings of IAU Symposium No. 19 on Site Testing.* (J. Rösch, ed.) Gauthier-Villars, Paris, p. 196 (1963).

Koch, R., *IAU Bull. No. 14*, 11 (1965).

Kuiper, G. P., and B. M. Middlehurst, *Telescopes*, Univ. of Chicago Press, Chicago, Ill., p. 240 (1960).

Merrill, J. E., Report of the Commission on Photometric Double Stars, *IAU Agenda and Draft Reports*, Thirteenth General Assembly, Prague, Aug. 22–31, 1967, pp. 936 *et seq.* (June 1967).

Neugebauer, G., and R. B. Leighton, *Sci. Amer. 219* (2), 51–60, 65 (1968).

Orsay Conference on New Methods in Spectrosopic Instrumentation, Colloque C2, *J. Phys., 28*, Suppl. to No. 3–4, C2-1–C2-341 (1967).

Panel on Astronomical Facilities, A. E. Whitford, chairman, *Ground-Based Astronomy: A Ten-Year Program*. NAS-NRC Publ. 1234, Nat. Acad. Sci.–Nat. Res. Council, Washington, D.C. (1966 printing).

Panel on Planetary Astronomy, J. S. Hall, Chairman, *Planetary Astronomy: An Appraisal of Ground-Based Opportunities*. NAS Publ. 1688, National Academy of Sciences, Washington, D.C. (1968).

Rogers, E. H., paper presented at AAS Meeting in Solar Astronomy, Tucson, Ariz. (Feb. 1–3, 1968).

Stock, J., in *Proceedings of the IAU Symposium No. 19 on Site Testing*. (J. Rösch, ed.) Gauthier-Villars, Paris, p. 49 (1963).

Whipple, F. L., Report of the Commission for the Study of the Physics of Comets, *IAU Agenda and Draft Reports*, Thirteenth General Assembly, Prague, Aug. 22–31, 1967, pp. 267–280 (June 1967).

Wilson, O. C., in *Stellar Atmospheres*, (J. Greenstein, ed.) Univ. of Chicago Press, Chicago, Ill., p. 441 (1960).

Zwicky, F., Report of the Committee for Research on Supernovae, *IAU Agenda and Draft Reports*, Thirteenth General Assembly, Prague, Aug. 22–31, 1967, pp. 594–595 (June 1967).

9

Polar Biology and Medicine

Biological research in the polar regions, prior to the 1940's, was conducted from sporadic and often hazardous expeditions of short duration. Medical research was limited to study by a few physicians and sanitation engineers. These individuals were accorded little more than polite attention by those living in milder climates who considered the illnesses and epidemics of the Far North an inevitable consequence of pioneer life. The realization of the significance of the attributes of polar organisms in developing biological theory, and of including these organisms in the inventory of world biological resources, and of the importance to wise management of ecological systems has changed earlier research patterns.

Largely as a consequence of World War II, many previously inaccessible areas of the Arctic and Subarctic were mapped, described, and settled. In 1950, the National Academy of Sciences convened the Alaskan Science Conference to focus attention on Far Northern research. Since that time, and with new impetus provided by the International Geophysical Year (1957–1958), study of the polar regions has loomed, and biological and medical research in the area has risen steadily. This is witnessed by the numerous recent meetings, symposia, and new publications on polar research. Also, the Arctic Institute of North America (AINA), a binational organization of scientists dedicated to the advancement of polar research, has been effective in stimulating U.S. and Canadian collaboration in arctic research. Within the context of the 12-nation Antarctic Treaty, the National Science Foundation sponsors a vigorous and comprehensive program in antarctic biological and biomedical research.

Although biological and biomedical research in the polar regions are still in their infancy, many challenging problems have been uncovered. Two earlier reports (Committee on Polar Research, 1961, 1963) included recommendations for

advancing polar biological research. Some of these have been implemented and have led to rewarding research programs; others were not implemented but are still valid today. These reports, however, gave little attention to human physiology, psychrobiology, and community health, which, because we feel that action is now necessary on these topics, are discussed in what follows.

SYSTEMATICS AND BIOGEOGRAPHY

The flora and fauna of the polar regions are now known in sufficient detail that the efforts of systematic botanists and zoologists can be applied to problems with special groups, in particular where identities and variations in parts of populations are critical to understanding of a larger problem. There will be few discoveries of new Linnean species among macroorganisms in the polar regions, but only the main lines of the taxonomy of microalgae and the fungi, the protista in general, and the microinvertebrates have been put in workable systems. Virtually all groups of plants and animals remain to be studied for their population biology, including the genetic and environmental causes of their variation, and this holds for the low and middle latitudes as well as the high latitudes.

We are probably at the point now when biologists must evaluate utility against cost and effort of pursuing biosystematic and population biology studies of different groups of organisms. We cannot hope to get all the necessary information in hand with our small cadre of qualified manpower, nor would we find the burden of indexing and curating the documentation of such knowledge worth the effort for all groups. It is doubtful that we shall ever have all the taxonomic specialists that we need. We can, however, continue to encourage young people to enter this field and then encourage them to give attention to groups of organisms that are in particular need of systematic treatment. We will need to exercise economy of specialized manpower resources in this area by considering priority of need for information. We may expect, however, that an organism such as a nematode known only to specialists may well be at the center of a problem that will allow it to compete with the need for research on some large and widespread vertebrate.

Biogeography and its subdivisions of phytogeography and zoogeography are undergoing a vigorous renaissance, spurred especially by new tools from population genetics and new key information from paleogeography (particularly paleomagnetism and the theory of continental drift). We have not outgrown our need for detailed knowledge of the distributions of species, modern and ancient. Instead, we now have new sets of accessory data to gather about habitat conditions, history of the site, and associated organisms. The polar regions have readily identifiable, distinctive biogeographical problems and provide unique contributions to the understanding of the biogeography, especially the historical biogeography, of other parts of the world. Hultén's works (1937, 1962) demonstrate the need for focusing attention on the circumpolar patterns. Hultén's recent book on the flora of Alaska and neighboring territories (1968) and the book of illustrated flora of Greenland by Böcher *et al.* (1966) are examples of excellent sources of systematic and distributional data on arctic and subarctic vascular flora. Nonvascular flora are less well known and described, and some progress is being made on them; an outstanding example is Krog's (1968) work on the macrolichens of Alaska.

A new departure in phytogeography has been made by Böcher (1963a, 1963b) in his combined geographical and phytosociological analyses of plant communities and vegetation districts in Greenland. The integration of life history, site preference, associated species, regional history, and total range information for each species in the vegetation involves great labor, even for a small flora; the resulting understanding of the units of vegetation is adequate compensation.

Zoogeography of the Arctic and Subarctic has received more attention from researchers in the Soviet Union and Scandinavia than in other nations, but Canadians, Danes, and Americans have produced some excellent contributions to the zoogeography of special groups. Two recent publications (Löve and Löve, 1964; Hopkins, 1967) have been particularly significant in drawing attention to the biogeography of boreal regions; and a set of symposium proceedings (Gressitt, 1964) draws together recent advances in knowledge of both boreal and austral regions.

The antarctic regions have been at the core of another set of biogeographical problems since Sir Joseph Dalton Hooker's discoveries there while he was a naturalist aboard HMS *Erebus* in 1839–1843 (Wace, 1965). More recently, the late C. J. F. Skottsberg, botanist of the Swedish Antarctic Expedition, 1901–1904, pointed out many of the fascinating phytogeographical facts of the antarctic and subantarctic regions. Darlington, in his summary of southern hemisphere biogeography (1965), has brought many of the salient features of plant and animal distributions under the light of the new concepts of continental drift and Late Cenozoic glacial history in Antarctica. The zoogeography of invertebrate groups on the fringes of the antarctic continent and islands in the Southern Oceans has recently received increased attention through works such as those by Brundin (1966), Janetschek (1963, 1964), Dalenius (1965), and Gressitt (1965, 1967). The Second Symposium on Antarctic Biology at Cambridge, England, in 1968 brought forth evidence of new opportunities and needs for biogeographical studies in antarctic regions, including surveys such as those being published in atlas format by the American Geographical Society under the direction of V. Bushnell (1964 continuing).

Recent concepts of continental drift have given the subantarctic region a major role in the interpretation of antarctic and south temperate distributions. Biosystematic and chemotaxonomic studies in the extremely isolated islands of the Subantarctic can contribute greatly to our understanding of antarctic biogeography, as well as shed light on the importance of long-distance dispersal and problems of insular isolation. The notion that dispersal by spores limits the usefulness of a plant group for biogeography has now been disproved, and it is time to evaluate in detail the distribution patterns of the lower plants (lichens and bryophytes) which constitute the bulk of the flora of polar regions (Llano, 1965, 1968; Rudolph, 1965).

Paleozoology and paleobotany provide the documentation from the geologic past for historical biogeography, and these remain areas of opportunity in the polar regions. Evidence from fossils is needed, especially in connection with the new data from paleomagnetism, studies of crustal movements, and paleoclimate studies based on diverse kinds of evidence. The origins of polar tundra flora and fauna and subpolar biota are still to be sought in the Cenozoic record, probably among the scarce fossil records of alpine biota of the mid-Cenozoic as Arnold (1959) and other authors have suggested. The antarctic regions could have been a center of origin of primitive woody angiosperm stocks as some have suggested. Although the lands bordering the Arctic Basin have been fairly well explored for their fossils, strange anomalies there remain to be explained. There is the puzzling fact of the extinction of many mammals in the Subarctic in the late Pleistocene when the physical conditions, at least, were seemingly less rigorous. Another mystery is the fact that the widely occurring Tertiary continental deposits of Alaska and adjacent Canada have not yielded a single scrap of evidence of terrestrial vertebrates (Dorr, 1964), yet there is abundant evidence of luxuriant mixed forests throughout the region. The general lack of invertebrate fossils in Antarctica is a comparable enigma that needs solving. It is indeed fair to say that both polar regions hold critical information for contemporary and historical biogeography.

TERRESTRIAL ECOSYSTEMS

Closely following systematic studies of the floras and faunas, techniques of plant ecology and animal ecology were applied in the Subarctic and Arctic in the early years of those disciplines. Studies such as Warming's treatment of Greenland vegetation and Elton's investigations of fluctuations in Canadian mammal populations were strong on the development of general theory in ecology. In more recent years, results of ecological investigations from boreal regions have had a prominent place in the general shaping of ecological thought, and this has been strongly bolstered in the past two decades by contributions from the more extreme polar environments of the Antarctic.

The biological sciences have, for the most part, centered on North Temperate Zone experiences and examples until recent years. Information from the Subarctic and Arctic provided some new ideas for ecological studies, and contributions from the Antarctic now share prominently in this role. Polar floras and faunas constitute a smaller number of entities, and biotic communities have fewer species that are organized in less complex structure. Organisms usually respond in obvious ways to physical stresses of the environment, in contrast to the greater complexities and less obvious responses of organisms in lower latitudes. We must promptly augment ecological investigations both in the tropics and in the polar regions in order to take advantage of the lessons to be gained from comparative ecologies before the wild species, native populations, and original ecological systems become any further altered or diminished.

Terrestrial ecology has in the past 20 years entered on two exciting new paths. One path is that of analysis pursuing relations of organism function to environment up to the stage where responsible physiological processes and population genetic mechanisms can be identified. The other path is one of synthesis that endeavors to find the larger systems within which those individual systems function and to measure the energy and materials flow through the communities of plants and animals.

The physiological ecology and "genecology" approaches are being pursued in the polar regions especially with birds (and small mammals in the Arctic) on land and with fishes and certain crustaceans in the sea. A little of such effort is currently directed toward terrestrial vascular plants in the Arctic. Most other groups of animals and plants are not receiving attention in this respect. Although the need for information has been demonstrated, as with nematodes, mites, bacteria, and yeasts and other fungi in soils and surface waters, a case can be made also for similar studies of the widespread mosses and lichens that compose so much of the vegetation cover over extensive areas. Terrestrial arthro-

pods of polar regions are being studied as special groups by only several score of qualified people, and they are forced to seek help from taxonomy specialists before it is possible to move ahead with ecological investigations. Terrestrial fungi are also very poorly known, other than those conspicuous "macrofungi" that have been collected more or less incidentally over most of the polar regions. Polar soils and rock surfaces support many different kinds of algae, even though the surface may be dry or frozen all but a short time during the year. The invertebrates and lower plants dwelling in soils and upon rock surfaces in polar regions are undoubtedly important as components of ecological systems, both small and great, and we dare not assume that these organisms possess the same attributes and ecosystem roles possessed by their nearest relatives in temperate climates.

Ecosystem studies to measure energy budgets and materials economies have been attempted only in a limited number of instances so far in terrestrial situations, in contrast to aquatic environments where the uniform medium simplifies the problem. This is testimony for the complexity of the systems on land in the high latitudes where the environment is characteristically strongly varied from point to point in space and undergoes strong changes in time over periods of hours, days, seasons, and years. We must face these complexities and understand these terrestrial ecosystems before we can manage them wisely. Our current failures in other regions to predict allowable limits for changes in populations and their ranges or tolerance levels for pollution stem from our lack of understanding of the biology of the species concerned and of the functioning of the ecological systems involved.

Cycling of materials in terrestrial ecosystems is in particular need of attention. In the past 15 years, there have been several major forward steps on this subject as a result of radionuclide monitoring that revealed unanticipated concentrations of strontium-90 and cesium-137 in selected tissues of certain large mammals in arctic America. Support from the Atomic Energy Commission's Plowshare Program made possible a detailed study of Cape Thompson on the northwest coast of Alaska (Wilimovsky and Wolfe, 1966). This is one of the most comprehensive studies of the biota, environments, and ecological systems of any polar region area, and yet the materials cycling regimen and energy budget were not entirely charted and integrated into a refined model of the ecosystem. Some of the added problems facing such investigations in the high latitudes are the frequency and intensity of catastrophes (snow, ice, or wind damage; fire; flooding), inconstancy of favorable conditions during the growing season, and lack of knowledge about actions of decomposer and reducer organisms. It is generally recognized that decomposition, or conversion to humus and finally to inorganic salts, proceeds more slowly under cold climates, but we do not have a good idea of how slowly and by exactly what processes. Only a few preliminary attempts have been made to promote primary production by the use of agricultural fertilizers, and those did not take into account the requirements of the wild vegetation treated or what chemical compounds the soil organisms could best handle. At least some of the wide fluctuations in land vertebrate populations have been laid to nutritional fluctuations, and it is possible that artificial fertilizers could smooth some of those fluctuations, although such approaches might give rise to quite different and less desirable consequences.

Microbiology has been little explored in polar regions. At the present time it is not possible to prepare a meaningful survey of the microbiology of the soils, freshwaters, or human settlements in the high latitudes or high altitudes. Some sampling of soils has been done in the Arctic and Subarctic (Boyd and Boyd, 1964), and there have been a few investigations in the Antarctic (Boyd, 1967; Benoit et al., 1968). Although soils that support some vegetation and animal life generally have been found to possess bacterial floras and some actinomycetes and yeasts, some polar soils have been found to be surprisingly sterile. Indications are that populations of soil microbes may be highly localized owing to long-term persistence of some organic matter (guano, animal carcasses) or presence of special suites of available minerals along with slight concentrations of organic matter. Aquatic and soil microbiology holds particular promise for discovery of new decomposer organisms and hitherto unknown decomposer systems. Benoit (personal communication) believes that yeasts may be far more widespread and significant in polar aquatic systems than has been suspected. He emphasizes the need for imaginative departures from routine microbiological assays in polar regions, having found different culture media, especially in dilute concentrations, along with relatively low-temperature incubation for periods of months necessary for culturing these organisms.

Microbiology in polar regions, in addition to contributing to the general advancement of biological knowledge, has two special missions. One is that of delineating microbiological systems of extreme cold and long-term drought conditions, conditions most similar of all earth environments to those on the moon and the more hospitable planets. The other is the task of investigating the microbiological problem attending the presence of man and his dwellings and settlements in polar regions. Sewage and garbage disposal, treatment of water supplies, interactions of disease systems between animals and man, and the behavior of man's microbial associates under polar conditions all need study.

One of the greatest inadequacies in our body of ecological knowledge today is the lack of comparability data for classes of organism-environment states, units of measurement, and standards for accuracy. This deficiency is particularly acute with respect to terrestrial ecosystem studies, and it may be a primary reason that knowledge of terrestrial systems is lagging behind knowledge of marine and freshwater systems. We could well begin rectifying this situation by setting standards of instrumentation, observa-

tion, and reporting of climatic and microclimatic information for biological research purposes. Another area in which to establish useful physical environment parameters would be the physical and chemical properties of soils. We should not be deterred by arguments that too little information is available to set standards for such measurements as base exchange capacity; where our knowledge is deficient there is even greater reason to ensure that we know the significance of measurements taken. The search for and establishment of standards of observation, measurement, and reporting are major goals of the International Biological Program (IBP), and those doing research in the polar regions should participate in that program. It is hoped that in time the IBP can pursue more studies in the polar regions. Establishment and continuing improvement of standards is a responsibility of research that is commonly left to evolve without guidance through testing and criticism of previous work. However, occasional efforts to review the status of standards for a given area of research, especially when done by the most experienced investigators, seldom fail to clear away some useless efforts and clarify the actual capability for acquiring new knowledge. Terrestrial ecology in polar regions is a case in point.

Biological phenomena of the Antarctic are too often regarded as entirely exceptional because of the paucity of comparable results from localities in the adjacent South Temperate Zone. The Subantarctic has not yet played a role in polar research comparable with that of the Subarctic. The more or less contiguous nature of the arctic and subarctic regions, and their relatively easy access, resulted in their simultaneous study. Unfortunately, the Antarctic and Subantarctic are not contiguous with regard to their land areas, and workers in the Antarctic have not had the benefit of data from the Subantarctic. Individual scientists have no access to this large expanse of the earth's surface, and consequently, available information is extremely fragmentary and based on incidental studies, usually by nonspecialists. Only recently has any attempt (Wace, 1965) been made to collate the data on vegetation. The paucity of species, coupled with the rather small size of the islands, makes these areas particularly susceptible to the effects of introduced species. Although some of the islands are now officially protected by conservation laws, it is imperative that the ecosystems be studied as promptly as possible, because for most of them change has been initiated and the original systems will become increasingly altered.

FRESHWATER ECOSYSTEMS

Limnology in the polar regions rests on a relatively small body of information about the physical and chemical characteristics of lakes and a still smaller amount of information about the lake organisms and their role in the ecosystem.

The information available indicates that the physical and chemical characteristics of the waters, with the possible expection of certain highly saline antarctic lakes, do not differ appreciably from waters encountered in temperate latitudes (Holdgate, 1969; Livingstone, 1963).

The few polar lakes studies reveal extremely low rates of primary production. Annual production rates are low in part because a relatively small percentage of the annual incident solar energy can enter the lakes. However, even after the disappearance of the ice in the thaw season, production rates are low, apparently in large part the result of a very small annual input of inorganic and organic nutrients.

The annual phytoplankton species composition is known only for a few lakes in northern Europe. These studies show a high proportion of small, nannoplankton species, which are not usually collected by North American algologists, who have in large part restricted their attention to the larger algae that can be taken with plankton nets. The information available suggests not only that most arctic species can also be found in North Temperate Zone lakes but also that plankton variety is not so much a function of latitude as of the intensity of sampling and the environmental conditions existing in particular lakes.

It has not been resolved how appreciable numbers of phytoplankton survive the polar winter without any resting stages. The very limited work to date suggests that the survival cannot be attributed solely to a heterotrophic existence but rather to the utilization of a combination of mechanisms.

The small amount of primary production in polar lakes is reflected in relatively low standing crops and low production rates at higher trophic levels. The number of arctic zooplankton species is small and generally declines with increasing latitude, while the entomostracan species (known only with respect to the ice-free-season parts of their life cycles) at least appear to be characterized by normally only one or less than one generation per year. Fish growth, too, is extremely slow; and although a few standing stocks estimates are available, fish production has not been measured.

The small number of species at trophic levels above the primary producers makes polar lakes very well suited to studies of energy flow and determinations of biological energy budgets. Several studies with these aims have been or will be shortly initiated in North America and Scandinavia under the auspices of the International Biological Program, but more such investigations are needed. Except for a little information on the physical and chemical characteristics of a few arctic and subarctic rivers and some observations on fish populations and their migrations (salmon in particular), studies of lotic environments are nonexistent.

Studies of antarctic freshwater ecosystems have for the most part been concentrated near antarctic research stations. Antarctica, considering its great land mass, is characterized by a paucity of water in the liquid state. Glaciers and precipitation in the form of snow do, however, provide water for a variety of shallow, often highly productive, lakes along the coast and on some of the islands. The lakes of Ross Island and Victoria Land have been surveyed and have been the subject of considerable investigative effort. The dry valleys hold some unique permanently frozen lakes of greater size than most of the coastal environments. They are of particular interest because of their sparse phytoplankton populations and their unusual chemical and thermal relationships which feature the storage of solar energy.

The "oases" of East Antarctica have a number of lakes which were surveyed by the Soviet Antarctic Expedition. The Japanese have worked around Showa Station and the Ongul Islands.

Antarctic lake basins are usually associated with ice action. Small lakes often develop on the surface of glaciers or along their margins, while others are formed in ice- or moraine-dammed valleys such as those in the dry valleys of Victoria Land (Péwé, 1962). Lake Vanda has been the most intensively studied lake. It occupies an undrained bedrock basin in the Wright Valley and at one time was about 185 ft above its present level. The Taylor Valley contains Lakes Bonney and Fryxell. These are shallower than Lake Vanda and have not yet been studied so intensively. The most southern of the dry valley lakes is Lake Miers (78°07′ S, 163°54′ E), which has been studied by Baker.

In Queen Maud Land (70°45′ S, 11°20′ E) the German expedition of 1938–1939 discovered a series of lakes formed in depressions between hills which have been deepened by ice erosion. They are supplied with meltwater from adjacent glaciers and snow fields during summer. Lakes in the smaller depressions dry up in winter and the larger ones grow smaller.

Antarctic lakes provide unique environments for ecological studies. Meromictic conditions may be maintained by a combination of permanent ice cover and chemical stabilization of their bottom waters. Even the shallow lakes along the Ross Sea that completely melt in summer may exhibit a cryogenic meromixis as the freezing-out phenomenon concentrates the salts at the bottom where they impart sufficient stability to resist wind mixing with the overlying water.

Lakes Bonney and Vanda have attracted a number of investigators. Some considered Lake Vanda to be a solar-energy trap, while others concluded that geothermal heating was largely responsible for the high water temperatures (25°C) of the brine layer near the lake bottom, with solar heating providing some additional heat during summer. There is general agreement that Lake Bonney derives its heat strictly from solar heating, and Lake Miers would fit the same category. The dry valley lakes characteristically have little snow cover and undergo considerable sublimation in the summer. Their surfaces are irregular and etched with meltwater patterns, and they melt in summer for a few feet around their margins.

There is really no suitable basis on which to frame a

general discussion of the chemistry of antarctic inland waters; the inland lakes that do exist are continually frozen. Most antarctic limnology has been carried out along the coast, and the waters encountered have reflected the rather special hydrologic conditions of coastal desert areas anywhere. The lakes of the Taylor and Wright dry valleys are deep, chemically stratified, desert lakes lying in glacial troughs that also contain brine pools and evidence of precipitates from previous lacustrine environments. Many biological specimens have been collected from small pools of meltwaters very near the coast, and occasionally water samples have been analyzed in conjunction with these collections. The analyses usually are not complete but generally reveal a preponderance of NaCl among the dissolved salts.

Small ponds in the Antarctic freeze solid during the long winter. The freezing out of salts introduces a severe annual fluctuation in the ionic content of the liquid phase so that a pond with moderate salinity in the summertime when it is free of ice may give rise to an ice sheet of low ionic content capping a thin layer of brine that may never freeze solid. Such is the environment of the algal felts that line the bottoms of small ponds in the McMurdo region.

The freshwater benthos and zooplankton have been less well recorded and studied. Rotifera, Tardigrada, Nematoda, and Turbellaria have been collected in the McMurdo area. A heliozoan protozoan was found in Lake Vanda, and the Russians sampling the lakes of East Antarctica found crustaceans which included copepods and one *Daphnia* among the net plankton. The micrometazoa were nearly always found in wet algal felt. Dougherty and Harris reported the red-pigmented rotifer *Philodina gregaria* as extremely abundant on the bottom of many shallow ponds of the Ross Island area. Dougherty and Harris also observed great abundance of tardigrades which are rarely as abundant in warmer climates. In 1958, Kiryanova recorded six species of freshwater nematodes, two of these endemic, from the Antarctic. At that time, about 30 species were known from the subantarctic regions.

Direct nitrogen fixation measurements on Signey Island reveal that, although appreciable fixation takes place at $0°C$, the optimal temperature for fixation is probably $10°C$. Some soil microorganisms of the Antarctic are able to carry out certain reactions of the nitrogen cycle at a very slow rate. Small clumps of blue-greens have been observed to move slowly through solid ice by absorbing solar radiation during summer days to provide a liquid microhabitat for the colony. It would be useful to check these for nitrogen fixation as the ice is extremely low in nutrients except where dust accumulates in the crevasses.

Low light level and angle of incidence are as much a characteristic of the antarctic environment as is low temperature. Studies of inhibition and injury to the photosynthetic mechanism from high light intensities of algae conducted *in situ* on Cape Evans, Ross Island, showed maxi-

mum photosynthetic rate to be at about 20 percent of incident light at noon. The over-all efficiency of photosynthesis was inverse to light intensity during the major part of austral summer days.

The aquatic freshwater flora of antarctic lakes can be considered as three assemblages occupying three distinct levels. The first are the meteorlike clumps of algae that have already been mentioned in the solid phase of the lakes. A second is the planktonic assemblage which exists when lakes are at least partially thawed; and the third is the rich growth of periphyton (largely *Nostoc* and *Phormidium*) to be found on the bottom of many of the shallow lakes.

Measurements of primary productivity with the oxygen method in Skua Lake and some other coastal environments show a range of 326 to 1008 mg of C m^{-3} day^{-1}. For accurate estimates of productivity, measurements throughout the day are essential since minimum rates may be measured at midday and maximum values during periods of lower (less-inhibiting) light intensity.

The importance of the periphyton production is particularly obvious from a two-season study of Alga and Skua Lakes on Cape Evans. In 1961–1962, the periphyton production was about three times the phytoplankton production in the highly turbid Skua Lake, while in the more transparent Alga Lake it was over twenty times as great. During the second season, the productivity of the periphyton was much higher in both lakes, nearly doubling in Alga. When the phytoplankton and periphyton from Skua and Alga Lakes are summed, productivity ranges from about 2 to nearly 5 g of C m^{-2} day^{-1} of lake surface. This is a very high rate and shows the high fertility of these environments when compared with the ultraoligotrophic dry valley lakes or, for that matter, with others anywhere on the globe. It should be kept in mind, however, that the summer growing season is very short, and its intensity is partly the result of continuous light.

There are unusual vertical profiles of productivity in the dry valley lakes. Despite the low light intensity below 50 m in Vanda (less than 1 percent of the surface), high temperature ($15-25°C$), nutrients, and concentration of nutrients resulted in a photosynthetic maximum at this depth.

Limiting nutrient studies have been conducted in the littoral water of Lake Vanda. Considerable stimulation (mainly double the control value) was obtained *in situ* with the addition of 0.5 mg of NO_3-N per liter. Phosphorus was only very slightly stimulating, and trace elements inhibited photosynthesis. In the skua-fertilized Cape Evans lakes, nutrient response was almost totally lacking. Nitrogen appears also to be the most likely candidate for nutrient limitation on Signey Island.

Limnologists are attracted to the antarctic lakes because they are nearly closed ecosystems. These have the advantage of simple trophic structure and rigorous climatic restriction. The organisms are adapted to withstand high light intensities and at the same time to endure many months of darkness. There is a particular need to continue and to improve the taxonomic work to better define antarctic endemism. Eventually, most of the organisms should be examined in pure culture.

The role of heterotrophy in summer as well as in winter darkness remains as yet unsolved. There is a need for biochemical studies of enzyme systems which continue to operate down to at least 0°C levels and of nitrogen fixation in the periphyton mats of the shallow lakes. The possibility that the biota is dependent on energy sources other than organic matter and light should not be neglected in future arctic and antarctic studies.

The establishment of a number of polar laboratories, the development of portable electronic equipment, and greatly improved air transport now permit much more comprehensive studies of polar freshwaters and their organisms. These studies should be pushed forward while the environments are still in a relatively unspoiled state.

RECOMMENDATIONS

1. Studies combining the taxonomy and ecology of polar phytoplankton and protozoa should be undertaken. Plankton net samples alone are not adequate in view of the great importance of nannoplankton in these waters; cell samples should also be taken.

2. Studies should be made of the role of environmental factors (light, temperature, nutrients) on the phytoplankton species composition and primary production.

3. Physiological–ecological studies on winter survival mechanisms of the phytoplankton should be undertaken.

4. There should be studies on the factors responsible for the long development period of entomostraca.

5. Investigations should be made on the ecology of rotifers in polar lakes, zooplankton activity during the winter, taxonomy of the benthos of lakes and rivers, biomass and production studies of the benthos, standing crop and production studies of fishes, fish ecology during the winter, and energy flow studies in lake and stream systems.

6. Studies on the abundance and role of bacteria should be undertaken. The practice of utilizing organic substrates for monitoring abundance of bacteria has proved of questionable value. New techniques for surveying bacterial floras in natural waters are urgently needed.

MARINE ECOSYSTEMS

Problems of organisms in polar seas present some of the greatest challenges to biological research today, and their solutions hold potentially handsome rewards in terms of both contributions to theory and yield from managed resources. Although there have been biological observations and collections in polar seas for about 150 years, knowledge of polar marine ecosystems is meager, especially those associated with pack ice and shelf ice. The very great productivity of seas south of the Antarctic Convergence has long been known to fishing fleets, and some observations indicate that productivity of systems associated with pack ice and certain shelf ice is greater than was hitherto suspected. Oceanographic work in and near ice, such as the North Polar Pack or Ice Islands, requires specially equipped vessels or platforms. The relatively few icebreaker-supported investigations, such as those from the USCGS *Glacier* in the Weddell Sea in 1968 and 1969 and by the icebreaker-accompanied R/V *Alpha Helix* in the Bering Sea in 1968, have shown the relative feasibility and value of work within ice packs. Greater effort, and use of submersibles, will be required for work on benthic organisms under shelf ice.

Marine research programs have been strongest in the systematics, zoogeography, physiology, and ecology of invertebrates. Common plants and animals of the plankton are well known taxonomically, but most are known only incompletely with respect to their individual life histories and population characteristics, while their precise roles in the ecological systems of which they are a part are largely unknown. Mammals of polar seas are probably best known of the organisms there, and fishes next. The physiology and life histories of both mammals and fishes are under investigation, but as yet we have almost no information about their population ecology, except for a few of the commercial species in the Arctic and Subarctic such as fur seals and salmon. There is a dearth of knowledge about the relationship between the trophic levels and the flow of energy through the antarctic marine ecosystem. This is primarily due to a paucity of data on estimates of biomass of the different trophic levels and our almost complete lack of knowledge of the metabolic rates and turnover rates of the antarctic marine organisms. The deficiencies in our knowledge of the antarctic marine ecosystem, together with the potential richness of its oceanic resources, are now ushering in a new phase of antarctic biology — a phase in which population dynamics and metabolic studies will have to be stressed. These studies are urgently needed for species with potential for exploitation or those species that are critical to the support of exploitable species.

Ecological systems of polar seas have been examined in only very limited ways so far. The largest bodies of information have accrued with respect to seals and whales and certain prominent plankters such as the krill (*Euphausia superba*) of antarctic seas. Primary and secondary productivity of the open seas is being charted slowly in both polar regions, with the Soviet Union leading with the most vigorous program. Primary and secondary productivity under annual and permanent pack ice is being investigated by a very small corps of workers except for the apparently continuous and well-staffed program of the Soviet Union in the

Arctic Ocean. The biology and ecology of marine waters beneath ice shelves are virtually unknown. A U.S. Antarctic Research Program project planned for the Ross Ice Shelf is designed to make exploratory probes by drilling into the subice waters. The presence of ice cover, either annual or perennial, and the formation of bottom ice near shore (Dayton et al., 1969) in the highest latitudes pose many very different environmental conditions for organisms in the sea, at least some of which need to be understood before we can undertake management of the biological productions in those waters.

Biological studies of subarctic seas are proceeding at a greater rate and with more emphasis on marketable species of fishes and mammals because of commercial exploitation. The U.S. Bureau of Commercial Fisheries has active programs in Alaskan waters, and the Fisheries Board in Canada has a vigorous program of investigations along that nation's eastern seaboard. A strong start was made with a marine biology program at the Naval Arctic Research Laboratory, Point Barrow, in the early 1950's by MacGinitie (1955) and his co-workers, but subsequently there have been only sporadic contributions from ice islands in the Arctic Ocean. There is obvious need for a more coherent program of marine biological investigations in the far northern seas, an effort in which icebreakers or platforms that could be frozen into pack ice of the Arctic Ocean gyre would be of great value.

Biological exploration of the Antarctic Ocean dates back to the expeditions of the *Erebus* and the *Terror* (1839-1843), but it was not until initiation of the *Discovery II* investigations in 1925 that a new era in the scientific exploration of the Antarctic Ocean was begun. In this era, the "cataloguing" or purely descriptive phase gave way to a broader approach in which the dynamic aspect of antarctic marine biology was stressed. Although the *Discovery II* investigations were primarily concerned with whales and whaling, studies of practically all the factors influencing their migration, food and feeding habits, breeding cycle, and the like have led to an intensive program of physical, chemical, and biological oceanography of the Southern Ocean. Other expeditions followed, such as those of the *Gauss* and the *Meteor,* but the credit goes to the *Discovery II* for initiating a continuous program.

Since the International Geophysical Year (1957-1958), scientific investigation in Antarctica has expanded and is still gaining momentum. The great interest in the biology of the Antarctic and its surrounding seas is reflected in the symposia of 1962 (Carrick et al., 1964) and 1968 (Holdgate, 1969); also in the Antarctic Research Series (1964 continuing) and the *Antarctic Map Folio Series* (Bushnell, 1964 continuing).

Great interest is now being shown in harvesting more of the marine living resources of the antarctic marine ecosystems. With the decline (85-90 percent) of the stock of

baleen whales in the past 40 years, attention has now been shifted to the krill, *Euphausia superba,* the potential catch of which has been estimated to be well in excess of the present total harvest of all fishes from all the oceans (60.5 million tons, according to 1967 Food and Agriculture Organization figures). If the krill is to be exploited wisely, it must be inventoried and its population dynamics understood. The awesome depletion of the California sardine and the antarctic baleen whale populations are testimonies of poor management of natural resources.

Before discussing the various components of the antarctic marine ecosystem, it is instructive to present here a brief account of the physical and chemical settings of the Southern Ocean, since these are necessary in explaining the biological phenomena to be discussed later.

The Antarctic Ocean is bounded to the south by the antarctic continent and to the north by the Antarctic Convergence. It is essentially a deep oceanic environment. One of the peculiar aspects of the Antarctic Ocean is the arrangement of its water masses (Deacon, 1964). The main transport of water is from west to east in what is known as the Circumpolar Current or West Wind Drift. North of the antarctic continent there are two boundary or frontal zones where surface-temperature increases of about 2 to 3°C occur. The Antarctic Convergence lies at about 50° to 60° S and extends completely around the continent. At about 40° S, a less well-defined zone exists—the Subtropical Convergence. The Antarctic Convergence is characterized by the sinking of the cold, less saline antarctic water beneath the warmer subantarctic water. At the Convergence, the antarctic surface water is overridden by the subantarctic water, and as it sinks down to 400 m it moves northward at depths of several hundred meters, forming the Antarctic Intermediate Water. At the edge of the continent (the Weddell Sea in particular), very cold water sinks and moves northward down the Shelf and into the deep, forming the Antarctic Bottom Water. This water is found all around the antarctic continent and even beyond the Equator in the Atlantic Ocean. To replace these northerly directed water masses, the warm deep water, with high salinity and rich in nutrient elements, moves southward at intermediate depths, rising close to the surface near the continent. The upwelling of these waters seems to account for the high productivity of the antarctic coastal region.

One unique aspect of the Antarctic Ocean is its nearly homeothermic nature. Sea temperature south of the convergence is very low; its variation with depth and season barely exceeds 4 or 5°C. Variations in salinity are also small —only some 0.1 percent. Thus from the surface to the bottom, the conservative properties of the antarctic waters show a high degree of uniformity (Currie, 1964).

For a region which lies in relatively high latitudes, the extreme variations in incoming solar radiation between summer and winter certainly have a pronounced effect on the metabolism of ice-fish pioneered modern investigations of metabolic rates of zooplankton and micronekton in the Antarctic. This was followed by workers who defined the problems in greater detail (DeVries and Wohlschlag, 1964; Hemmingsen and Douglas, 1967; Hemmingsen and Grigg, 1967; Morris, 1967; Somero and DeVries, 1967; Somero and Giese, 1967). Further metabolic studies are needed, not only for the phytoplankton, zooplankton, seals, winged birds, penguins, fishes, and squids but also for the altraplankton and microbenthic flora and fauna.

In the light of the history of man's decimation of the whale stocks and the potential economic harvest of the krill populations, there are clear practical reasons for seeking to better understand the antarctic marine ecosystem. Because of its highly unique character, this system also provides many compelling theoretical reasons for attempting to understand the system as a whole.

Modern technology is presenting real threats to biological systems of the seas. For example, discovery and proving of large petroleum reserves in northeastern Alaska and the lower Mackenzie Valley generated the problem of how to transport oil from those remote areas to the markets. Overland transport is outside the realm of economic feasibility, and severe economic disadvantages appear to argue against transport through long pipelines. Transport by aircraft is not yet economical and will probably not develop in the foreseeable future. Ocean tanker transport is the most likely means remaining. The petroleum industry has indicated a willingness to acknowledge the chance of loss of a conventional tanker in Arctic Ocean ice, and reporters of industry news have suggested that planners would accept the loss of one tanker in a hundred trips as keeping within the zone of economic feasibility. It is difficult to imagine the disaster of 100,000 or more barrels of crude oil in the ice-choked surface waters of the Arctic Ocean! A tanker cargo spill in the temperate north Atlantic is a catastrophe of some three months' duration, but in that time certain microorganisms and perhaps inorganic chemical reactions, both assisted by wind and waves in breaking up oil films and allowing gaseous oxygen to diffuse into the surface waters, do "digest" and render harmless the petroleum. In the Arctic Ocean, however, the spill of a tanker might turn out to be a poisonous, life-extinguishing blot on the ice-mantled surface for years rather than months. Wind and wind waves have less opportunity to assist diffusion of oxygen into the water. The water temperature, at or slightly below $0°C$, would probably cause some of the aliphatic hydrocarbon components to become as sticky as congealed fat and certainly would slow the rates of microbiological activity. A tanker spill several hundred square miles in area on the Arctic Ocean would most likely threaten delicate biological systems for an unpredictable number of years. Actually we do not know and do not have the information with which to make worthwhile estimates. This example is not a

unique one. Other problems in prospect are the consequences of stirring up ocean-floor sediments by undersea mining, thus releasing suddenly into suspension and solution materials that had been put out of circulation by enclosure in sediments for long periods of time. We must prepare to meet these problems by accelerating our investigations of marine ecosystems and by focusing attention on problems certain to require at least partial answers within a few years.

RECOMMENDATIONS

1. Strong encouragements and inducement should be given to scientists and students to investigate polar marine organisms from the standpoint of ecosystems—functional units of associated organisms interacting with each other and with their environments. Team effort, coherent area studies, collaborative projects, and other special arrangements may be necessary to advance knowledge in this subject area. Special consideration should be given to determinations of trophic levels and estimation of the biomass in each and its turnover rate, pathways in the ecosystem of nutrient materials and energy and approximations of flow rates, and the physical and chemical context within which the community operates.

2. Systematic scientific surveys and experiments should be carried out within the arctic and subarctic seas of organisms subject to intensive exploitation. More fundamental information concerning extensive and precise new knowledge is needed as a basis for international deliberation and agreement on the wise exploitation of these resources for the benefit of all concerned.

3. We should learn more about the population dynamics and ecology of krill (*Euphausia superba*), which, in the past, has supported enormous stocks of whales and now is subject to potential large-scale harvesting.

4. Variation in biological phenomena from place to place and from season to season makes necessary the repetition of observations, serial observations in space and time, so that major seasonal changes and main gradients and water masses are sampled.

5. Marine ecological systems involving ice, pack ice, shelf ice, or fast ice should be studied in greater detail. They have been little explored but are potentially of considerable interest, especially with respect to nutrition of the ice microflora and the possible degree of heterotrophic growth.

6. Greater efficiency of observation and data processing should be achieved by standardization of all basic routine techniques used in polar marine biological investigations. Search for improved or superior new methods and techniques should be pressed. Additional and improved handbooks, especially for difficult groups, such as the diatoms and dinoflagellates, need to be prepared to facilitate critical studies of plankton.

lated pockets in the latter where moderate chlorophyll *a* concentrations ranging between 0.50 and 0.99 mg m^{-3} were

Antarctica.

Knowledge of the distribution and abundance of the

7. Investigations within the ice-covered waters of the Amundsen and Bellingshausen Seas of the Antarctic and the Chukchi and Beaufort Seas of the Arctic should be undertaken, employing icebreakers that are designed or modified to support oceanographic research. The International Weddell Sea Oceanographic Expedition (IWSOE, 1968-1969) and the Scripps Institution of Oceanography Bering Sea Expedition in 1968 (with the R/V *Alpha Helix* supported by the USCGC *Northwind*) are examples of the types of investigations that are proposed.

8. Search for new techniques and equipment for subice and subshelf ice investigations should be encouraged. Potentially valuable techniques range from scuba to submarine operations, the latter obviously requiring collaboration with the U.S. Navy, the U.S. Coast Guard, or both.

COMPARATIVE PHYSIOLOGY

Of particular importance with respect to polar region organisms are psychrobiology and cryobiology, studies of responses to cold environments and reactions of organisms, tissues, and cells to intense cold to far below the freezing point of water. Research in this field should be encouraged and sponsored, for studies of plants as well as animals. As Billings and Mooney (1968, p. 483) point out,

By studying arctic and alpine plants we can hope to learn how this relative handful of species in the world's flora has succeeded not only in surviving low temperatures during dormancy but in manufacturing relatively large amounts of food at low temperatures in very short periods of time.

Many of the problems with plants, as well as with animals, require laboratory experimentation with the aid of controlled environment chambers, for example, studies of relative sexuality-asexuality in plants as related to temperature, photoperiod, and growing season.

The physiological mechanisms underlying adaptations to cold are now understood only to the extent that many kinds of such adaptations have been recognized and have excited the interest of the observers. Morphological adaptations have been identified in great profusion, but in most instances without experimental evidence to fully support the case for cold adaptation. It has been found (Somero and DeVries, 1967) that several species of marine fish are so strongly adapted to water of $-1.8°C$ in McMurdo Sound, Antarctica, that they die when warmed to $6°C$ or higher. At least one enzyme from the muscles of one of these fishes has been found to be irreversibly damaged when warmed to $15°C$ or higher. On the other hand, certain activities go on much faster in these cold-adapted fish in the cold than they do in warmer-adapted fish or in warm-blooded animals. For example, the bloods of cold-adapted fish clot rapidly at $0°C$, a temperature at which human or

rabbit blood clots only very slowly (Robert E. Feeney, personal communication). The physiological bases of animal adaptations to cold and to changes in pressure (air or water) are in need of study, especially for guidance in acculturing man for high altitudes, deep dives, and low temperatures in the environments where he will inevitably probe.

Medical research is largely responsible for initiating research on low-temperature effects on cells, tissues, and organisms, both with respect to damage through freezing and especially with respect to the search for beneficial applications of hypothermia, rapid freezing, and freezing to very low temperatures in surgical and other techniques. There is a need for polar-region biologists to work closely with those already active in the new field of cryobiology.

Considering the variety of antarctic marine environments, there has been limited scientific analysis of them, particularly in the areas of behavior and comparative physiology. Physiology entails some special problems because of the logistic complications inherent in much of the delicate equipment required for thorough investigations. U.S. support of intensive marine physiological studies is possible at all the coastal stations, i.e., at or near McMurdo, Hallett, and Palmer Stations, and aboard the USNS *Eltanin* and the R/V *Hero*. Most activities are restricted to nearby laboratory facilities, and more programs are designed for the summertime when the organisms are available. The result is numerous studies of a few species and environments near these stations. The untapped areas that would yield valuable scientific information, as well as reduce disturbance and drain on animal populations near the major stations, could be reached only by icebreaker or helicopter support. An example of this problem is presented by studies of the emperor penguin. From a physiological point of view it is one of the most interesting of birds; yet, *in situ* physiological studies of this bird at McMurdo Station have been restricted for lack of an easily available source of specimens. The nearest collecting site is nearly 20 miles away at Cape Crozier, and access to this site is dependent on ice conditions and weather. The area is not a dependable source of birds, since the rookery has been subjected to severe mortality losses by the breakup of the shelf ice and storms at Cape Crozier. Because it is a small colony, the area is designated a "specially protected area" where a population study is being conducted. Other sources for emperor penguins in the Ross Sea can be used for experimental birds, but this requires logistic planning. Similar examples could be cited for other species. A solution to this dilemma possibly could be found in some instances with portable laboratories that can be established in interesting areas for periods of time and then removed.

Perhaps even more pressing than a diversification of our inshore studies is to initiate study of the pack-ice environment. This is assumed to be the area of concentration of

4. Studies of behavior under stresses of isolation, extreme climates, and polar light regimes should be expanded for both man and animals. Few studies on human behavior are under way at present, yet with increasing human populations, both temporary and permanent, in the high latitudes and with men pushing into extraterrestrial regions, requirements for the information are growing rapidly.

HUMAN BIOLOGY

Human biology is considered here to include human physiology, medicine, psychiatry, and psychology, and attention will be largely restricted to those aspects which might be profitably pursued in polar environments. The U.S. Antarctic Research Program has initiated sponsorship of research in human physiology and medicine only recently, whereas the British and the Russians have for many years maintained active programs in polar physiology. The extensive and systematic physiological work carried out under the British Antarctic Survey has been summarized by Lewis and Masterton (1963), Edholm and Lewis (1964), and Edholm (1965). Early physiological studies were concerned primarily with adaptation to cold, diurnal rhythms, work loads and food consumption, metabolic and hormonal changes, cardiovascular functions, and relationships between meteorological weather and microclimate on skin temperature. Measurements often were made under difficult conditions, and generally only crude instruments were available.

Wilson (1965) provided a comprehensive review of physiological research through 1962, including blood chemistry studies and the severe effects of altitude and extreme cold on physiological functions as reported at Vostok by Tichomirov and others. Relatively few studies of psychological adjustment in winter parties were available at that time.

Recently an *ad hoc* Subcommittee on Human Physiology of the Scientific Committee on Antarctic Research (SCAR) outlined proposals for a basic program in physiological research utilizing simple and standardized techniques of measurement. These proposals were regarded as preliminary steps toward developing more systematic investigations and permitting replications at various sites by different research teams.

Medical problems and health programs in the arctic regions have been thoroughly reviewed in two international conferences. The Conference on Medicine and Public Health in the Arctic and Antarctic, sponsored by the World Health Organization, was held in Geneva, Switzerland, in August 1962. This conference was an exploratory exchange of information pertaining to the ecologic characteristics of the north polar regions, descriptions of the populations living there, and the health problems of high latitudes and cold climates. The Symposium on Circumpolar Health Related

Problems, sponsored by the Arctic Institute of North America and funded by the U.S. Public Health Service, was held in Fairbanks, Alaska, in July 1967. Scientists from eight nations that share the arctic frontier participated. This symposium covered a wide range of health problems and environmental stresses encountered in the Far North. A large proportion of the medical investigations conducted in the Arctic have been devoted to endemic and chronic disease. These studies were primarily concerned with needs for and delivery of medical and public health services to the small settlements scattered across the northern latitudes.

The Antarctic has neither indigenous populations nor industrial or commercial enterprise and, therefore, presents quite different kinds of human biology problems for investigation. Although problems of, for example, adaptation to cold and social isolation are basically similar in the Arctic and Antarctic, the greater severity of these conditions in the Antarctic and the complete isolation of groups for several months provide an unparalleled situation for long-term study of physiological and behavioral adaptations in a closed environment. Inhabitants of Antarctica, typically, are temperate zone dwellers temporarily transported to the Antarctic environment for a specific period (usually one year) after which they return to an urban environment in a temperate zone. The Antarctic, then, provides a natural laboratory in which to study many important problems of psychobiological and medical adaptation for urban dwellers from temperate zones. Problem areas in human biology which could be investigated in the Antarctic with great benefit to medical and behavioral science are described in more detail below.

The trend of research effort in medicine has slowly turned from the goal of curing disease, where it has always been centered, toward the prevention of disease and disability, especially through public-health-type efforts, and toward the goal of optimization of performance of healthy individuals, as in combat medicine, in aerospace and undersea exploration, and particularly in the relatively new specialty of sports medicine.

Sociopsychological factors become the predominant ones in improving human performance beyond that already achieved, and it is precisely here that the greatest gaps exist in knowledge, the greatest complexities impede our efforts, and the least manpower and scientific tradition exist. It is possible now to point out some of the substantive areas where biomedical and biobehavioral investigations of man in the arctic and antarctic regions are needed and which approaches are amenable to systematic scientific investigation.

HEALTH AND MORBIDITY

Implicit in many of the medical investigations conducted on the Antarctic continent is the assumption that the particular environmental stresses encountered here adversely affect physical and mental health. While this is a plausible hypothesis in view of an abundance of anecdotal reports, the actual effects of living for a year in the Antarctic upon health and general functioning are still largely unknown. Living for a year in the antarctic environment is certainly an unusual experience and contrasts sharply in many ways with urban life in temperate zones, but much more about the specific nature of the stresses experienced and their physiological and psychological effects needs to be learned. This type of investigation requires extended periods of observation beginning with a control period prior to living in the Antarctic and ending with follow-up observations after returning home. This type of longitudinal research design is much more satisfactory than simply demonstrating that differences exist between people who normally live in polar regions and subjects who reside there temporarily.

An unforgettable fact of existence at all stations on the interior of an ice cap is that neither evacuation nor outside help are possible during several months of the year. Thus, the possibility of physiological or psychological breakdown in this situation is viewed with grave concern. The risks of different types of illness or injury can be objectively established by analysis of medical records at antarctic bases over a period of years. Preliminary morbidity data reported by Hedblom (1961) and by Gunderson (1968) have shown that the risk of injury or psychiatric disorder for naval personnel in Antarctica tends to be low but somewhat higher than elsewhere. In studies of relative health risks, McMurdo Station and ships in antarctic seas can be used as control conditions in the sense that they represent situations of lesser environmental stress as compared with the extremely rigorous conditions prevailing at interior continental stations.

In any population at risk, health problems appear to be concentrated in a relatively small proportion of the population (Hinkle et al., 1956). Furthermore, susceptible persons incur a variety of illnesses involving many different organ systems (Thurlow, 1967), and those having multiple illness episodes tend to experience them in clusters, that is, concentrated during particular time periods characterized by unusual life stress (Hinkle and Wolff, 1958; Schmale, 1966).

Recent investigations have suggested that the amount of life change or stress experienced by individuals affects the probability of incurring illness shortly thereafter (Rahe, 1968). Both interview methods and questionnaires, reflecting recent changes in the subject's personal, family, and community life with particular reference to his occupation, residence, engagements or marriage, finances, social behavior, and recreation, have provided "life crisis" indices that correlated significantly with concurrent or future illness in a variety of populations.

Prior health history also is significantly correlated with future illness episodes. Objective health records and self-reports of major illnesses and injuries over recent time

periods may predict illnesses during the antarctic winter.

Self-perceptions of health status have been shown to relate to illness onset in a number of settings. One widely used health questionnaire, the Cornell Medical Index, has predicted medical problems during short-term, acute environmental stress and has predicted the onset of psychiatric illness. Application of this type of instrument prior to, during, and after deployment in the Antarctic or at remote arctic sites would throw considerable light on the kinds and degrees of subjective physical and mental distress experienced in this novel situation.

The following factors should be systematically examined in relation to illness incidence at antarctic stations: (1) demographic and social background information, (2) psychological needs and personality traits, (3) recent health history, (4) recent life crises and adjustment problems, (5) self-perceptions of health, (6) current life status factors (occupational level, educational level, etc.), (7) occupational specialty, (8) work schedule at the station, and (9) job satisfaction.

PHYSIOLOGICAL AND BIOCHEMICAL STUDIES

The comprehensive psychophysiological research program conducted by Shurley and sponsored by the Office of Antarctic Programs at the South Pole Station during the 1967 and 1968 seasons established a valuable framework for long-term psychrobiological investigations. The results obtained during the first two years of the project will lay the groundwork for more specialized studies of sleep and activity cycles and their physiological and psychological correlates in future expeditions.

The recommendations for biochemical research set forth below are drawn from a different context and are based on recent work at a number of university and military laboratories. Within the past decade many studies have tended to show relationships between psychological and behavioral variables and levels of serum cholesterol and uric acid. It has been noted that elevations of uric acid correlate with achievement orientation, leadership behavior, and vigorous responses to environmental demands and life challenges (Brooks and Mueller, 1966). Persons with high cholesterol concentrations have been described as overburdened or overwhelmed by situational demands (Wolf et al., 1962; Peterson et al., 1962; Wertlake et al., 1958). Biochemical determinations and behavioral data taken during arduous and stressful frogman training tended to support earlier observations that high serum uric acid levels were associated with eager acceptance of difficult tasks and successful accomplishment; serum cholesterol levels were low during periods of heavy physical exertion but high during boring or frustrating portions of the training program. Mood, symptom, and motivational measures gathered simultane-

Range, on the central Pacific coast of Alaska, has already become a large oil-producing area. Amchitka, one of the islands in the Aleutian Chain, was considerably disturbed by military activities in World War II, reverted to an abandoned state, and recently has become a very busy center for underground testing of nuclear devices, with all the attendant scientific, surveying, and engineering activities that undertaking entails. The scheme for building a dam at Rampart on the Yukon in Alaska, to make a reservoir on the Yukon Flats larger than Lake Erie and inundate one of the major waterfowl breeding areas in northwestern North America, was put aside once after much debate, and now interest is rising for another look at the possibilities. Many other projects, both active and in the planning stage, can be expected to have significant effects on Alaska's biota. Other areas in the North are coming under similar pressures. There cannot be occupancy, development, and use without some disruption or damage to the original natural systems; but we must use the available means to marshall all possible information that will permit the best choices for long-term use of the resources and spaces.

We must expect the pressure of exploitation of the natural resources of polar regions to increase drastically in the years to come. It will be mandatory that intelligent control be exercised over this process, so that scientific and aesthetic interests in the polar regions are given fair consideration. This cannot be accomplished without an increase in the scientific and educational programs regarding the polar regions. The south polar regions are at least to some degree protected through natural isolation and by the Antarctic Treaty and the growing body of Agreed Measures for Conservation under the Treaty. In the Arctic, however, time is already running out. We desperately need to establish an inviolate system of natural areas in the Far North, both for scientific research and for long-range development as recreation areas. Over most of the temperate land areas and the larger part of tropical land areas it is no longer possible to find parcels of complete original ecosystems on scales large enough to serve as baseline systems against which to measure environmental and biotic changes; we can only look for sites that exhibit least disturbance. In the polar regions we know of many still unspoiled areas. Let us secure some, set up the programs of study, and begin making the measurements that will become so useful in monitoring the conditions affecting human health and comfort.

The whole problem of introduction and establishment of organisms in polar regions has received little more than casual attention so far. The potential dangers of the introduction of a disease of domestic fowl into antarctic penguin populations is readily apparent. With trial models of introduction processes that are now available (e.g., in MacArthur and Wilson, 1967), it would be possible to conduct at least some pilot experiments on small scales to secure some be-

ginning information for selected organisms. Newly exposed glacial moraine surfaces and remote areas on the Antarctic or Greenland Ice Cap might be feasible areas for certain kinds of field experiments of this nature. It would also be valuable to establish study areas in which the vegetation was destroyed in order to investigate regeneration and/or establishment of plants and animals and at the same time test the available theoretical models.

Significant aid would be given to conservation of species and environments in polar regions by making available to persons entering these regions information about the landscapes, their faunas and floras, and summaries of human disturbances to date. For centers of scientific activity, such as McMurdo Station in the Antarctic and the Naval Arctic Research Laboratory on the north coast of Alaska, there are needs for inexpensive and easily emendable guidebooks for the local areas. These would include tables of common plants and animals, with notations of those that are in any way specially protected, lists of reservations for conservation purposes or for scientific projects in progress, and lists of features such as lakes with annotations including literature citations about previous work on the feature and summaries about characteristics such as seasonal changes in ice cover. These guidebooks should also include accounts in appropriate detail of the history of human activity in the area, as this becomes increasingly significant to biological investigations and to planning for further human occupation.

For most centers of activity at least two versions of a guidebook will be necessary, one for scientific investigators and another for the support staff and conducted visitors, the latter version avoiding specialized terminology and problems and including more of the engineering design and management considerations. Where the general public has access to one of these areas, still a third version of the guidebook would be desirable; it would be a means of providing information to which the general public should have ready access and at the same time be a device for educating the reader in the necessity for careful use of the area and its resources. Our work in polar regions has a strong and wide appeal to the general public interest, and these steps would help to serve that need as well as gain some ground toward wise use and management of polar areas and their resources.

It is sometimes said that polar ecosystems are "fragile" with respect to disturbance. The extreme specializations or narrow adaptations of the organisms constitute one responsible cause of this fragility, and the relative simplicity of structure (i.e., few species) in the ecosystems is another cause. Moderate disturbances, such as pollution (Sladen *et al.*, 1966) and approach of helicopters, may have profound effects. For instance, on approach of helicopters, penguins show excitement and temporarily abandon their nests, permitting skuas to steal the penguin eggs. Plants grow slowly in the Antarctic, so that destruction of vegetation may have a long-lasting effect. Disturbances, such as trampling of moss-mats by man and grading for stations, camps and airstrips, may exterminate colonies of plants. Survival of some plants may be endangered if their insect associates are killed off. Many arthropod species are highly localized in known distribution and could quite conceivably be exterminated by relatively slight changes in their environment through disturbance. Since most of the antarctic macroscopic species—birds, seals, arthropods, and plants—are endemic to the antarctic region, general steps should be taken to provide adequate protection for all the species. Many are restricted in occurrence. Not only should preserves be set aside, but all visitors to the continent should be thoroughly indoctrinated regarding the urgency of protecting the natural environment with the biota. The biological investigators who work in the polar regions have responsibility for providing guidelines for administrative authorities to follow in order to ensure the preservation of the unique biota.

The two polar regions are in strong contrast with respect to their resource planning and conservation problems. The Arctic has had small centers of indigenous human population for at least several thousand years. Exploration, exploitation of resources, and modern settlement in the Arctic began more than 100 years earlier than parallel activity in the Antarctic, and the access overland from temperate latitude population centers into northern areas made a difference. We are already engaged in a vigorous debate about what we may yet keep inviolate of the arctic lands. The Antarctic is still sufficiently remote and economically unattractive that the Antarctic Treaty Nations are setting up Agreed Measures for Conservation of Biota and Specially Protected Areas in a pattern more nearly ideal than has been seen for any other part of the earth.

The riches of the Antarctic, it appears, are the biological resources of the seas in the vicinity of the Antarctic Convergence. Eventually some agreements by nations in accord will be necessary in order to husband those resources. So far the high seas have been open to all, the rights of the high seas being vigorously defended in every instance. But territorial waters are being extended by some nations to protect fishing grounds, and some valuable species of high seas fisheries are being harvested to extinction. This course cannot be followed much longer without prejudicing some of the primary sources of protein for human populations and key portions of major world ecosystems. We must begin now to face this problem of international accord on resource planning of high seas productions and areas such as the antarctic continent.

Although it at first sounds paradoxical, polar areas nearly devoid of living things, such as the Inland Ice of Greenland and the Antarctic Ice Cap, may prove to be a valuable resource. These areas could become sites for biological experimentation in which freedom from contamination is important. It has also been suggested that these nearly barren areas might be used as quarantine localities for exiting or entering space vehicles making contact with extraterrestrial bodies. The point to be made here is that we dare not use any area or resource on the earth without consideration for other uses in the future.

LOGISTICS

Biological investigations in polar regions pose special logistic problems because of (1) the difficulties of obtaining observations in the field throughout the year, especially with cumbersome but delicate equipment requiring electric power supply, (2) the remoteness of laboratories in which certain critical observations must be made, and (3) the characteristics of the organisms themselves, requiring control of temperature, diurnal rhythms, or food for maintenance in near-natural condition. Establishment and progressive development of the Naval Arctic Research Laboratory (NARL) at Point Barrow, Alaska, and more recently the Biological Laboratories at McMurdo, Hallett, and Palmer Stations in the Antarctic were milestones toward the solution of adequate facilities in the polar regions and serve as models for more that are needed. Some very modest installations, little more than clusters of huts supplied annually, such as the Devon Island Station of the Arctic Institute, and American and Soviet Union stations on sea ice and ice islands of the Arctic Ocean, have given handsome returns in biological research for the investment of money and effort, but not in terms of problems requiring sophisticated facilities. Observations in the field are being facilitated by design and routine manufacture of more and more compact, lightweight, and still dependable field instruments. This problem will be aided in its solution also by development and installation of automatic observing stations, at first for basic observations of microclimates on land and of temperature, current, and salinity in water, but eventually for such measurements as plant respiration, soil "respiration," and carbonate and bicarbonate ion concentration in waters. Toward solution of study of polar organisms under experimental conditions we must provide for more environmental chamber facilities capable of simulating closely the polar climates and microclimates. Low-temperature freezer compartments are not good enough; we need to control atmospheric quality, solar band radiation, and moisture relations to a much better degree than has been done in most facilities so far.

Marine biology logistic problems can be solved largely by ships of appropriate characteristics with respect to sea conditions, cruise schedules, and shipboard facilities for scientific work. The USNS *Eltanin* of the U.S. Antarctic Research Program is a conventional ship modified for biological, geophysical, oceanographic, and upper-atmosphere work that has been a great aid in conducting high-seas scientific investigations in antarctic waters, although it has recognized deficiencies for work in ice and in tight inshore areas. The R/V *Hero*, a smaller, wooden-type vessel, specially designed for behavioral studies (acoustic) with marine mammals, was built for general support of the U.S. Antarctic Research Program in the Antarctic Peninsula particularly along the Continental Shelf.

INTERNATIONAL COOPERATION

International cooperation in biological research in arctic and subarctic regions has been in frequent need of stimulation throughout the history of exploration and development. Biologists were able to append field surveys and investigations to the several International Geophysical Year (1957–1958) efforts, and during that year marine biology of the Arctic Ocean Basin was a part of the effort in oceanography conducted primarily by Canada, the Soviet Union, and the United States. Cooperation between the United States and Canada in the Arctic has become so informal, especially through the Arctic Institute of North America, that we often forget to include these binational undertakings in the category of international cooperation. The Danish Government and its Greenland Department have also been most cooperative in matters of the western hemisphere Arctic. Nevertheless, constant and vigorous collaboration in biological research does not, in fact, exist among all the nations concerned with the North Polar regions. This state of affairs has been made conspicuous by the remarkable collaboration in research made possible in the south polar regions by the Antarctic Treaty. The responsibilities for sharing data, and the opportunities for exchanging scientific and technical personnel, have created in the Antarctic a new political climate for research, with all the advantages of free exchange of information and persons.

International cooperation is critical to several aspects of biological and medical research, especially surveys of widespread populations of animals, synoptic studies of phenological events or population fluctuations, surveys of the spread of infectious diseases, conservation of endangered species, and enforcement of protection for given species and given areas. As we are forced by reason of biological losses and catastrophes to maintain global watchfulness of certain organisms and environmental conditions (Sladen *et al.*, 1966), we are pressed into international cooperation, without which many of these problems cannot be solved. The great whales are now reduced to such small populations that they are probably doomed to extinction, because efforts at international control were too late and too feeble. We should not let this pattern be repeated.

The International Biological Program (IBP) is helping to advance cooperation between nations active in polar research. Among antarctic scientists there is a feeling that

international cooperation has been achieved to an adequate degree through SCAR (the Scientific Committee on Antarctic Research of the International Council of Scientific Unions). Actually, further benefits are available even to antarctic research through still other international cooperation, as through the IBP, for example, in collaborative research comparing alpine conditions at lower latitudes with those in the Antarctic. But it is arctic and subarctic research that needs far wider and more constant international collaboration, such as that being developed under IBP projects, for example, the international study of Eskimos (Milan, 1968). An international study of the polar bear, from the standpoint of its role at the summit of the trophic pyramid in the Arctic Basin, failed to get the international support needed to make it viable; it is to be hoped that another international study of the polar bear, oriented around the protection of the species, can be carried out under the IUCN (International Union for the Conservation of Nature).

The *sine qua non* of productive international efforts in biological and medical research is free communication between the scientists making the observations and conducting the analyses. When information must be passed up through formal channels to administrative officials of one government for transmittal by way of administrative chains of another government to reach the other scientists who will make some use of the information, the chances of loss, error, and delay are so great as to make the whole procedure of doubtful value. Information exchange internationally is facilitated especially by symposia of international gatherings of scientists, international excursions to specialized laboratories and field areas where work is in progress, and international exchange of personnel in laboratories and institutions of higher learning. There are many circumstances under which a private foundation or research institute, such as the Arctic Institute of North America or the Scott Polar Research Institute can provide arrangements for accomplishing such undertakings when government agencies and even universities might find it too complicated. By that mechanism, the arrangements for the exchange are being essentially put into the hands of a group of scientists widely informed and deeply concerned with polar research. The results obtained in this way have been so satisfactory over the past 20 years that it seems reasonable to recommend that more of the arrangements be entrusted to private institutes of an international nature.

REFERENCES

Antarctic Research Series, 13 vols. through 1968, Amer. Geophys. Union, Washington, D.C. (1964 continuing).

Arnold, C. A., "Some Paleobotanical Aspects of Tundra Development," *Ecology*, 40, 146–148 (1959).

Balech, E., "Dinoflagellates," *Atlas Folio Series No. 10*. (V. Bushnell, ed.) Amer. Geographical Soc., New York (1968).

Belyaev, G. M., "Some Patterns in the Quantitative Distribution of the Bottom Fauna in the Antarctic," *Soviet Antarctic Information Bulletin I*, 119–121 (1958).

Benoit, R. E., C. L. Hall, Jr., and R. E. Cameron, "Microbial Ecology of Some Dry Valley Soils of Victorialand," *Proceedings of the Second Symposium on Antarctic Biology July 28–Aug. 3, 1968, Cambridge, U.K.* (M. W. Holdgate, ed.) Academic Press, N.Y. (1968).

Billings, W. D., and H. A. Mooney, "The Ecology of Arctic and Alpine Plants," in *Biological Reviews*. Cambridge University Press, N.Y., pp. 43, 481–529 (1968).

Böcher, T. W., "Oceanic and Continental Vegetational Complexes in Southwest Grønland," *Medd. Grønland, 148* (3) (1963a).

Böcher, T. W., "Phytogeography of Middle West Grønland," *Medd. Grønland, 148* (3) (1963b).

Böcher, T. W., K. Holmen, and K. Jakobsen, *Grønlands Flora*. P. Haase and Sons, Forlag, Copenhagen (1966).

Boyd, W. L., "Ecology and Physiology of Soil Microorganisms in Polar Regions," *Proc. Symp. on Pacific-Antarctic Sci. II*. Pac. Sci. Congr., Tokyo, Japan (1967).

Boyd, W. L., and J. W. Boyd, "The Presence of Bacteria in Permafrost of the Alaskan Arctic," *Can. J. Microbiol., 10*, 917–919 (1964).

Brooks, G. E., and E. Mueller, "Serum Urate Concentrations Among University Professors: Relation to Drive, Achievement, and Leadership," *J. Amer. Med. Ass., 196*, 415–418 (1966).

Brundin, L., "Transantarctic Relationships and their Significance, as Evidenced by Chironomid Midges," *Monograph of the Subfamilies* Podonominae *and* Aphrotentinae *and the Austral* Heptagyiae, *Kungl. Svenska Vetensk., Handl. Fjärde, ser. 11* (1), 1–472 (1966).

Burkholder, P. B., and E. F. Mandelli, "Productivity of Microalgae in Antarctic Sea Ice," *Science, 149*, 872–874 (1965).

Bunney, W. E., and J. A. Fawcett, "Possibility of a Biochemical Test for Suicidal Potential," *Arch. Gen. Psychiat., 13*, 232–239 (1965).

Bushnell, V. (ed.), *Antarctic Map Folio Series*, 11 vols. through 1968, Amer. Geographical Soc., N.Y. (1964 continuing).

Carrick, R., M. Holdgate, and J. Prévost (eds.), *Antarctic Biology*, Report of the First Symposium on Antarctic Biology, Paris, France, Sept. 2–8, 1962, sponsored by SCAR and IUBS. Hermann, Paris (1964).

Clowes, A. I., "Phosphate and Silicate in the Southern Ocean," *Discovery Reports XIX*, Cambridge University Press, N.Y., pp. 1–120 (1938).

Committee on Polar Research, *Science in Antarctica, Part I, The Life Sciences in Antarctica*, NAS-NRC Publ. 839, Nat. Acad. Sci.-Nat. Res. Council, Washington, D.C. (1961).

Committee on Polar Research, *Science in the Arctic Ocean Basin*, NAS-NRC Publ. 1086, Nat. Acad. Sci.-Nat. Res. Council, Washington, D.C. (1963).

Currie, R. I., "Environmental Features in the Ecology of the Antarctic Seas," in *Antarctic Biology*. (R. Carrick, M. Holdgate, and J. Prévost, eds.) Hermann, Paris, pp. 87–94 (1964).

Dalenius, P., "The Acarology of the Antarctic Regions," in *Biogeography and Ecology in Antarctica. Monographiae Biologicae, 15*. (J. van Mieghem, P. van Oye, and J. Schell, eds.) W. Junk, The Hague, pp. 414–430 (1965).

Darlington, P. J., *Biogeography of the Southern End of the World*. Harvard University Press, Cambridge, Mass., p. 236 (1965).

Dayton, P. K., G. A. Robilliard, and A. L. DeVries, "Anchor Ice Formation in McMurdo Sound, Antarctica, and Its Biological Effects," *Science, 163*, 273–274 (Jan. 17, 1969).

Deacon, G. E. R., "Antarctic Oceanography: the Physical Environment," in *Antarctic Biology*. (R. Carrick, M. Holdgate, and J. Prévost, eds.) Hermann, Paris, pp. 81–86 (1964).

Deacon, G. E. R., "Note on the Dynamics of the Southern Ocean," *Discovery Reports, XV*. Cambridge University Press, N.Y., pp. 125–152 (1937).

DeVries, A. L., and D. E. Wohlschlag, "Diving Depths of the Weddell Seal," *Science, 145*, 292 (July 17, 1964).

Dorr, J. A., "Tertiary Non-Marine Vertebrates in Alaska–the Lack Thereof," *Bull. Amer. Ass. Petrol. Geol., 48* (7), 1198–1202 (1964).

Edholm, O. G., "Medical Research by the British Antarctic Survey," *Polar Record, 12*, 575–582 (1965).

Edholm, O. G., and H. E. Lewis, "Terrestrial Animals in Cold: Men in Polar Regions," in *Handbook of Physiology*. (D. B. Dill, E. F. Adolph, and C. G. Wilber, eds.) Amer. Physiol. Soc., Washington, D.C., pp. 435–446 (1964).

El-Sayed, S. Z., "Dynamics of Trophic Relationships in the Southern Ocean." Paper presented at the AAAS Antarctic Research Symposium, Dallas, Texas (Dec. 28, 1968).

Foxton, P., "The Standing Crop of Zooplankton in the Southern Ocean," *Discovery Reports, XXVIII*. Cambridge University Press, N.Y., pp. 193–235 (1956).

Gressitt, J. L., "Biogeography and Ecology of Land Arthropods of Antarctica. Biogeography and Ecology in Antarctica," *Monogr. Biolog., 15*, 431–490 (1965).

Gressitt, J. L. (ed.), "Entomology of Antarctica," *Antarctic Research Series 10*. Amer. Geophys. Union, Washington, D.C. (1967).

Gressitt, J. L. (ed.), *Pacific Basin Biogeography–A Symposium*. Bishop Museum Press, Honolulu (1964).

Gunderson, E. K. E., "Mental Health Problems in Antarctica," *Arch. Environ. Health, 17*, 558–564 (1968).

Hedblom, E. E., "The Medical Problems Encountered in Antarctica," *Military Med., 126*, 818–824 (1961).

Hemmingsen, E. A., and E. Douglas, "Snow Blindness in Animals," *Antarctic J. U.S., 2* (4), 99–100 (July–Aug. 1967).

Hemmingsen, E. A., and G. C. Grigg, "Oxygen Consumption in a Hemoglobin-Free Fish," *Antarctic J. U.S., 2* (4), 104–105 (July–Aug. 1967).

Hinkle, L. E., Jr., R. H. Pinsky, I. D. J. Bross, and N. Plummer, "The Distribution of Sickness Disability in a Homogeneous Group of Healthy Adult Men," *Amer. J. Hyg., 64*, 220–242 (1956).

Hinkle, L. E., Jr., and H. G. Wolff, "Ecologic Investigations of the Relationship Between Illness, Life Experiences and the Social Environment," *Ann. Int. Med., 49*, 1373–1388 (1958).

Holdgate, M. W., "The Antarctic Ecosystem," *Phil. Trans. Ser. B, 252* (777), 363–383 (1967).

Holdgate, M. W. (ed.), *Proceedings of the Second Symposium on Antarctic Biology, July 28–Aug. 3, 1968, Cambridge, U.K.*, sponsored by SCAR and IUBS, Academic Press, New York (1969).

Hopkins, D. M. (ed.), *The Bering Land Bridge*. Stanford University Press, Stanford, Calif. (1967).

Hopkins, T. L., "Zooplankton Standing Crop in the Atlantic Sector of the Antarctic Ocean," *Second Int. Oceanogr. Congr. Abstr.*, A. P. Vinogradov (ed.), Nauka, Moscow, p. 160 (1966).

Hopkins, T. L., "Zooplankton Standing Crop in the Pacific Sector of the Antarctic" (unpublished manuscript).

Hultén, E., *Flora of Alaska and Neighboring Territories: a Manual of the Vascular Plants*. Stanford University Press, Stanford, Calif. (1968).

Hultén, E., *Outline of the History of Arctic and Boreal Biota during the Quaternary Period*. Bokförlage aktiebolaget Thule, Stockholm, p. 168 (1937).

Hultén, E., "The Circumpolar Plants, I," *Kungl. Avensk Vetensk., Handl.*, ser. 4, 8 (5), 275 (1962).

Janetschek, H., "On the Biology of Antarctica" ("Zur Biologie von Antarktika," text in German), *Naturw.-Med. Ver. in Innsbruck, Ber.*, 53, 235–246 (1963).

Janetschek, H., "The Level of Microphytes (A New Concept and Program)," ("Die Mikrophytenstufe. Ein neuer Begriff und ein Programm," text in German), *Akad. Wiss., Vienna Math.-Naturwiss. Kl. Anz.*, 9, 185–191 (1964).

Krog, H., *The Macrolichens of Alaska*, Norsk Polarinstitutt, Skrifter No. 144, Oslo Universitets Sforlaget (1968).

Llano, G. A., "The Flora of Antarctica," in *Antarctica.* (T. Hatherton, ed.) Frederick A. Praeger, N.Y., pp. 331–350 (1965).

Llano, G. A., "Plant Life," *Australian Natural History*, 108–114 (1968).

Lester, J. T., Jr., "Behavioral Research During the 1963 American Mt. Everest Expedition," *Final Report* (Sept. 1964).

Lewis, H. E., and J. P. Masterton, "Polar Physiology: Its Development in Britain," *Lancet*, 1, 1009–1114 (1963).

Livingstone, D. A., "Alaska, Yukon, Northwest Territories, and Greenland," in *Limnology in North America.* (D. G. Frey, ed.) University of Wisconsin Press, Madison, Wisc., pp. 559–574 (1963).

Löve, A., and D. Löve (eds.), *North Atlantic Biota and Their History.* Macmillan, N.Y. (1963).

MacArthur, R. H., and E. O. Wilson, *The Theory of Island Biogeography.* Princeton University Press, Princeton, N.J. (1967).

MacGinitie, G. E., "Distribution and Ecology of the Marine Invertebrates of Point Barrow, Alaska," *Smithsonian Misc. Coll.*, 128 (9), 201 (1955).

Mackintosh, N. A., "The Seasonal Circulation of the Antarctic Macroplankton," *Discovery Reports, XVI.* Cambridge University Press, N.Y., pp. 365–412 (1937).

Mackintosh, N. A., and S. G. Brown, "Preliminary Estimates of the Southern Populations of the Larger Baleen Whales," *Norsk Hvalfanstlid*, 5, 469–480 (1956).

Marr, J. W. S., "The Natural History and Geography of the Antarctic Krill (*Euphausia Superba* Dana)," *Discovery Reports, XXXII,* Cambridge University Press, N.Y., pp. 433–464 (1962)

McWhinnie, M. A., and P. L. Marciniack, "Temperature Responses and Tissue Respiration in Antarctic Crustacea with Particular Reference to the Krill *Euphausia superba.*" *Antarctic Research Series 1.* (M. O. Lee, ed.) Amer. Geophys. Union, Washington, D.C., pp. 63–72 (1964).

Milan, F. A., "The International Study of Eskimos," *Arctic*, 21 (3), 123–126 (1968).

Morris, R. W., "Thermal-Metabolic Relationships in Stenothermal Fishes," *Antarctic J. U.S.*, 2 (4), 107–108 (July–Aug. 1967).

Peterson, J. E., R. A. Keith, and A. A. Wilcox, "Hourly Changes in Serum Cholesterol Concentration: Effects of the Anticipation of Stress," *Circulation*, 25, 798–803 (1962).

Péwé, T. L., "Age of Moraines in Victoria Land, Antarctica," *J. Glaciol.*, 4, 93–100 (1962).

Radloff, R., and R. Helmreich, *Groups Under Stress: Psychological Research in SEALAB II.* Appleton-Century-Crofts, N.Y. (1968).

Rahe, R. H., "Life-Change Measurement as a Predictor of Illness," *Proc. Roy. Soc. Med.*, 61, 1124–1126 (1968).

Rahe, R. H., R. T. Rubin, R. J. Arthur, and B. R. Clark, "Serum Uric Acid and Cholesterol Variability," *J. Amer. Med. Assoc.*, 206, 2875–2880 (1968).

Ray, C., "Physiological Ecology of Marine Mammals at McMurdo Sound, Antarctica," *BioScience*, 15 (4), 274–277 (Apr. 1965).

Ray, C., and M. S. R. Smith, "Thermoregulation of the Adult and Pup Weddell Seal, *Leptonychotes weddellii* (Lesson), in Antarctica," *Zoologica*, 53 (1), 33–48 (1968).

Rudolph, E. D., "Antarctic Lichens and Vascular Plants: Their Significance," *BioScience*, 15 (4), 285–287 (1965).

Schmale, A. H., Jr., "Object, Loss, Giving Up, and Disease Onset," in *Symposium on Medical Aspects of Stress in Military Climate*, Walter Reed Army Institute of Research, Walter Reed Army Medical Center, Washington, D.C., April 22–24, 1964. U.S. Government Printing Office, Washington, D.C., pp. 433–443 (1966).

Shurley, J. T., "Study of Sleeping, Dreaming, and Waking Patterns of Antarctic Wintering-Over Personnel," *Antarctic J. U.S.*, 2 (5), 197 (1967).

Sladen, W. J. L., "Ornithological Research in Antarctica," *BioScience*, 15 (4), 264–268 (Apr. 1965a).

Sladen, W. J. L., "Staphylococci in Noses and Streptococci in Throats of Isolated and Semi-isolated Communities," *J. Hyg.*, 63 (1), 105–116 (1965b).

Sladen, W. J. L., C. M. Menzie, and W. L. Reichel, "DDT Residues in Adelie Penguins and a Crabeater Seal from Antarctica: Ecological Implications," *Nature*, 210, 670–673 (1966).

Smith, W. M., "Scientific Personnel in Antarctica: Their Recruitment, Selection, and Performance," *Psychol. Rep.*, 9, 163–182 (Monogr. Suppl. 1-V9) (1961).

Smith, W. M., "Observations over the Lifetime of a Small Isolated Group: Structure, Danger, Boredom, and Vision," *Psychol. Rep.*, 19, 475–514 (Monogr. Suppl. 1-V19) (1966).

Smith, W. M., and M. B. Jones, "Astronauts, Antarctic Scientists and Personal Autonomy," *J. Aerospace Med.*, 33, 162–166 (1962).

Somero, G. N., and A. L. DeVries, "Temperature Tolerance of Some Antarctic Fishes," *Science*, 156, 257–258 (Apr. 14, 1967).

Somero, G., and A. C. Giese, "Physiological and Biochemical Mechanics of Cold Adaptation in Fishes of McMurdo Sound," *Antarctic J. U.S.*, 2 (5), 189–190 (Sept.–Oct. 1967).

Thurlow, H. J., "General Susceptibility to Illness: A Selective Review," *Can. Med. Ass. J.*, 97, 1397–1404 (1967).

Ushakov, P. V., "Some Characteristics of the Distribution of the Bottom Fauna off the Coast of East Antarctica," *Sov. Antarctic Expedition Information Bull. 4*, 287–292 (1962).

Wace, N. M., "Vascular Plants," in *Biogeography and Ecology in Antarctica.* W. Junk, The Hague, pp. 201–266 (1965).

Wertlake, P. T., A. A. Wilcox, M. I. Haley, and J. E. Peterson, "Relationship of Mental and Emotional Stress to Serum Cholesterol Levels," *Proc. Soc. Exp. Biol. Med.*, 97, 163–165 (1958).

Wilimovsky, N. J., and J. N. Wolfe, *Environment of the Cape Thompson Region, Alaska.* U.S. Atomic Energy Commission, Oak Ridge, Tenn. (1966).

Wilson, O., "Human Adaptation to Life in Antarctica," in *Monographia Biologia: Biogeography and Ecology in Antarctica.* (J. Van Mieghem and P. Van Oye, eds.) W. Junk, The Hague, (1965).

Wolf, S., W. R. McCabe, C. Yamamoto, C. A. Adsett, and W. W. Schottstaedt, "Changes in Serum Lipids in Relation to Emotional Stress During Rigid Control of Diet and Exercise," *Circulation*, 26, 379–387 (1962).

Committee and Panel Members

LAURENCE M. GOULD, *Chairman*   University of Arizona
DANA K. BAILEY   Institute for Telecommunication Sciences and Aeronomy, ESSA
WILLIAM S. BENNINGHOFF   University of Michigan
SIDNEY A. BOWHILL   University of Illinois
CAMPBELL CRADDOCK   University of Wisconsin
WILLIAM O. FIELD   American Geographical Society
RICHARD M. GOODY   Harvard University
BERNHARD HAURWITZ   National Center for Atmospheric Research
KENNETH L. HUNKINS   Lamont-Doherty Geological Observatory
WALDO K. LYON   USN Arctic Submarine Research Laboratory
JACK E. OLIVER   Lamont-Doherty Geological Observatory
MARTIN A. POMERANTZ   Bartol Research Foundation
ALAN H. SHAPLEY   Institute for Telecommunication Sciences and Aeronomy, ESSA
RUPERT B. SOUTHARD, JR.   U.S. Geological Survey
A. LINCOLN WASHBURN   University of Washington
LOUIS DeGOES, *Executive Secretary*

Liaison Members: T. O. JONES (National Science Foundation), A. P. CRARY (National Science Foundation),
LOUIS O. QUAM (National Science Foundation), Rear Admiral DAVID F. WELCH (U.S. Naval Support Force—Antarctica),
MAX E. BRITTON (Office of Naval Research), CHARLES C. BATES (U.S. Coast Guard), LEONARD S. WILSON
(U.S. Army Office of the Chief R&D), JOHN C. REED (Arctic Institute of North America)

Panel on Biological and Medical Sciences

WILLIAM S. BENNINGHOFF, *Chairman*   University of Michigan
ROBERT E. BENOIT   Virginia Polytechnic Institute
SAYED Z. EL-SAYED   Texas A&M University
ROBERT E. FEENEY   University of California, Davis
J. LINSLEY GRESSITT   Bernice P. Bishop Museum
MARGARET L. LANTIS   University of Kentucky
PETER R. MORRISON   University of Alaska
RICHARD L. PENNEY   New York Zoological Society
ROBERT L. RAUSCH   Arctic Health Research Laboratory, USPHS
G. CARLETON RAY   The Johns Hopkins University

JAY T. SHURLEY   Oklahoma Medical Research Foundation
WILLIAM C. STEERE   New York Botanical Garden
HERBERT G. SHEPLER, *Secretary*

GEORGE A. LLANO (Liaison Member)   National Science Foundation

Panel on Geodesy and Cartography

RUPERT B. SOUTHARD, JR., *Chairman*   U. S. Geological Survey
PETER F. BERMEL   U. S. Geological Survey
VIVIAN C. BUSHNELL   American Geographical Society
FREDERICK M. EDVALSON   U. S. Naval Oceanographic Office
JULES D. FRIEDMAN   U. S. Geological Survey
WILLIAM R. MacDONALD   U.S. Geological Survey
ERIC H. RUTSCHEIDT   U.S. Army Topographic Command
HELLMUT H. SCHMID   Institute for Earth Sciences, ESSA
CHARLES A. WHITTEN   U.S. Coast and Geodetic Survey
DEAN P. KASTEL, *Secretary*

WALTER R. SEELIG (Liaison Member)   National Science Foundation

Panel on Geology and Solid Earth Geophysics

CAMPBELL CRADDOCK, *Chairman*   University of Wisconsin
CHARLES R. BENTLEY   University of Wisconsin
COLIN BULL   The Ohio State University
GEORGE GRYC   U. S. Geological Survey
WILLIAM R. MacDONALD   U.S. Geological Survey
NED A. OSTENSO   Office of Naval Research
FRED ROOTS   Canadian Geological Survey
ROBERT H. RUTFORD   University of South Dakota
DWIGHT L. SCHMIDT   U.S. Geological Survey
LYNN SYKES   Lamont-Doherty Geological Observatory
F. ALTON WADE   Texas Technological University
DEAN P. KASTEL, *Secretary*

MORT D. TURNER (Liaison Member)   National Science Foundation

Panel on Glaciology

A. LINCOLN WASHBURN, *Chairman*   University of Washington
FRANKLIN I. BADGLEY   University of Washington
JAMES A. BENDER   USA–Cold Regions Research and Engineering Laboratory
CARL S. BENSON   University of Alaska
CHARLES R. BENTLEY   University of Wisconsin
COLIN BULL   The Ohio State University
WILLIAM O. FIELD   American Geographical Society
RICHARD P. GOLDTHWAIT   The Ohio State University
EDWARD R. LACHAPELLE   University of Washington
CHESTER C. LANGWAY, JR.   USA–Cold Regions Research and Engineering Laboratory
M. MARTINELLI, JR.   U.S. Forest Service
MARK F. MEIER   U.S. Geological Survey

FRITZ MÜLLER   McGill University
LAURENCE H. NOBLES   Northwestern University
NORBERT UNTERSTEINER   University of Washington
WILFORD F. WEEKS   USA–Cold Regions Research and Engineering Laboratory
JOHANNES WEERTMAN   Northwestern University
JAMES H. ZUMBERGE   University of Arizona
PEMBROKE J. HART, *Secretary*

MORT D. TURNER (Liaison Member)   National Science Foundation

Panel on Meteorology and Climatology

RICHARD M. GOODY, *Chairman*   Harvard University
RICHARD CADLE   National Center for Atmospheric Research
ROBERT G. FLEAGLE   University of Washington
ROBERT A. HELLIWELLL   Stanford University
SVENN ORVIG   McGill University
RICHARD J. REED   University of Washington
MORT J. RUBIN   Environmental Science Services Administration
WERNER SCHWERDTFEGER   University of Wisconsin
NORBERT UNTERSTEINER   University of Washington
LOUIS DeGOES, *Secretary*

RAY R. HEER, JR. (Liaison Member)   National Science Foundation

Panel on Oceanography

KENNETH L. HUNKINS, *Chairman*   Lamont-Doherty Geological Observatory
ALAN BEAL   USN Arctic Submarine Research Laboratory
JOOST BUSINGER   University of Washington
BRUCE C. HEEZEN   Lamont-Doherty Geological Observatory
DONALD W. HOOD   University of Alaska
ARTHUR H. LACHENBRUCH   U.S. Geological Survey
HENRY M. STOMMEL   Massachusetts Institute of Technology
NORBERT UNTERSTEINER   University of Washington
L. V. WORTHINGTON   Woods Hole Oceanographic Institution
DEAN P. KASTEL, *Secretary*

MORT D. TURNER (Liaison Member)   National Science Foundation

Panel on Upper Atmosphere Physics

SIDNEY A. BOWHILL, *Chairman*   University of Illinois
SYUN-ICHI AKASOFU   University of Alaska
W. I. AXFORD   University of California, San Diego
JAMES R. BARCUS   University of Denver
MICHAEL GADSDEN   Institute for Telecommunication Sciences and Aeronomy, ESSA
ROBERT A. HELLIWELL   Stanford University
FRANCIS S. JOHNSON   Southwest Center for Advanced Studies

WILLIAM NORDBERG   Goddard Space Flight Center, NASA
BRIAN J. O'BRIEN   Rice University
MARTIN A. POMERANTZ   Bartol Research Foundation
GEORGE C. REID   High Latitude Ionospheric Laboratory, ESSA
LOUIS DeGOES, *Secretary*

RAY R. HEER, JR. (Liaison Member)   National Science Foundation

Key to Place Names

1. Axel Heiberg Island

2. Bathurst Island

3. Cornwallis Island

4. Devon Island

5. Ellef Rignes Island

6. Melville Island

7. Prince Patrick Island

8. Prince of Wales Island

9. Cook Inlet

10. Franklin Bay

11. Frobisher Bay

12. King William Peninsula

13. Lena River Delta

14. Mackenzie River Delta

15. Viscount Melville Sound

16. Boothia Peninsula

17. Cape Morris Jesup